STUDIES IN
PURE MATHEMATICS

Richard Rado

STUDIES IN PURE MATHEMATICS

PAPERS IN COMBINATORIAL THEORY, ANALYSIS, GEOMETRY, ALGEBRA, AND THE THEORY OF NUMBERS

presented to

RICHARD RADO

on the occasion of his sixty-fifth birthday

edited by

L. MIRSKY

1971

Academic Press: London and New York

ACADEMIC PRESS INC. (LONDON) LTD
Berkeley Square House
Berkeley Square
London, W1X 6BA

U.S. Edition published by
ACADEMIC PRESS INC.
111 Fifth Avenue
New York, New York 10003

Library of Congress Catalog Card Number: 78-129790

ISBN: 0-12-498450-9

Printed in Great Britain by
ROYSTAN PRINTERS LIMITED

Preface

On 28 April 1971 Richard Rado, Professor of Pure Mathematics in the University of Reading, celebrates his sixty-fifth birthday; and a number of his friends and colleagues who share his interests welcome this opportunity to pay tribute to a remarkable mathematician and a man held in universal regard.

In an age when specialization has become the norm, Rado's long series of imaginative and highly individual discoveries testifies to a degree of versatility that is altogether out of the common. Classical analysis and the study of inequalities, the theory of numbers and algebra, geometry and the exploration of convexity, measure theory and transfinite arithmetic have all been grist to his mill. Yet his deepest insight has been displayed in combinatorial mathematics, and it is as the leading figure in this field of research that he is most widely known. To gauge the magnitude of Rado's contribution to combinatorial studies, it suffices to recall the selection principle now linked with his name, his work on 'regular' systems, on linear combinatorial topology, on the theory of graphs, on independence structures and independent transversals, and above all his extensions of Ramsay's theorem and the resulting development of the 'partition calculus'.

The papers offered here are intended to reflect both aspects of Rado's work: its broad range as well as the dominance of combinatorial questions. The authors wish Richard Rado many further years of fruitful mathematical activity, and they are confident that their good wishes will be echoed and their admiration for his achievement shared by a much wider circle of mathematicians than that formally associated with the present volume.

University of Sheffield
January, 1971

L. MIRSKY

Contents

The Determination of Groups by their Groups of Automorphisms

REINHOLD BAER

It has been noticed quite often that restrictions, imposed upon the group of automorphisms, lead to even stronger restrictions of the structure of the underlying group. It is the objective of the present note to offer a few further instances of this phenomenon.

If ω is some class of groups, then one may define a class ω^* of groups by the property:

$G \in \omega^*$ if, and only if, Aut $F \in \omega$ for every factor [= epimorphic image of a subgroup] F of G.

In Chapter 1 we investigate the class ω^*, in case ω is the class of abelian groups or the class of countable groups or that of locally finite groups.

Chapters 2 and 3 are devoted to a characterization of the class of all almost cyclic groups [= groups with a cyclic subgroup of infinite index]. Generalizing Plotkin's class of radical groups we term the group G an $\mathfrak{N}$-group if every epimorphic image, not 1, of G possesses an accessible subgroup, not 1, which is locally finite or locally nilpotent. Our principal result, obtained in Chapter 3, may now be stated as follows: The class of almost cyclic groups is the most comprehensive class $\mathfrak{K}$ of groups with the following two properties:

Factors and groups of automorphisms of $\mathfrak{K}$-groups are $\mathfrak{K}$-groups; and every $\mathfrak{K}$-group, not 1, possesses an accessible locally-$\mathfrak{N}$-subgroup, not 1.

An important step in the proof of this result is constituted by the proof of the fact that every locally-almost-cyclic group G possesses a characteristic locally finite subgroup L such that G/L is either 1 or a torsionfree abelian group of rank 1 or a non-abelian extension of a torsionfree abelian group of rank 1 by a group of order 2.

Notations

Aut G = group of all automorphisms of the group G
$\mathfrak{c}_X Y$ = centralizer of Y in X
$\mathfrak{z}G$ = center of G
$A \lhd B :=: A$ is a normal subgroup of B

$A \subset B$: = : A is a proper subgroup of B
$\{\ldots\ldots\}$: = : subgroup generated by enclosed set
G' = commutator subgroup of G = derived group of G

Definitions

Normal Chain: If C_σ is for every ordinal σ with $0 \leqslant \sigma \leqslant \beta$ a subgroup of the group G, if

$$C_\sigma \lhd C_{\sigma+1} \text{ for } 0 \leqslant \sigma < \beta \text{ and}$$

$$C_\lambda = \bigcup_{\sigma<\lambda} C_\sigma \text{ for every limit ordinal } \lambda \leqslant \beta,$$

then we say that these subgroups C_σ form a normal chain, connecting C_0 and C_β, which we denote by $C = [C_\sigma : 0 \leqslant \sigma \leqslant \beta]$. The quotient groups $C_{\sigma+1}/C_\sigma$ are the factors of this normal chain.

Accessible Subgroups: The subgroup S of G is termed an accessible subgroup of G, if there exists a normal chain, connecting S and G.

Factor of a group : = : epimorphic image of a subgroup.

Group of rank n : = : group whose finitely generated subgroups may be generated by at most n elements.

Noetherian group : = : group whose subgroups are finitely generated.

Soluble group : = : group almost all of whose derived subgroups are trivial.

Polycyclic groups : = : noetherian + soluble groups.

Nilpotent groups : = : groups of finite class : = : groups with finite central chain from top to bottom.

Almost-ω-groups : = : groups with ω-subgroup of finite index.

Locally-ω-groups : = : groups whose finitely generated subgroups have property ω.

Radical groups [in the sense of Plotkin] : = : groups whose non-trivial epimorphic images possess non-trivial locally nilpotent normal subgroups.

1. Characterization of groups in terms of their groups of automorphisms

This is our problem: given a more or less well-known class ω of groups, to determine all groups G with the property: Aut $F \in \omega$ for every factor F of G.

THEOREM 1.1. *The following properties of the group G are equivalent*:

(i) *G is abelian of rank* 1.

(ii) Aut *F is abelian for every factor F of G*.

(iii) Aut F *is locally nilpotent for every factor* F *of* G.

(iv) $\begin{cases} \text{(a) } \textit{Elementary abelian, primary factors of } G \textit{ are cyclic.} \\ \text{(b) } G \textit{ is locally nilpotent.} \end{cases}$

Proof. If G is abelian of rank 1, so is every factor F of G. It is well-known and almost obvious that then Aut F is abelian: (i) implies (ii).

It is clear that (ii) implies (iii). If A is an elementary abelian p-group of order p^2, then Aut A is finite, though not nilpotent. Hence Aut A is not locally nilpotent—actually Aut A is soluble if, and only if, $p = 2, 3$. Thus, if (iii) is satisfied by G, such an A cannot be a factor of G. Hence (iv. a) is a consequence of (iii). A second consequence of (iii) is the local nilpotency of the group of inner automorphisms of G. Thus $G/\mathfrak{z}G$ is locally nilpotent so that (iv. b) is a consequence of (iii).

Assume next the validity of (iv). If the factor P of G is an abelian p-group, then the set $\tilde{P}$ of all elements $x \in P$ with $x^p = 1$ is an elementary abelian p-factor of G; and as such $\tilde{P}$ is cyclic by (iv. a). It is well-known and easily verified that consequently P is of rank 1. If next the factor T of G is an abelian torsion group, then the primary components of T are primary abelian factors of G; and as such they have been shown to be of rank 1. It follows that T itself is of rank 1; and we have shown that

(1) abelian torsion factors of G are of rank 1.

Suppose that the factor A of G is torsionfree abelian. There exists a free abelian subgroup F of A with A/F a torsion group. Then F/F^2 is an elementary abelian 2-factor of G; and it follows from (iv. a) (or (1)) that F/F^2 is cyclic. Hence F is cyclic so that A is of rank 1; and we have shown that

(2) torsionfree abelian factors are of rank 1.

Assume that the abelian group A is neither a torsion group nor torsionfree. Then A contains an infinite cyclic subgroup C and a cyclic subgroup P of order a prime p. The factor CP/C^p of A is elementary abelian of order p^2; and hence by (iv. a) it is not a factor of G. But then A itself is not a factor of G; and we have shown that

(3) abelian factors of G are either torsionfree or torsion groups.

Combination of (1), (2), (3) shows that

(4) abelian factors of G are of rank 1.

Consider a pair a, b of elements in G. Then $S = \{a, b\}$ is nilpotent by (iv. b). It is a consequence of (4) that the finitely generated abelian factor S/S' of G is cyclic. If S were not abelian, then $S' \neq 1$; and the nilpotency of S implies that $S \circ S' \subset S'$; here $S \circ S'$ is the subgroup, generated by all commutators of elements in S by elements in S'. But $S/S \circ S'$ is an extension of the subgroup

$S/S \circ S'$ of $\mathfrak{z}[S/S \circ S']$ by the cyclic group S/S'. Groups with cyclic central quotient group are well-known and easily seen to be abelian. Hence

$$S' \subseteq S \circ S' \subset S',$$

a contradiction showing the commutativity of S. Hence $ab = ba$, proving that

(5) G is abelian.

But (4) + (5) = (i) so that (i) is a consequence of (iv), proving the equivalence of (i)–(iv).

Discussion of Theorem 1.1: $\mathfrak{A}$. If G is a direct product of an infinite cyclic group and a cyclic group of order 2, then the subgroups of G are either cyclic or isomorphic to G. In the latter case their group of automorphisms is elementary abelian of order 4. Thus it does not suffice to require in Theorem 1.1 the commutativity of Aut S for every subgroup S.

$\mathfrak{B}$. If G is the direct product of a group of type 2^∞ and a cyclic group of order 2, then an epimorphic image of G is either of rank 1 or isomorphic to G. In the latter case its group of automorphisms is abelian; see e.g. Fuchs **5**, (p. 222, Theorem 58.3). Thus it does not suffice to require in Theorem 1.1 the commutativity of Aut E for every epimorphic image E of G.

$\mathfrak{C}$. Since the groups of automorphisms of the elementary abelian groups of orders 4 and 9 are soluble, it is impossible to substitute 'soluble' for 'abelian' in (ii) and for 'locally nilpotent' in (iii).

THEOREM 1.2. *The group G is noetherian if and only if G meets the following two requirements*:

(a) Aut *F is countable for every factor F of G.*

(b) *If the set $\mathfrak{M}$ of finitely generated subgroups of the subgroup S of G is not vacuous, and if all the subgroups in $\mathfrak{M}$ have the same centralizer in S, then there exists a maximal subgroup in $\mathfrak{M}$.*

Proof. If G is noetherian, then every factor of G is finitely generated so that its group of automorphisms is countable; see Baer (**3**; p. 37, Hilfssatz II.4). Thus (a) is satisfied by G and (b) is just a (very) special case of the maximum condition for subgroups of G.

Assume conversely the validity of conditions (a) + (b).

Consider a subgroup S of G and denote by $\mathfrak{M}$ the set of finitely generated subgroups X of S with $\mathfrak{c}_S X = \mathfrak{z}S$. It is a consequence of (a) that Aut B is countable for every epimorphic image B of S. Application of Baer (**3**; p. 46, Satz III.4) shows therefore the existence of a finite subset E of S with the property:

1 is the only automorphism of S fixing every element in E.

Naturally $\mathfrak{z}S \subseteq \mathfrak{c}_S E = \mathfrak{c}_S\{E\}$. If s belongs to $\mathfrak{c}_S E$, then every element in E is a fixed element of the automorphism of S, induced by s. It follows that s induces the 1-automorphism in S so that s belongs to $\mathfrak{z}S$, proving $\mathfrak{c}_S E \subseteq \mathfrak{z}S$. Hence $\mathfrak{z}S = \mathfrak{c}_S\{E\}$, showing that $\{E\} \in \mathfrak{M}$. It is consequently possible to apply condition (b) on the set $\mathfrak{M}$. Hence there exists a maximal subgroup W in $\mathfrak{M}$. If x is any element in S, then $\{W, x\}$ is a finitely generated subgroup of S with $\mathfrak{z}S = \mathfrak{c}_S\{W, x\}$ because of $\mathfrak{z}S = \mathfrak{c}_S W$. Hence $\{W, x\} \in \mathfrak{M}$; and we deduce $W = \{W, x\}$ from the maximality of W. But this shows that $x \in W$ for every $x \in S$. Hence $S = W$ is finitely generated, proving that G is noetherian.

THEOREM 1.3. *The following properties of the group G are equivalent*:

(i) *There exists a cyclic subgroup C of G with* $C \subseteq \mathfrak{z}G$ *and finite* G/C.

(ii) Aut *F is finite for every factor F of G.*

(iii) Aut *F is locally finite for every factor F of G.*

(iv) (a) $G/\mathfrak{z}G$ *is locally finite.*
(b) Aut *A is a torsion group for every abelian factor A of G.*

Proof. If G has property (i), so has every factor F of G. It follows that F is almost cyclic with finite $F/\mathfrak{z}F$; and the finiteness of Aut F is readily deduced from $F/\mathfrak{z}F \cong$ Inn F and Baer (**4**; Satz 1, (D)). Hence (ii) is a consequence of (i).

It is clear that (iii) is a consequence of (ii); and (iv) is a consequence of (iii) because of $G/\mathfrak{z}G \cong$ Inn G.

Assume finally the validity of (iv) and consider a primary elementary abelian factor A of G. If A were infinite, then it would be a direct product

$$A = \prod_{i=-\infty}^{\infty} A_i$$

of isomorphic direct factors $A_i \neq 1$. One sees readily the existence of an automorphism σ of A with $A_i^\sigma = A_{i+1}$ for every i so that Aut A would not be a torsion group. Application of (iv. b) shows:

(1) Every primary elementary abelian factor of G is finite.

Consider a primary abelian factor A of G. Because of (1) and Fuchs (**5**, p. 68, Exercise 19 and p. 65, Theorem 19.2) A is the direct product of finitely many groups of rank 1. But groups of type p^∞ have a group of automorphisms, isomorphic to the multiplicative group of p-adic integers, prime to p. These are not torsion groups. Thus application of (iv. b) shows that A is a direct product of finitely many cyclic groups. Hence

(2) every primary abelian factor of G is finite.

Suppose now that A is an abelian torsion factor of G. Denote by $\mathfrak{p}$ the set of odd primes that are orders of elements in A. Then A contains a subgroup S which is a direct product

$$S = \prod_{p \in \mathfrak{p}} S_p$$

of cyclic subgroups S_p of order p. Since Aut S_p is cyclic of order $p - 1$, there exists an automorphism of S_p whose order is $p - 1$; and there exists an automorphism σ of S which induces in S_p an automorphism of order $p - 1$ (for every $p \in \mathfrak{p}$). If $\mathfrak{p}$ were infinite, then σ would not be of finite order and Aut S would not be a torsion group, contradicting (iv. b). Hence $\mathfrak{p}$ is finite so that almost all primary components of A are trivial. Combine this with (2) to show that A is finite. We note this:

(3) Every abelian torsion factor of G is finite.

Consider an abelian factor A of G. Then every torsion-factor of A is finite by (3); and we deduce from Baer (**3**; p. 11, Folgerung I.3] that A is finitely generated. Suppose now that $B = \{b'\} \otimes \{b''\}$ is a free abelian subgroup of rank 2 of A. Then there exists one and only one automorphism λ of B with $b'^{\lambda} = b'\,b''$ and $b''^{\lambda} = b''$. It is clear that λ is not of finite order and that therefore Aut B is not a torsion group, contradicting (iv. b). Since A is finitely generated, A is a direct product of finitely many cyclic groups; and it follows from our last remark that at most one of these finitely many cyclic direct factors is infinite. Thus we have shown that

(4) abelian factors of G are almost-cyclic.

Application of (4) shows that $\mathfrak{z}G$ is almost cyclic. Application of (iv. a) shows that $G/\mathfrak{z}G$ is locally finite and its abelian subgroups are finite by (3). Application of the Theorem of P. Hall + C. R. Kulatilaka and Kargapolov shows the finiteness of $G/\mathfrak{z}G$. It follows that G is an almost cyclic group with finite central quotient group: (i) is a consequence of (iv), proving the equivalence of (i)–(iv).

Remark: A closely related result is due to Alperin; see Scott (**8**, p. 445, Theorem 15.1.19).

2. A generalization of Malcev's theorem

This chapter has been added for the reader's convenience, since its results will be needed in Chapter 3. Professor Bernd Amberg (Austin, Texas) has obtained more far-reaching results.

The compositum $\mathfrak{L}\mathfrak{F}G$ of all locally finite accessible subgroups of G is clearly a well determined characteristic subgroup of G.

LEMMA 2.1. (A) $\mathfrak{L}\mathfrak{F}\mathfrak{G}$ *is locally finite.*

(B) *The group G is locally finite if and only if every epimorphic image, not* 1, *of G possesses a locally finite accessible subgroup, not* 1.

Proof. Local finiteness is a totally inherited [= vollvererblich in the sense of Baer (**1**; p. 49)] group-theoretical property; see e.g. Baer (**1**; p. 53). Now our lemma is an immediate consequence of Baer (**1**; p. 52, Lemma 2.5).

It is well-known that locally nilpotent groups are also locally noetherian. The compositum $\mathfrak{L}\mathfrak{N}G$ of all locally nilpotent accessible subgroups of the group G is a well determined characteristic subgroup of G.

LEMMA 2.2: *$\mathfrak{L}\mathfrak{N}G$ is locally nilpotent.*

This shows among other things that $\mathfrak{L}\mathfrak{N}G$ is the Hirsch–Plotkin radical of G.

This result is an immediate consequence of Baer (**1**; p. 57, Lemma 3.1 and the attached remark).

It will be convenient to let $\mathfrak{L}G = \mathfrak{L}\mathfrak{F}G\ \mathfrak{L}\mathfrak{N}G$ for every group G. This is again a well determined characteristic subgroup of G. It is a consequence of Lemmas 2.1 and 2.2 that $\mathfrak{L}G$ is the compositum of all accessible subgroups of G which are locally finite or locally nilpotent.

LEMMA 2.3. *Every epimorphic image, not* 1, *of the group G possesses an accessible subgroup, not* 1, *which is locally finite or locally nilpotent if and only if*

$$\mathfrak{L}H \neq 1 \text{ for every epimorphic image } H \neq 1 \text{ of } G.$$

This is an immediate consequence of Lemmas 2.1 and 2.2.

Groups with the equivalent properties of Lemma 2.3 will be termed $\mathfrak{R}$-*groups*. It is immediately obvious that every radical group in the sense of Plotkin is an $\mathfrak{R}$-group; thus $\mathfrak{R}$-group may be thought to stand for generalized radical group. Note, however, that every locally finite group is likewise an $\mathfrak{R}$-group.

PROPOSITION 2.4. (A) *Factors of $\mathfrak{R}$-groups are $\mathfrak{R}$-groups.*

(B) *The group G is an $\mathfrak{R}$-group if there exists a normal chain connecting* 1 *and G, whose factors are $\mathfrak{R}$-groups.*

(C) *The compositum $\mathfrak{R}G$ of all accessible $\mathfrak{R}$-subgroups of G is a characteristic $\mathfrak{R}$-subgroup of G; and $\mathfrak{R}[G/\mathfrak{R}G] = 1$.*

Proof. That epimorphic images of $\mathfrak{R}$-groups are $\mathfrak{R}$-groups is immediately clear from the definition. That subgroups of $\mathfrak{R}$-groups are $\mathfrak{R}$-groups, may be verified by the customary arguments, if one only remembers that subgroups of locally $\left\{\begin{matrix}\text{finite}\\ \text{nilpotent}\end{matrix}\right\}$ groups are locally $\left\{\begin{matrix}\text{finite}\\ \text{nilpotent}\end{matrix}\right\}$. This proves (A).

Suppose next that there exists a normal chain of the group G, connecting 1 and G, whose factors are $\mathfrak{R}$-groups. Consider an epimorphic image $H \neq 1$ of

G. Then there exists a normal chain $C = [C_\sigma; 0 \leqslant \sigma \leqslant \beta]$ of H, connecting 1 and H, whose factors are $\mathfrak{R}$-groups. Then $1 = C_0$ and $C_\beta = H$; and we may assume without loss in generality that $C_1 \neq 1$. Then $C_1 = C_1/C_0$ is an $\mathfrak{R}$-group so that $C_1 \neq 1$ implies $\mathfrak{L}C_1 \neq 1$. Consequently $\mathfrak{L}\mathfrak{F}C_1 \neq 1$ or $\mathfrak{L}\mathfrak{N}C_1 \neq 1$. As characteristic subgroups of the accessible subgroup C_1 of H both $\mathfrak{L}\mathfrak{F}C_1$ and $\mathfrak{L}\mathfrak{N}C_1$ are accessible subgroups of H. Hence H possesses an accessible subgroup, not 1, which is locally finite or locally nilpotent (Lemmas 2.1 and 2.2) so that G is consequently an $\mathfrak{R}$-group, proving (B).

The validity of (C) is a consequence of (A), (B) and Baer (**1**; p. 49, Satz 2.1).

PROPOSITION 2.5. *The group G is almost polycyclic if and only if G is an $\mathfrak{R}$-group whose abelian subgroups are finitely generated.*

Proof. Almost-polycyclic groups are noetherian so that their abelian subgroups are finitely generated. Almost-polycyclic groups are almost-soluble; they possess consequently a soluble normal subgroup of finite index and are therefore $\mathfrak{R}$-groups.

Assume conversely that G is an $\mathfrak{R}$-group whose abelian subgroups are finitely generated. Denote by G^* the compositum of all those accessible subgroups of G which are radical in the sense of Plotkin. Suppose that σ is an epimorphism of G^* upon $H \neq 1$. Then there exists at least one accessible radical subgroup S of G^* with $S^\sigma \neq 1$. Then S^σ is an accessible radical subgroup, not 1, of H. There exists consequently an accessible, locally nilpotent subgroup $T \neq 1$ of S^σ. As an accessible subgroup of an accessible subgroup, T is an accessible subgroup. Hence $1 \subset T \subseteq \mathfrak{L}\mathfrak{N}H$ by Lemma 2.2. Thus we have shown that the Hirsch–Plotkin radical $\mathfrak{L}\mathfrak{N}H \neq 1$ for every epimorphic image $H \neq 1$ of G^*. Hence we have shown that G^* is a radical group. But a radical group whose abelian subgroups are finitely generated is polycyclic; see Baer (**2**; p. 359/360, Hauptsatz 8.15, $\mathfrak{N}$, equivalence of conditions (1) and (5)). Thus we have shown:

(1) G^* is polycyclic.

If S/G^* is an accessible radical subgroup of G/G^*, then S is an accessible radical subgroup of G, so that $S \subseteq G^*$, proving:

(2) 1 is the only accessible radical subgroup of G/G^*.

Every abelian subgroup of G/G^* has the form A/G^*. Then A is, by (1), soluble; and the abelian subgroups of A are by hypothesis finitely generated. It is an immediate consequence of a well-known theorem of Mal'cev—see e.g. Baer (**2**; p. 359/360, Hauptsatz 8.15, **N**)—that A is noetherian. Hence A/G^* is finitely generated; and we have shown:

(3) Abelian subgroups of G/G^* are finitely generated.

Let $H = G/G^*$. Then $\mathfrak{L}\mathfrak{F}H$ is by Lemma 2.1 locally finite. The abelian subgroups of $\mathfrak{L}\mathfrak{F}H$ are, by (3), finitely generated and hence finite. Thus we may apply the Theorem of P. Hall + Kulatilaka and Kargapolov on $\mathfrak{L}\mathfrak{F}H$. It follows that

(4) $\mathfrak{L}\mathfrak{F}H$ is finite.

Since $\mathfrak{L}\mathfrak{F}H$ is a characteristic subgroup of H, so is its centralizer $C = \mathfrak{c}_H\mathfrak{L}\mathfrak{F}H$. Then $C \cap \mathfrak{L}\mathfrak{F}H = \mathfrak{z}H$ is a characteristic abelian subgroup of H which is trivial by (2). We note this:

(5) $\mathfrak{L}\mathfrak{F}H \cap C = 1$.

Assume by way of contradiction that H is infinite. Then $H \neq \mathfrak{L}\mathfrak{F}H$ by (4) so that $\mathfrak{L}[H/\mathfrak{L}\mathfrak{F}H] \neq 1$ since $H/\mathfrak{L}\mathfrak{F}H$ is a non-trivial epimorphic image of the $\mathfrak{R}$-group G. Consequently $\mathfrak{L}\mathfrak{F}[H/\mathfrak{L}\mathfrak{F}H] \neq 1$ or $\mathfrak{L}\mathfrak{N}[H/\mathfrak{L}\mathfrak{F}H] \neq 1$; and this is equivalent with the existence of a subgroup W with the following properties:

$\mathfrak{L}\mathfrak{F}H \subset W \lhd H$ and $W/\mathfrak{L}\mathfrak{F}H$ is locally finite or locally nilpotent.

If $W/\mathfrak{L}\mathfrak{F}H$ were locally finite, then the extension W of the (by (4)) finite group $\mathfrak{L}\mathfrak{F}H$ by the locally finite group $W/\mathfrak{L}\mathfrak{F}H$ would be a locally finite normal subgroup of H so that $W \subseteq \mathfrak{L}\mathfrak{F}H \subset W$, a contradiction. It follows that $W/\mathfrak{L}\mathfrak{F}H$ is locally nilpotent. From (5) we deduce that

$$W \cap C = (W \cap C)/(\mathfrak{L}\mathfrak{F}H \cap C) \cong \mathfrak{L}\mathfrak{F}H(W \cap C)/\mathfrak{L}\mathfrak{F}H \subseteq W/\mathfrak{L}\mathfrak{F}H.$$

Hence $W \cap C$ is a locally nilpotent normal subgroup of H so that $W \cap C = 1$ by (2). Consequently

$$W = W/(W \cap C) \cong WC/C \subseteq H/C = H/\mathfrak{c}_H\mathfrak{L}\mathfrak{F}H.$$

Since $\mathfrak{L}\mathfrak{F}H$ is finite by (4), so is $H/\mathfrak{c}_H\mathfrak{L}\mathfrak{F}H$, showing the finiteness of the normal subgroup W of H. Hence $W \subseteq \mathfrak{L}\mathfrak{F}H \subset W$, a contradiction proving the finiteness of $H = G/G^*$. Combine this with (1) to see that G is almost polycyclic.

3. The class of almost-cyclic groups

We preface our discussion by some considerations on finite and finitely generated abelian groups which will prove useful in the sequel.

PROPOSITION 3.1. *The following properties of the abelian torsion group A are equivalent*:

(i) *A is finite.*

(ii) Aut *A is a torsion group.*

(iii) *Free abelian automorphism groups of A are of finite rank.*

Proof. It is clear that (i) implies (ii) and that (ii) implies (iii). We assume now the validity of (iii).

Suppose that P is the totality of p-elements in A. Since A is a torsion group, P is a direct factor of A. If x is an integral p-adic number, prime to p, then there exists one and only one automorphism x^* of A which fixes every element in the direct factor of A, complementary to P, and which maps the element a in P onto a^x. The mapping $x \to x^*$ is a homomorphism of the multiplicative group $\mathfrak{J}_p$ of p-adic integers prime to p into Aut A. Since $\mathfrak{J}_p$ contains free abelian subgroups of uncountably infinite rank, the mapping $x \to x^*$ cannot be a monomorphism; and it is readily seen that this implies the following fact:

(1) If A_p is the p-component of the abelian torsion group A, then there exists a positive integer $n = n(p)$ such that $A_p^{p^n} = 1$.

Suppose next that the direct factor F of A is the direct product of an infinity of isomorphic groups, not 1. Then

$$A = F \otimes F^*;$$

and there exist isomorphic subgroups $F_{i,j} \neq 1$ of F where the i, j range over all the integers (positive, negative or 0) such that

$$F = \prod_{i,j} F_{i,j} \text{ is the direct product of the } F_{i,j}.$$

To every integer i, there exists an automorphism σ_i which maps $F_{i,j}$ upon $F_{i,j+1}$ and fixes every element in F^* and in $F_{k,j}$ for $k \neq i$. One verifies easily that the automorphisms σ_i form a free basis of a free subgroup of Aut A; and this contradicts (iii). Thus, we have shown:

(2) There does not exist a direct factor of A which is the direct product of infinitely many isomorphic groups, not 1.

If A_p is the p-component of A, then it follows from (1) and Fuchs (**5**, p. 44, Theorem 11.2) that A_p is a direct product of cyclic groups (of bounded order). Note that A_p is a direct factor of the torsion group A. If A_p were infinite, then A_p and consequently A would possess a direct factor which is the direct product of infinitely many cyclic groups of equal order, not 1. But this contradicts (2); and thus we have shown:

(3) Every primary component of A is finite.

Denote by ω the set of all odd primes p with $A_p \neq 1$. Since every A_p is a finite group and hence a direct product of cyclic groups, there exists for every $p \in \omega$ a cyclic direct factor $C_p \neq 1$ of A_p. Then

$$C = \prod_{p \in \omega} C_p$$

is the direct product of the C_p and a direct factor of A so that

$$A = C \otimes D.$$

Assume by way of contradiction the infinity of ω. Then there exists a partition of ω into infinitely many infinite components ω_i. We note next that C_p is for every p in ω a cyclic group of odd prime power order, not 1, so that Aut C_p is cyclic; see e.g. Hecke (**7**, p. 48, Satz 44). Denote by λ_p an automorphism, generating Aut C_p. Note that the order of λ_p grows beyond all bounds as p tends to infinity.

Denote by σ_i the well-determined automorphism of A which fixes every element in D, every element in C_p for p not in ω_i and which induces λ_p in C_p for p in ω_i. One verifies readily that the σ_i form a free basis of a free subgroup of Aut A; and this contradicts (iii). Hence ω is finite; and we have shown that

(4) $A_p = 1$ for almost all p.

Combination of (3) and (4) shows the finiteness of A.

COROLLARY 3.2. *The following properties of the abelian group A are equivalent*:

(i) *A is finitely generated.*

(ii) *If the epimorphic image J of A is a torsion group, then J is finite.*

(iii) *If the epimorphic image J of A is a torsion group, then* Aut *J is a torsion group.*

(iv) *If the epimorphic image J of A is a torsion group, then free abelian subgroups of* Aut *J are of finite rank.*

Proof. The equivalence of (i) and (ii) is a consequence of Baer (**3**; p. 11, Folgerung I.3); and the equivalence of (ii)–(iv) is contained in Proposition 3.1.

Discussion of Proposition 3.1 and Corollary 3.2: $\mathfrak{A}$. It is an immediate consequence of Theorem 1.3 and Corollary 3.2 that an abelian group is almost cyclic if and only if the automorphism groups of its factors are finite.

$\mathfrak{B}$. The abelian group of type p^∞ is not almost-cyclic, though the free groups of automorphisms of its factors are cyclic. This shows the impossibility of substituting for condition (iii) of Proposition 3.1 and for condition (iv) of Corollary 3.2 an analogous condition, involving free groups only.

LEMMA 3.3. *If the group G is locally almost-cyclic, then* $G/\mathfrak{L}\mathfrak{F}G$ *is* 1 *or torsion-free abelian of rank* 1 *or a non-abelian extension of a torsionfree abelian group of rank* 1 *by a cyclic group of order* 2.

Proof. If G happens to be a torsion group, then G is locally finite, so that $G/\mathfrak{L}\mathfrak{F}G = 1$. We assume consequently in the sequel that G is not a torsion group.

Denote by S the set of all elements g in G with the property:

(+) g centralizes some infinite cyclic subgroup of G.

If a and b are elements in S, then there exist infinite cyclic subgroups A and B of G such that A is centralized by a and B is centralized by b. Since $\{A, B, a, b\}$ is finitely generated, it is an almost-cyclic subgroup of G. It follows that $A \cap B$ is an infinite cyclic group, since both A and B have finite index in $\{A, B, a, b\}$; see Baer (**4**; Satz 1, (C)). Clearly $A \cap B$ is centralized by ab^{-1} so that $ab^{-1} \in S$. Hence S is a subgroup of G; and by its definition S is a characteristic subgroup of G. It is clear that S contains every infinite cyclic subgroup of G.

Consider elements u and v in G neither of which is contained in S. Since G is, by hypothesis, not a torsion group, there exists an infinite cyclic subgroup Z of G. Since $\{Z, u, v\}$ is finitely generated, it is an infinite almost-cyclic group. By Baer (**4**; Satz 1, (B)) there exists a cyclic characteristic subgroup C of $\{Z, u, v\}$ with finite $\{Z, u, v\}/C$. Clearly C is infinite and C is normalized by u and v; but since neither u nor v is in S, neither of these elements centralizes C. Hence u and v induce in C the same automorphism which maps every element in C onto its inverse. It follows that C is centralized by uv^{-1} so that uv^{-1} belongs to S. Thus we have shown:

(1) S is a characteristic subgroup of G and either $S = G$ or else G/S has order 2 and each element, not in S, inverts the elements in some infinite cyclic subgroup of G.

Consider a finitely generated subgroup F of S. Either F is finite or else F is an infinite almost-cyclic group. In the latter case there exists by Baer (**4**; Satz 1, (B)) a cyclic characteristic subgroup C of F with finite F/C. Clearly C is infinite. Consider an element $a \in F \subseteq S$. Then there exists an infinite cyclic subgroup A of G which is centralized by a. Since $\{F, A\}$ is a finitely generated subgroup of G, it is almost-cyclic. It follows from Baer (**4**; Satz 1, (C)) that every infinite subgroup of $\{F, A\}$ has finite index in $\{F, A\}$. Hence C, A and consequently $C \cap A$ has finite index in $\{F, A\}$ and *a fortiori* in A and C. Since a centralizes A, it centralizes $C \cap A$; and since a normalizes the cyclic characteristic subgroup C of F, it follows that a centralizes C. Thus C is centralized by every element in F so that $C \subseteq \mathfrak{z}F$; and this implies the finiteness of $F/\mathfrak{z}F$. It is well-known that this implies the finiteness of F'; see e.g. Scott (**8**, p. 443, 15.1.13). Thus we have shown:

(2) F' is finite for every finitely generated subgroup $F \subseteq S$.

If E is a finite subset of S', then there exists a finitely generated subgroup F of S such that that E is part of F'. But F' is finite by (2); and this implies the finiteness of $\{E\}$. Thus we have shown:

(3) S' is locally finite.

Since S is a characteristic subgroup, so is S'. Denote by T the uniquely determined subgroup with $S' \subseteq T \subseteq S$ and T/S' the torsion subgroup of the abelian subgroup S/S'. Since S, S' and the torsion subgroup of an abelian group are characteristic subgroups, T is a characteristic subgroup of G. Since T/S' is an abelian torsion group, it is locally finite. Since S' is locally finite, and since extensions of locally finite groups by locally finite groups are locally finite (Lemma 2.1, (B)), T is a locally finite characteristic subgroup of G. If u and v are elements in S, but not in T, then $\{S' u\}$ and $\{S' v\}$ are infinite cyclic groups so that $\{u\}$ and $\{v\}$ are infinite cyclic groups. As before $\{u, v\}$ is almost-cyclic and $\{u\}$ and $\{v\}$ are infinite cyclic subgroups of $\{u, v\}$ with finite index, by Baer (**4**; Satz 1, (C)). Hence $\{u\} \cap \{v\}$ has finite index in the infinite group $\{u, v\}$, so that $\{u\} \cap \{v\}$ is an infinite cyclic group. Since S/T is a torsionfree abelian group, and since any two infinite cyclic subgroups of S/T have non-trivial intersection, it follows that S/T is torsionfree abelian of rank 1. It follows that

(4) $T \subseteq S \cap \mathfrak{LF}G$ and S/T is torsionfree abelian of rank 1.

It follows that $S\,\mathfrak{LF}G/\mathfrak{LF}G$ is an epimorphic image of S/T and as such it is abelian of rank 1. If it were not torsionfree, then this abelian group of rank 1 would be a torsion group and hence locally finite. Then $S\,\mathfrak{LF}G$ would be locally finite as an extension of the locally finite group $\mathfrak{LF}G$ by the locally finite group $S\,\mathfrak{LF}G/\mathfrak{LF}G$; see Lemma 2.1, (B). But S contains all infinite cyclic subgroups of G and is consequently not a torsion group. Thus we have shown that

(5) $S\,\mathfrak{LF}G/\mathfrak{LF}G$ is torsionfree abelian of rank 1.

Our Lemma is now an immediate consequence of (1) and (5).

Remark: $\mathfrak{A}$. If the group G is obtained by adjoining to a normal subgroup N, isomorphic to the additive group of rational numbers, an element g, subject to the relations

$$g^2 = 1, \qquad gag = a^{-1} \text{ for } a \in N,$$

then G is readily seen to be locally almost-cyclic with $\mathfrak{LF}G = 1$ and G not almost-cyclic.

$\mathfrak{B}$. Simple examples like the wreath product of a cyclic group of order a prime with an infinite cyclic group show that the properties of locally-almost-cyclic groups, enumerated in Lemma 3.3, are not sufficient for a group to be locally almost-cyclic. It would be easy to complete these conditions in such a way as to make them necessary and sufficient.

PROPOSITION 3.4. *The following properties of the group G are equivalent*:

(i) *G is almost cyclic.*

(ii) $\begin{cases} \text{(a) Aut } F \textit{ is noetherian for every factor } F \textit{ of an abelian subgroup of } G. \\ \text{(b) Aut } E \textit{ is an } \mathfrak{N}\textit{-group for every finitely generated subgroup } E \textit{ of } G. \end{cases}$

(iii) $\begin{cases} \text{(a) } \textit{Abelian subgroups of } G \textit{ are almost-cyclic.} \\ \text{(b) } G \textit{ is a locally-}\mathfrak{N}\textit{-group.} \end{cases}$

(iv) $\begin{cases} \text{(a) } \textit{Abelian subgroups of } G \textit{ are finitely generated.} \\ \text{(b) } G \textit{ is locally almost-cyclic.} \end{cases}$

Proof. If G is almost cyclic, then Aut F is almost cyclic for every factor F of G; see Baer (**4**; Satz 1, (A)). Thus (ii) is a consequence of (i).

Assume next the validity of (ii). If A is an abelian subgroup of G, then Aut F is noetherian for every factor F of A. It follows from (ii. a) that condition (vii) of Baer (**4**; Hauptsatz 4) is satisfied by A. Hence A is almost cyclic: (iii. a) is a consequence of (ii. a). Consider next a finitely generated subgroup E of G. Then Aut E is an $\mathfrak{N}$-group. Hence the group of inner automorphisms of E is likewise an $\mathfrak{N}$-group. This is equivalent to saying that $E/\mathfrak{z}E \in \mathfrak{N}$. But $\mathfrak{z}E$ is abelian and hence noetherian (as we have shown already). Hence $E \in \mathfrak{N}$ so that G is a locally-$\mathfrak{N}$-group: (iii) is a consequence of (ii).

Assume now the validity of (iii). It is clear that (iii. a) implies (iv. a). Consider a finitely generated subgroup E of G. It is a consequence of (iii) that E is an $\mathfrak{N}$-group whose abelian subgroups are almost cyclic. Since the abelian subgroups of E are in particular finitely generated, application of Proposition 2.5 shows that E is almost polycyclic; and it is a consequence of (iii. a) that the free abelian subgroups of E are cyclic. Thus condition (iii) of Baer (**4**; Hauptsatz 4) is satisfied by E so that E is almost-cyclic and G is locally almost-cyclic: (iv) is a consequence of (iii).

Assume finally the validity of (iv). It is a consequence of (iv. b) and Lemma 3.3 that G is an $\mathfrak{N}$-group whose abelian subgroups are, by (iv. a), finitely generated. Thus it follows from Proposition 2.5 that G is noetherian. Apply (iv. b) to see that G is almost-cyclic: (i) is a consequence of (iv) so that (i)–(iv) are equivalent.

PROPOSITION 3.5. *If factors and automorphism groups of $\mathfrak{K}$-groups are $\mathfrak{K}$-groups, then the following properties of the class $\mathfrak{K}$ of groups are equivalent:*

(i) *Every locally-$\mathfrak{N}$-group in $\mathfrak{K}$ is almost-cyclic.*

(ii) *Free abelian groups in $\mathfrak{K}$ are cyclic.*

(iii) *Free groups in $\mathfrak{K}$ are cyclic.*

(iv) *$\mathfrak{K}$ does not contain all countable groups.*

Proof. Suppose first that every locally-$\mathfrak{N}$-group in $\mathfrak{K}$ is almost-cyclic. Consider a free abelian group F in $\mathfrak{K}$. Then F is a (locally-) $\mathfrak{N}$-group and hence by (i) almost cyclic. Consequently there exists a cyclic subgroup S of F with finite F/S so that the free abelian group F is cyclic too: (i) implies (ii).

If (ii) is satisfied by $\mathfrak{K}$, then $\mathfrak{K}$ does not contain the free abelian group of rank 2. Since this group is countably infinite, (iv) is a consequence of (ii).

If $\mathfrak{K}$ contains a non-cyclic free group, then $\mathfrak{K}$ contains in particular a free group of degree 2. It is well-known that the commutator subgroup of the free group of degree 2 is a free group of countably infinite degree which then belongs to $\mathfrak{K}$ too. But every countable group is an epimorphic image of the free group of countably infinite degree so that $\mathfrak{K}$ contains every countable group: if (iii) is false, so is (iv). Hence (iii) is a consequence of (iv).

Suppose that A is the free abelian group of rank 2. Then it is well-known that Aut A contains a free subgroup of degree 2. Hence (iii) is false if (ii) is false so that (ii) is a consequence of (iii); we have shown the equivalence of the conditions (ii)–(iv).

Assume now the validity of the equivalent conditions (ii)–(iv). Consider an abelian group A in $\mathfrak{K}$. If the epimorphic image J of A is a torsion group, then every group of automorphisms of J belongs to $\mathfrak{K}$. It follows from (ii) that free abelian groups of automorphisms of J are cyclic. Hence condition (iv) of Corollary 3.2 is satisfied by A so that A is finitely generated.

If G is an $\mathfrak{R}$-group in $\mathfrak{K}$, then the abelian subgroups of G belong to $\mathfrak{K}$ and are consequently finitely generated. Application of Proposition 2.5 shows that G is almost-polycyclic. Thus G is an almost-polycyclic group whose free abelian subgroups are $\mathfrak{K}$-groups and consequently, by (ii), cyclic. Thus condition (iii) of Baer (**4**; Hauptsatz 4) is satisfied by G so that G is almost-cyclic. Assume next that the $\mathfrak{K}$-group G is a locally-$\mathfrak{R}$-group. Then every $\mathfrak{R}$-subgroup of G is a $\mathfrak{K}$-group and hence almost-cyclic so that G is locally almost-cyclic. Abelian subgroups of G are in particular abelian $\mathfrak{K}$-groups; and we have shown already that abelian $\mathfrak{K}$-groups are finitely generated. Apply Proposition 3.4 to see that G is almost-cyclic: we have deduced condition (i) from the equivalent conditions (ii)–(iv), proving the equivalence of conditions (i)–(iv).

THEOREM 3.6. *The class of all almost-cyclic groups is the most comprehensive class $\mathfrak{K}$ of groups with the following two properties:*

$\mathfrak{A}$. *Factors and automorphism groups of $\mathfrak{K}$-groups are $\mathfrak{K}$-groups.*

$\mathfrak{B}$. *$\mathfrak{K}$-groups, not* 1, *possess accessible locally-$\mathfrak{R}$-subgroups, not* 1.

Proof. That factors and automorphism groups of almost-cyclic groups are almost cyclic, is a consequence of Baer (**4**; Satz 1, (A)). Furthermore every almost-cyclic group G possesses by Baer (**4**; Satz 1, (B)) a cyclic characteristic subgroup C with finite G/C. It follows that the class of almost cyclic-groups meets requirements $\mathfrak{A}$ and $\mathfrak{B}$.

Consider next a class $\mathfrak{K}$ of groups, meeting requirements $\mathfrak{A}$ and $\mathfrak{B}$. Note that a free $\mathfrak{R}$-group is cyclic. If L is a free locally-$\mathfrak{R}$-group, then we remember that every finitely generated subgroup of L is, by Schreier's Theorem, a free $\mathfrak{R}$-group and hence cyclic. Thus we have shown that free locally-$\mathfrak{R}$-groups are cyclic. If a free group possesses an accessible cyclic subgroup, not 1, then it is cyclic, since cyclic subgroups, not 1, of non-abelian free groups are not normal. Thus $\mathfrak{B}$ implies in particular that free $\mathfrak{K}$-groups are cyclic. Proposition 3.5 shows therefore that every locally-$\mathfrak{R}$-group in $\mathfrak{K}$ is almost cyclic. Thus $\mathfrak{K}$-groups, not 1, possess accessible almost-cyclic subgroups, not 1. By Baer (**4**; Satz 1, (B)) almost-cyclic groups possess cyclic characteristic subgroups with finite quotient group. Hence every $\mathfrak{K}$-group, not 1, possesses an accessible subgroup, not 1, which is cyclic or finite. It follows that all $\mathfrak{K}$-groups are $\mathfrak{R}$-groups and as such they are almost-cyclic.

References

1. BAER, REINHOLD. Erreichbare und engelsche Gruppenelemente. *Abhandlungen Math. Seminar Hamburg* **27** (1964), 44–74.
2. BAER, REINHOLD. Auflösbare, artinsche, noethersche Gruppen. *Math. Annalen* **168** (1967), 325–363.
3. BAER, REINHOLD. Gruppen mit abzählbaren Automorphismengruppen. *Hamburger Math. Einzelschriften*. Neue Folge, Heft 2 (1969).
4. BAER, REINHOLD. Fast-Zyklische Gruppen. *Archiv der Math.* **21** (1970), 225–239.
5. FUCHS, L. *Abelian Groups* (Budapest, 1968).
6. HALL, P. and KULATILAKA, C. R. A property of locally finite groups. *J. London Math. Soc.* **39** (1964), 235–239.
7. HECKE, ERICH. *Theorie der algebraischen Zahlen*. (Leipzig, 1923).
8. SCOTT, W. R. *Group Theory* (Prentice Hall Inc., 1964).

A General Linking Theorem in Directed Graphs

R. A. BRUALDI* AND J. S. PYM

There is a class of questions in the theory of transversals of families of sets which have significant generalizations to the theory of graphs. The most important example is probably the theorem of P. Hall, which is a special case of Menger's Theorem. The Mapping Theorem of Banach (**1**) (which gives a little more information than the Schroeder–Bernstein Theorem) which is an important tool in the theory of common transversals can be viewed as a theorem on bipartite graphs, and is a special case of the Linking Theorem of (**7**). The present paper offers another result in this tradition.

We shall describe in a loose way the antecedents of our result in Transversal Theory. Suppose we wish to find a common transversal of two families $\mathfrak{A}$ and $\mathfrak{B}$ which satisfies a set C of conditions. Then one method of attack is to find a transversal of $\mathfrak{A}$ satisfying conditions C, a transversal of $\mathfrak{B}$ satisfying conditions C, and to construct the common transversal from the first two transversals. It is the last step to which our theorem may apply. The precise condition we have in mind is that the transversal should contain a prescribed set of elements, or in technical language, we are concerned with the problem of 'marginal elements' for common transversals. We state and prove a theorem of this kind in §4 (Corollary 4). A result more general than Corollary 4 is true (**3**, **4**), but our main result does not appear to be strong enough to contain it.

There are two main approaches to the proof of a theorem of the kind we are presenting. One is to deal with the finite case first (perhaps using induction) and extend the result to the infinite situation using Rado's Selection Principle. This depends, of course, on finding some form of local finiteness in the problem—and this is often present in Transversal Theory for other reasons. This method was applied successfully in (**8**). The other approach derives its basic inspiration from proofs of Banach's Mapping Theorem, and its power is demonstrated in (**2**, **4**). We describe how this second method can be applied directly to prove our main theorem in §3. However, the proof we offer the reader in §2, although basically the same, shortens the work by using the Banach Mapping

* Research supported by a N.A.T.O. postdoctoral fellowship.

Theorem (or rather, the Mapping Theorem of (**6**)). The construction we use to produce a bipartite graph from a general graph might be of interest.

There are some technical points which should be mentioned here. Often in graph theory, restrictions are placed on the kinds of path allowed; for example, cyclic paths are usually forbidden. In §5, we give examples to show that even when we begin with a set of finite non-cyclic paths, the results of our construction may contain degenerate, cyclic or infinite paths. We have therefore allowed paths of these kinds from the beginning, though we give in §4 corollaries of the main theorem which give conditions under which they cannot occur.

We begin by formally introducing our terminology and notation.

1. Definitions and notation

A *directed graph* Γ consists of a set N, whose members are called *nodes*, together with a subset E of $\{(x, y) : x, y \in N, x \neq y\}$, whose members are called *edges*. A *path* in Γ is a system of distinct nodes of Γ of one of the following five types.

(1) A *finite linear path* is a linearly ordered finite set $(x_0, x_1, \ldots, x_n)$ of distinct nodes of Γ, where n is a non-negative integer and $(x_{r-1}, x_r) \in E$ $(1 \leqslant r \leqslant n)$. Observe that (x_0) is a finite linear path (which we shall sometimes call *degenerate*).

(2) A sequence $(x_0, x_1, x_2, \ldots)$ of distinct nodes such that $(x_{r-1}, x_r) \in E$ $(1 \leqslant r < \infty)$ is called an *unending linear path.*

(3) A system $(\ldots, x_{-2}, x_{-1}, x_0)$ of distinct nodes with $(x_{r-1}, x_r) \in E$ $(-\infty < r \leqslant 0)$ is called an *unbeginning linear path.*

(4) A system $(\ldots, x_{-2}, x_{-1}, x_0, x_1, x_2, \ldots)$ of distinct nodes with (x_{r-1}, x_r) $\in E$ $(-\infty < r < \infty)$ is called a *doubly-infinite linear path.*

(5) A *cyclic path* or *cycle* is a cyclically ordered system $(x_0, x_1, \ldots, x_n)_c$ of distinct nodes of Γ where n is a non-negative integer, $(x_{r-1}, x_r) \in E$ $(1 \leqslant r \leqslant n)$ and $(x_n, x_0) \in E$. (Observe that $(x_0)_c$ cannot be a cycle.) For any r $(1 \leqslant r \leqslant n)$, the path $(x_r, \ldots, x_n, x_0, x_1, \ldots, x_{r-1})_c$ is regarded as identical with $(x_0, x_1, \ldots, x_n)_c$.

If a path θ has a first node (i.e. if θ is of type 1 or of type 2) this node is called its *initial* node, and denoted by $\mathrm{In}\,\theta$. If θ has a last node (i.e. θ is of type 1 or type 3), this node is called its *terminal* node, and denoted by $\mathrm{Ter}\,\theta$. If Θ is a set of paths, we write $\mathrm{In}\,\Theta = \{\mathrm{In}\,\theta : \theta \in \Theta\}$, $\mathrm{Ter}\,\Theta = \{\mathrm{Ter}\,\theta : \theta \in \Theta\}$.

We denote by $\mathrm{Nod}\,\theta$ the set of all nodes lying on the path θ. If Θ is a set of paths, $\mathrm{Nod}\,\Theta = \cup\{\mathrm{Nod}\,\theta : \theta \in \Theta\}$. We call Θ *pairwise node disjoint* if $\theta_1, \theta_2 \in \Theta$ and $\theta_1 \neq \theta_2$ imply $\mathrm{Nod}\,\theta_1 \cap \mathrm{Nod}\,\theta_2 = \emptyset$. We shall use $\mathrm{Ed}\,\theta$ to denote the set of all edges belonging to the path θ, and when Θ is a set of paths, $\mathrm{Ed}\,\Theta = \cup\{\mathrm{Ed}\,\theta : \theta \in \Theta\}$.

Let θ be a path in Γ. If $\theta = (x_0, \ldots, x_n)$ and $0 \leqslant r \leqslant n$, we denote by $x_r.\theta$ the path $(x_r, x_{r+1}, \ldots, x_n)$. If $\theta = (x_0, x_1, \ldots)$ and $r \geqslant 0$ or $\theta = (\ldots x_{-1}, x_0, x_1, \ldots)$ and r is any integer, then $x_r.\theta = (x_r, x_{r+1}, \ldots)$. If $\theta = (\ldots, x_{-1}, x_0)$ and $r \leqslant 0$, then $x_r.\theta = (x_r, x_{r+1}, \ldots, x_0)$. In a similar way, if y is a node on a linear path θ we can define $\theta.y$. Then if x and y are two nodes of a linear path and y lies on $x.\theta$ (or equivalently, x lies on $\theta.y$), $x.\theta.y$ is defined to be $(x.\theta).y$ or $x.(\theta.y)$. Finally if x_r and x_s lie on a cycle $\theta = (x_0, x_1, \ldots, x_n)_c$, then if $r < s$, $x_r.\theta.x_s$ is by definition the linear path $(x_r, x_{r+1}, \ldots, x_s)$; if $r > s$, $x_r.\theta.x_s$ is $(x_r, x_{r+1}, \ldots, x_n, x_0, \ldots, x_s)$; while if $r = s$, $x_r.\theta.x_s$ is taken to be θ itself. Any of the paths we have just described is called a *part* (or *subpath*) of θ.

2. The main result

We are now in a position to give a precise statement of our main theorem.

THE GENERAL LINKING THEOREM. *Let Γ be a directed graph and let Θ and Φ be two sets of pairwise node disjoint paths of Γ. Then there exists a set Π of pairwise node disjoint paths of Γ with* $\text{Ed}\,\Pi \subseteq \text{Ed}(\Theta \cup \Phi)$ *which satisfies the following conditions*:

(a) $\text{In}\,\Theta \subseteq \text{In}\,\Pi \subseteq \text{In}\,\Theta \cup \text{In}\,\Phi$;

(b) $\text{Ter}\,\Phi \subseteq \text{Ter}\,\Pi \subseteq \text{Ter}\,\Theta \cup \text{Ter}\,\Phi$;

(c) $\text{Nod}\,\Theta \cap \text{Nod}\,\Phi \subseteq \text{Nod}\,\Pi \subseteq \text{Nod}\,\Theta \cup \text{Nod}\,\Phi$.

It is easy to give an outline of the proof, though the details are a little complicated. Basically, we shall split the paths of Θ and Φ into parts; we shall construct a bipartite graph G in which each part corresponds to an edge; we shall use the mapping theorem of **(6)** which we reformulate below to select certain of those parts; and we shall reassemble the chosen parts to form Π.

The last of the steps we have described is easy. It is accomplished by means of the following lemma, whose proof is obvious.

ASSEMBLING LEMMA. *Let Ω be a collection of paths of Γ. Suppose that if two paths of Ω intersect, it is where the terminal node of one is the initial node of the other. Then there is a unique collection Π of pairwise node disjoint paths of Γ such that* $\text{Nod}\,\Omega = \text{Nod}\,\Pi$ *and* $\text{Ed}\,\Pi = \text{Ed}\,\Omega$.

The main tool in our proof is the mapping theorem, which turns out to be a special case of the main theorem. We shall state it in a convenient form, and we offer a short proof, but we leave to the reader the task of verifying that our statement reduces to Theorem 1 of **(6)**.

THE MAPPING THEOREM. *Let the hypotheses of the General Linking Theorem hold, and suppose in addition that each path of* Θ *and of* Φ *consists of one edge (and so two nodes) and that* $\operatorname{In}(\Theta \cup \Phi) \cap \operatorname{Ter}(\Theta \cup \Phi) = \varnothing$. *Then the conclusions of that theorem hold.*

(In fact, part (c) of the conclusion has no content here, since every element of $\operatorname{Nod}\Theta \cap \operatorname{Nod}\Phi$ is either in $\operatorname{In}\Theta$ or else in $\operatorname{Ter}\Phi$.)

To prove the mapping theorem, we form for each path $\theta \in \Theta$ a maximal sequence $\theta_1 = \theta, \phi_1, \theta_2, \phi_2, \theta_3, \ldots$ with the properties that $\operatorname{Ter}\theta_i = \operatorname{Ter}\phi_i$ and $\operatorname{In}\phi_i = \operatorname{In}\theta_{i+1}$ $(i = 1, 2, \ldots)$. Since the paths of Θ and Φ are pairwise node disjoint, the sets $A(\theta) = \{\theta_1, \theta_2, \ldots\}$ and $B(\theta) = \{\phi_1, \phi_2, \ldots\}$ are uniquely determined by θ. The sequence $\theta_1, \phi_1, \theta_2, \ldots$ may be finite or infinite; observe that if it is finite and the last path is $\theta_k \in \Theta$, then $\operatorname{Ter}\theta_k \notin \operatorname{Ter}\Phi$, while if the last path is $\phi_k \in \Phi$, then $\operatorname{In}\phi_k \notin \operatorname{In}\Theta$.

Now write

$$\overline{\Theta} = \cup\{A(\theta) : \operatorname{In}\theta \notin \operatorname{In}\Phi\},$$
$$\overline{\Phi} = \Phi - \cup\{B(\theta) : \operatorname{In}\theta \notin \operatorname{In}\Phi\},$$
$$\Pi = \overline{\Theta} \cup \overline{\Phi}.$$

Then it is not difficult to check from the above observations that Π satisfies the desired conditions.

We shall now give a proof of the General Linking Theorem. We use the elements of $\operatorname{Nod}\Theta \cap \operatorname{Nod}\Phi$, which we shall call *intersection nodes*, to split the paths of Θ (resp. Φ) into parts, and we shall denote the set of these parts by $\Sigma(\Theta)$ (resp. $\Sigma(\Phi)$). Let $\theta \in \Theta$. If no intersection node lies on θ, we demand $\theta \in \Sigma(\Theta)$. If there is a first intersection node x on θ, then $\theta . x \in \Sigma(\Theta)$ (notice that it can happen that $\theta . x$ is degenerate). If there is a last intersection node y on θ, then $y . \theta \in \Sigma(\Theta)$. Finally, if x and y are intersection nodes on θ, if $x . \theta . y$ contains no intersection nodes other than x and y, and if $x . \theta . y$ is not degenerate (though we allow $x = y$ if θ is a cycle) then we require that $x . \theta . y \in \Sigma(\Theta)$. It is easy to see that every intersection node lies on some path in $\Sigma(\Theta)$, and that all intersection nodes are terminal nodes of paths of $\Sigma(\Theta)$. Moreover, $\Sigma(\Theta)$ satisfies the conditions required of Ω in the Assembling Lemma, and the set Π the Lemma produces is exactly Θ itself.

The set $\Sigma(\Phi)$ is constructed in an analogous way.

Next, we construct the bipartite graph G, and we describe first its set of nodes. We begin by taking a set X_I such that there is a bijection $x \to x_I$ of $\operatorname{In}\Theta \cup \operatorname{In}\Phi$ to X_I. Next we take a set X' such that there is a bijection $x \to x'$ of $\operatorname{Nod}\Theta \cap \operatorname{Nod}\Phi$ to X'. Finally, we take a set X_∞ such that to each path $\theta \in \Theta$ (resp. $\phi \in \Phi$) which has no initial node there corresponds one and only one element x_θ (resp. x_ϕ). We ask that the three sets X_I, X', X_∞ shall form a partition of a set X. In a similar way, we form X_T such that there is a bijection $x \to x_T$ of $\operatorname{Ter}\Theta \cup \operatorname{Ter}\Phi$ to X_T; X'' such that there is a bijection $x \to x''$ of $\operatorname{Nod}\Theta \cap \operatorname{Nod}\Phi$ to X''; and a set Y_∞ such that to each path $\theta \in \Theta$ (resp. $\phi \in \Phi$) with no terminal node there corresponds one and only one node y_θ (resp. y_ϕ) of Y_∞. Then we demand that X_T, X'' and Y_∞ form a partition of a set Y. We ask that $X \cap Y = \emptyset$, and take $\operatorname{Nod} G = X \cup Y$.

For each path σ in $\Sigma(\Theta)$ we construct an edge $\tilde{\sigma}$ of G in the following way. If $\sigma = \theta$, so that θ has no intersection nodes, then if θ has initial node x and terminal node y, $\tilde{\theta}$ shall be (x_I, y_T); if θ has initial node x and no terminal node, $\tilde{\theta}$ shall be (x_I, y_θ); if θ has no initial node and terminal node y, $\tilde{\theta}$ shall be (x_θ, y_T); and if θ has neither initial nor terminal node, $\tilde{\theta}$ shall be (x_θ, y_θ). If $\sigma = \theta . x$, where x is the first intersection node on θ, then $\widetilde{\theta . x}$ is (z_I, x'') if θ has initial node z, and is (x_θ, x'') if θ has no initial node. If $\sigma = x . \theta$ where x is the last intersection node on θ, then $\widetilde{x . \theta}$ is (x', y_T) if θ has terminal node y, and (x', y_θ) if θ has no terminal node. Finally, if $\sigma = x . \theta . y$ where both x and y are intersection nodes, $x . \theta . y$ is (x', y''). If we consider the set $\tilde{\Sigma}(\Theta)$ we have just described as a set of paths, then it is obviously pairwise node disjoint and satisfies $\{x_I : x \in \operatorname{In}\Theta\} \cup X' \subseteq \operatorname{In}\tilde{\Sigma}(\Theta) \subseteq X$, $\operatorname{Ter}\tilde{\Sigma}(\Theta) \subseteq Y$.

We define a set $\tilde{\Sigma}(\Phi)$ in the same way to satisfy

$$\{x_T : x \in \operatorname{Ter}\Phi\} \cup X'' \subseteq \operatorname{Ter}\tilde{\Sigma}(\Phi) \subseteq Y, \qquad \operatorname{In}\tilde{\Sigma}(\Phi) \subseteq X.$$

We take $\tilde{\Sigma}(\Theta) \cup \tilde{\Sigma}(\Phi)$ to be the set of edges of G.

We now apply the Mapping Theorem to obtain a set $\tilde{\Omega} \subseteq \tilde{\Sigma}(\Theta) \cup \tilde{\Sigma}(\Phi)$ of pairwise node disjoint paths which satisfies the relationships

$$\{x_I : x \in \operatorname{In}\Theta\} \cup X' \subseteq \operatorname{In}\tilde{\Omega} \subseteq X \tag{2.1}$$

and

$$\{x_T : x \in \operatorname{Ter}\Phi\} \cup X'' \subseteq \operatorname{Ter}\tilde{\Omega} \subseteq Y. \tag{2.2}$$

We let $\Omega \subseteq \Sigma(\Theta) \cup \Sigma(\Phi)$ be the collection of paths σ such that $\tilde{\sigma} \in \tilde{\Omega}$.

We show Ω satisfies the conditions of the Assembling Lemma. Let $\sigma_1, \sigma_2 \in \Omega$, and suppose x lies on both σ_1 and σ_2. Then x must be an intersection node, and is therefore either an initial node or a terminal node of σ_1 and σ_2. Now if x is initial for both σ_1 and σ_2, x' lies on both $\tilde{\sigma}_1$ and $\tilde{\sigma}_2$, which contradicts the assertion that $\tilde{\Omega}$ is pairwise node disjoint. In the same way, x cannot be terminal for both σ_1 and σ_2. Thus, x is initial for one and terminal for the other.

We can now apply the Assembling Lemma to form the set Π of pairwise node disjoint paths. We must check that Π satisfies (a), (b) and (c).

First, since $\Omega \subseteq \Sigma(\Theta) \cup \Sigma(\Phi)$, we have

$$\operatorname{Nod}\Pi = \operatorname{Nod}\Omega \subseteq \operatorname{Nod}\Theta \cup \operatorname{Nod}\Phi.$$

Also, if $x \in \operatorname{Nod}\Theta \cap \operatorname{Nod}\Phi$, $x' \in X' \subseteq \operatorname{In}\tilde{\Omega}$ (by 2.1), so that x is the initial node of some path of Ω, and therefore $x \in \operatorname{Nod}\Pi$. Thus, (c) is proved.

Next, if $x \in \operatorname{In}\Theta$, $x_I \in \operatorname{In}\tilde{\Omega}$ (by 2.1). Suppose that $x \notin \operatorname{In}\Pi$. Then there must be a non-degenerate path in Ω which has x as terminal node, and therefore for some $z \in X$ with $z \neq x_I$, $(z, x'') \in \tilde{\Omega}$. But this means that x is an intersection node, and so by construction, $(x_I, x'') \in \tilde{\Sigma}(\Theta)$. Moreover, (x_I, x'') is the only path of $\tilde{\Sigma}(\Theta) \cup \tilde{\Sigma}(\Phi)$ which contains the node x_I, and therefore $(x_I, x'') \in \tilde{\Omega}$. Since $\tilde{\Omega}$ is pairwise node disjoint, $z = x_I$, which is a contradiction. We have shown $\operatorname{In}\Theta \subseteq \operatorname{In}\Pi$.

Now let $x \in \operatorname{In}\Pi$. Then x must be the initial node of some path of Ω, and so either $x_I \in X_I$ when $x \in \operatorname{In}\Theta \cup \operatorname{In}\Phi$ or $x' \in X'$ (paths of $\tilde{\Omega}$ with initial nodes not in $X_I \cup X'$ correspond to paths in Ω without initial nodes). If $x' \in X'$, then x is an intersection node, and so also $x'' \in X''$. We can then find $z \in X$ with $(z, x'') \in \tilde{\Omega}$. The path σ in Ω with $\tilde{\sigma} = (z, x'')$ has x as terminal node, and therefore if x is the initial node of a path of Π, σ must also have x as initial node. By construction of the paths of $\tilde{\Sigma}(\Theta) \cup \tilde{\Sigma}(\Phi)$, this can only happen if $z = x_I$, and this means that $x \in \operatorname{In}\Theta \cup \operatorname{In}\Phi$. We have shown $\operatorname{In}\Pi \subseteq \operatorname{In}\Theta \cup \operatorname{In}\Phi$, and (a) is completely proved.

The relations (b) follow in a similar way.

3. An alternative method

The proof of the general linking theorem given in the last section was in a sense constructive: for a finite graph, it would be possible to trace the steps of the proof to find a set Π of paths from given sets Θ, Φ. We shall now describe an easier way of forming the paths of Π. We shall not prove our assertions, but the method could be used to give an alternative proof of our main theorem.

We first give a method of labelling certain of the intersection nodes. Each node may receive the label A or the label B or both. If $x \in \operatorname{Ter}\Phi - \operatorname{Ter}\Theta$, it lies on exactly one path $\phi \in \Phi$. If $\phi = \phi . x$ contains any intersection nodes then there is a last such node x' on ϕ (observe that if $x \in \operatorname{Nod}\Theta$, then $x' = x$). We label x' with A. We carry out this procedure for each $x \in \operatorname{Ter}\Phi - \operatorname{Ter}\Theta$.

Suppose now that certain of the intersection nodes have been labelled. We describe an inductive procedure for labelling further nodes. Each node x having A among its labels lies on exactly one path $\theta \in \Theta$. We give the label B to the first intersection node on θ which comes after x (if θ is a cycle, this node could be x itself). Each node x having B among its labels lies on exactly one path $\phi \in \Phi$. We give the label A to the last intersection node on ϕ which comes before x (again, this could be x itself if ϕ is a cycle). After a countable number of steps, all the labels will have been assigned.

We now indicate how to construct a set Π of paths. First, Π is to contain all those paths of Θ which have no label, and all those paths ϕ of Φ for which

Ter $\phi \in$ Ter Φ − Ter Θ and which have no label. The remaining paths of Π contain intersection nodes. Now these paths are made up of parts of paths of Θ and parts of paths of Φ, and all changes from paths of one kind to paths of the other occur at labelled nodes. It will be enough to describe how these changes are made. If x has only the label A, then the path π_x of Π through x must enter x as part of a path of Θ and leave as part of a path of Φ. If x has only the label B, then π_x must enter x as part of a path of Φ and leave as part of a path of Θ. If x has both labels A and B, then π_x both enters and leaves x as part of a path of Φ. Thus, the typical sequence of labels on a path of Π is ... *ABABA* ..., though it may be ... *A*(*BA*)*BA* ... where the brackets indicate that both labels are given to one node.

4. Special cases and applications

We indicate in this section some special cases of interest of the main theorem, and then we give some applications to transversal theory.

COROLLARY 1. *Let Γ be a directed graph having no infinite paths. Let Θ, Φ be two sets of pairwise node disjoint paths in Γ. Then there is a set Π of pairwise node disjoint finite paths in Γ satisfying* (a), (b) *and* (c).

This corollary follows immediately from the General Linking Theorem. It is enough to assume that there are no infinite paths in Γ which contain nodes in $\{\text{Nod}\,\Theta\} \cap \{\text{Nod}\,\Phi\}$. The assumption on infinite paths is, of course, always satisfied if Γ is a *finite* directed graph (i.e. the set of nodes is finite).

If a directed graph Γ has no cyclic paths, then the main theorem remains true if everywhere the word 'path' is replaced by 'linear path'. An important circumstance in which this happens is given in the next corollary.

COROLLARY 2. *Let Γ be a directed graph and suppose that the set N of nodes of Γ can be partitioned into sets N_k $(1 \leqslant k \leqslant m)$ such that if (x, y) is an edge of Γ, then $x \in N_i$, $y \in N_j$ for some i, j with $1 \leqslant i < j \leqslant m$. Let Θ, Φ be two sets of pairwise node disjoint finite linear paths in Γ. Then there is a set Π of pairwise node disjoint finite linear paths in Γ which satisfies* (a), (b) *and* (c).

It is plain that Γ, in this case, has no cyclic paths.

In (**7**, **8**) was proved a theorem which is related to Corollary 1. This theorem says that if Θ and Φ are two sets of pairwise node disjoint finite linear paths in a directed graph Γ, then there is a set Π' of pairwise node disjoint *finite* linear paths in Γ satisfying (a) and (b). In case the directed graph Γ has no infinite paths, then this theorem can be deduced from Corollary 1, by taking Π' to be the set of all *linear* paths in Π. However, if the directed graph Γ has infinite paths it does not seem possible to derive this result from the General Linking Theorem. This is due to the presence in Π of unending or unbeginning paths. The cyclic paths and doubly-infinite paths can be eliminated from Π, for their presence in Π is solely for the purpose of obtaining the intersection nodes which are neither initial nodes of Θ nor terminal nodes of Φ; however, the unbeginning or unending paths cannot be eliminated, for they are needed to obtain some of the initial nodes of Θ and some of the terminal nodes of Φ.

The main theorem can also be used to obtain a theorem about undirected graphs. An *undirected* graph G consists of a set N, whose elements are called *nodes*, together with a collection of two-element subsets of N which are called *edges*. A *path* is an undirected graph G is a linearly or cyclically ordered set of nodes such that each pair of adjacent nodes is an edge of G. Since paths are ordered sets, the notions of initial and terminal nodes, defined for directed graphs, are still appropriate.

COROLLARY 3. *Let Θ, Φ be two sets of pairwise node disjoint paths in an undirected graph G. Then there is a set Π of pairwise node disjoint paths in G which satisfies* (a), (b) *and* (c).

To obtain this corollary from Theorem 1, define a directed graph Γ whose set of nodes is also N and whose edges are the ordered pairs (x, y) where x and y are adjacent nodes in a path of Θ or a path of Φ with x preceding y. Then Θ and Φ become sets of pairwise node disjoint paths in Γ to which we can apply the theorem.

We now turn to some applications of our results to transversal theory. If $\mathfrak{A}(I) = (A_i : i \in I)$ is a family of subsets of a set E, then a set $T \subseteq E$ is a *transversal* of $\mathfrak{A}(I)$ if there exists a bijection $\rho : T \to I$ such that $x \in A_{\rho(x)}\,(x \in T)$. If $I' \subseteq I$, then $\mathfrak{A}(I') = (A_i : i \in I')$ is a *subfamily* of $\mathfrak{A}$(I). *Let* $\mathfrak{B}(J) = (B_j : j \in J)$ be another family of subsets of E. A set $T \subseteq E$ is a *common transversal* of $\mathfrak{A}(I)$ and $\mathfrak{B}(J)$ provided it is a transversal of both.

COROLLARY 4. *Let $\mathfrak{A}(I) = (A_i : i \in I)$ and $\mathfrak{B}(J) = (B_j : j \in J)$ be two families of subsets of a set E. Let $M \subseteq E$. Suppose the family of sets $(I_k : k \in K)$ partitions I and the family of sets $(J_l : l \in L)$ partitions J. Let a_k, b_k be integers with $0 \leqslant a_k \leqslant b_k\ (k \in K)$, and let c_l, d_l be integers with $0 \leqslant c_l \leqslant d_l\ (l \in L)$. Suppose there exist $I' \subseteq I$, $J' \subseteq J$ such that $\mathfrak{A}(I')$ and $\mathfrak{B}(J')$ have a common transversal T' with $M \subseteq T'$ where*

$$|I_k \cap I'| \leqslant b_k \quad (k \in K), \qquad c_l \leqslant |J_l \cap J'| \quad (l \in L),$$

and suppose there exist $I'' \subseteq I$, $J'' \subseteq J$ such that $\mathfrak{A}(I'')$ and $\mathfrak{B}(J'')$ have a common transversal T'' with $M \subseteq T''$ where

$$a_k \leqslant |I_k \cap I''| \quad (k \in K), \qquad |J_l \cap J''| \leqslant d_l \quad (l \in L).$$

Then there exist $\bar{I} \subseteq I$, $\bar{J} \subseteq J$ *such that* $\mathfrak{A}(\bar{I})$ *and* $\mathfrak{B}(\bar{J})$ *have a common transversal* $\bar{T}$ *with* $M \subseteq \bar{T}$ *where*

$$a_k \leqslant |I_k \cap \bar{I}| \leqslant b_k \quad (k \in K), \qquad c_l \leqslant |J_l \cap \bar{J}| \leqslant d_l \quad (l \in L).$$

We may assume without loss in generality that I, J, E are pairwise disjoint sets. We construct a directed graph Γ in two stages. First we construct the directed graph $\bar{\Gamma}$ associated with the two families $\mathfrak{A}(I)$ and $\mathfrak{B}(J)$ of subsets of E. The nodes of $\bar{\Gamma}$ are the elements of $I \cup E \cup J$; the edges of $\bar{\Gamma}$ are the ordered pairs of the form (i, e) where $e \in A_i$ $(i \in I, e \in E)$ and those of the form (e, j) where $e \in B_j$ $(e \in E, j \in J)$. Since $\mathfrak{A}(I')$ and $\mathfrak{B}(J')$ have a common transversal containing M, there is a set of pairwise node disjoint paths Φ' in $\bar{\Gamma}$ with $\text{In}\,\Phi' = I'$, $\text{Ter}\,\Phi' = J'$, and $M \subseteq \text{Nod}\,\Phi'$. Likewise there is a set of pairwise node disjoint paths Θ'' in $\bar{\Gamma}$ with $\text{In}\,\Theta'' = I''$, $\text{Ter}\,\Theta'' = J''$, and $M \subseteq \text{Nod}\,\Theta''$.

Let $I_k{}^*$ be a set with $\{I' \cap I''\} \cap I_k \subseteq I_k{}^* \subseteq I'' \cap I_k$ and $a_k \leqslant |I_k{}^*| \leqslant b_k$ $(k \in K)$. Because of the inequalities satisfied by I', I'', such sets exist. Likewise there exist sets $J_l{}^*$ with $\{J' \cap J''\} \cap J_l \subseteq J_l{}^* \subseteq J' \cap J_l$ and $c_l \leqslant |J_l{}^*| \leqslant d_l$ $(l \in L)$. Let $I^* = \bigcup_{k \in K} I_k{}^*$ and $J^* = \bigcup_{l \in L} J_l{}^*$. Now let $(P_k : k \in K)$ be a family of pairwise disjoint sets with $|P_k| = b_k$ $(k \in K)$, let $(Q_l : l \in L)$ be a family of pairwise disjoint sets with $|Q_l| = d_l$ $(l \in L)$, let U be a set with the cardinal number of U equal, say, to the cardinal number of I, and let V be a set with the cardinal number of V equal, say, to the cardinal number of J. Assume, as we surely may, that I, J, E, $P = \bigcup_{k \in K} P_k$, $Q = \bigcup_{l \in L} Q_l$, U, V are pairwise disjoint sets. The directed graph Γ is constructed from $\bar{\Gamma}$ by enlarging $\bar{\Gamma}$ to include the elements of $P \cup Q \cup U \cup V$ as nodes and the elements of $\bigcup_{k \in K} \{P_k \times I_k\}$, $\bigcup_{l \in L} \{J_l \times Q_l\}$, $I'' \times U$, $V \times J'$ as edges. The graph $\bar{\Gamma}$ has no cyclic or infinite paths.

We define a set Θ of pairwise node disjoint paths in Γ as follows. Let θ'' be a path in Θ''. We construct a path $\theta \in \Theta$ from θ''. If θ'' has initial node in $I_k{}^*$ $(k \in K)$, we enlarge θ'' to have initial node in P_k; if θ'' has initial node in $I'' - I^*$, we do not alter its initial node. If θ'' has terminal node in $J_l \cap J''$ $(l \in L)$, we enlarge θ'' to have terminal node in Q_l $(l \in L)$. The set Θ is to include the paths constructed in this way; because of our definition of Γ we may perform these constructions in such a way that we obtain a set of pairwise node disjoint paths in Γ. In addition to these paths, Θ is to include a set of pairwise node disjoint paths (each having two nodes) whose set of initial nodes is contained in V and whose set of terminal nodes equals $J' - J^*$. Thus Θ is a set of pairwise node disjoint paths in Γ with

$$\text{In}\,\Theta \subseteq P \cup V \cup \{I'' - I^*\},$$
$$\text{Ter}\,\Theta \subseteq Q \cup \{J' - J^*\},$$
$$M \subseteq \text{Nod}\,\Theta,$$
$$a_k \leqslant |\{\text{In}\,\Theta\} \cap P_k| \leqslant b_k \qquad (k \in K).$$

Likewise we may construct from Φ' a set Φ of pairwise node disjoint paths in Γ with

$$\operatorname{In}\Phi \subseteq P \cup \{I'' - I^*\},$$
$$\operatorname{Ter}\Phi \subseteq Q \cup U \cup \{J' - J^*\},$$
$$M \subseteq \operatorname{Nod}\Phi,$$
$$c_l \leqslant |\{\operatorname{Ter}\Phi\} \cap Q_l| \leqslant d_l \qquad (l \in L).$$

We now apply the General Linking Theorem to conclude the existence of a set Π of pairwise node disjoint paths in Γ satisfying (a), (b) and (c).

Let $\bar{\Pi}$ be the set of pairwise node disjoint paths in $\bar{\Gamma}$ obtained from Π by eliminating the nodes not in $I \cup E \cup J$ (and eliminating degenerate paths which result). Then $\operatorname{In}\bar{\Pi} \subseteq I, \operatorname{Ter}\bar{\Pi} \subseteq J, M \subseteq \operatorname{Nod}\bar{\Pi}$. Because $\operatorname{Ter}\Phi \subseteq \operatorname{Ter}\Pi$, $\{I'' - I^*\} \cap \{\operatorname{In}\bar{\Pi}\} = \varnothing$; hence because $\{\operatorname{In}\Theta\} \subseteq \operatorname{In}\Pi, a_k \leqslant |\{\operatorname{In}\bar{\Pi}\} \cap I_k| \leqslant b_k$ $(k \in K)$. Likewise $c_l \leqslant |\{\operatorname{Ter}\bar{\Pi}\} \cap J_l| \leqslant d_l$ $(l \in L)$. Since $\mathfrak{A}(\operatorname{In}\bar{\Pi})$ and $\mathfrak{B}(\operatorname{Ter}\bar{\Pi})$ have a common transversal containing M, the proof is complete.

There is a special case of this corollary which is worth mentioning. It can be derived by applying the General Linking Theorem to the directed graph $\bar{\Gamma}$ constructed above (the additional constructions are unnecessary).

COROLLARY 5. *Let $\mathfrak{A}(I) = (A_i : i \in I)$ and $\mathfrak{B}(J) = (B_j : j \in J)$ be two families of subsets of a set E. Let $M \subseteq E$. Suppose there exist $I' \subseteq I$, $J' \subseteq J$ such that $\mathfrak{A}(I')$ and $\mathfrak{B}J(')$ have a common transversal containing M, and suppose there exist $I'' \subseteq I$, $J'' \subseteq J$ such that $\mathfrak{A}(I'')$ and $\mathfrak{B}(J'')$ have a common transversal containing M. Then there exists sets $\bar{I}, \bar{J}$ with $I' \subseteq \bar{I} \subseteq I' \cup I''$, $J'' \subseteq \bar{J} \subseteq J' \cup J''$ such that $\mathfrak{A}(\bar{I})$ and $\mathfrak{B}(\bar{J})$ have a common transversal containing M.*

The special case obtained by taking $I' = I$, $J' = J$ (in which case $\bar{I} = I$, $\bar{J} = J$) is also of considerable interest. Theorems about transversals of a single family can also be obtained from it (or one can go back to the main theorem). For further discussion on these matters, one may consult (**2, 3, 4, 6, 7**).

If in Corollary 4 the set $M = \varnothing$, then one also obtains a result of interest. In (**3**) a theorem was proved which contains this as a special case: rather than having prescribed upper and lower bounds on $|I_k \cap \bar{I}|$, etc., there is prescribed upper and lower bounds on the 'defects' $|I_k - \bar{I}|$, etc. It was remarked in (**4**) that the proof as given in (**3**) for $M = \varnothing$, with virtually no change also works for arbitrary M. It does not seem possible to obtain the 'defect' version of Corollary 4 from the General Linking Theorem.

5. Examples

We give in this section some examples which illustrate the proof of the main result. In addition, these examples will show how cyclic paths, degenerate paths (consisting of only one node), and infinite paths may occur in the collection Π even if neither of the collections Θ and Φ have such paths. We shall use below the letters A and B (if necessary, subscripted) both to designate the labels attached to a node as a result of the labelling procedure described in §3 and to identify the node. In drawing the graphs we shall follow the custom of representing nodes by dots and edges by lines with arrows.

In the directed graph of Figure 1, Θ consists of the one linear path indicated

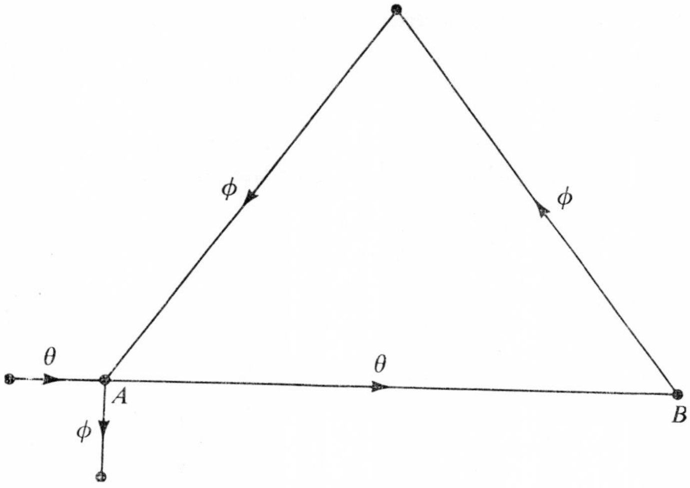

FIGURE 1

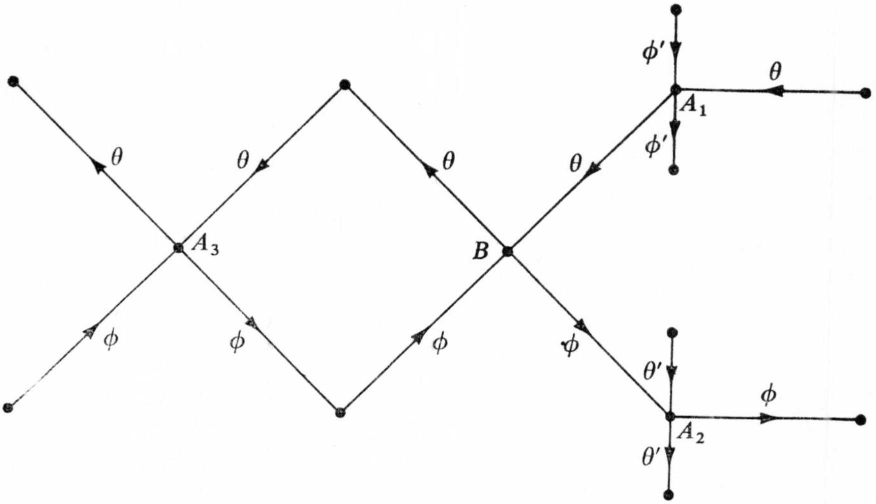

FIGURE 2

by θ while Φ consists of the one linear path indicated by ϕ. The set Π as constructed in §3 consists of the two paths $\theta.A.\phi$ and (B). It is easy to see that this is the only set of paths satisfying the conclusion of the theorem, so that paths consisting of a single node are absolutely necessary for the validity of the main theorem.

In the directed graph of Figure 2, Θ and Φ each consist of two linear paths which are indicated by θ, θ' and ϕ, ϕ', respectively. The set Π as constructed in §3 consists of the three paths (two linear and one cyclic) $\theta.A_1.\phi'$, $\theta'.A_2.\phi$, $A_3.\phi.B.\theta.A_3$. It is also easy to see that this is the only set of paths satisfying the conclusion of the theorem, so that cyclic paths are absolutely necessary for its validity.

The final example is one of an infinite directed graph. For each $i = 0$, ± 1, ± 2, ..., there is defined by Figure 3 a finite directed graph Γ_i. There are

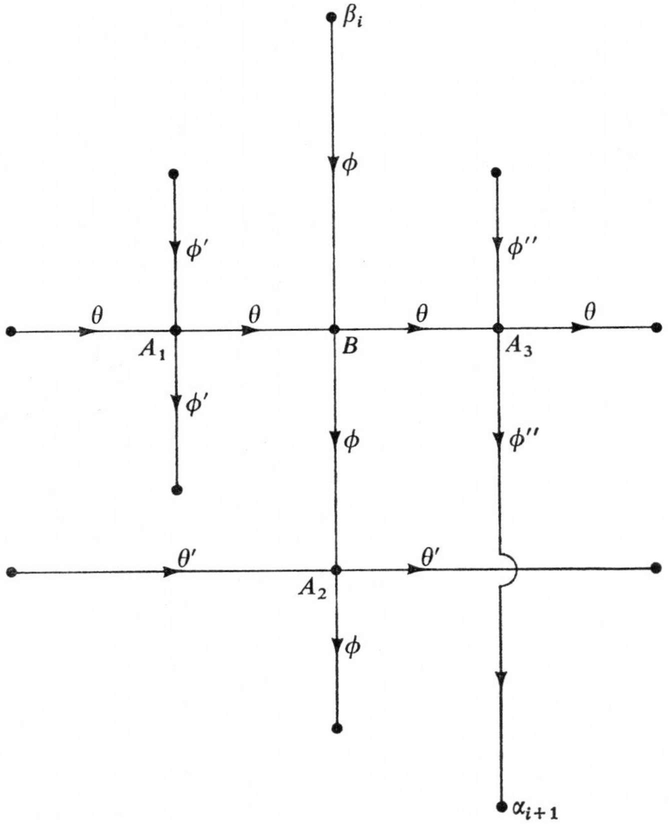

FIGURE 3

two collections of finite linear paths in Γ_i defined in figure 3. The set Θ_i consists of the two linear paths indicated by θ and θ' respectively; the set Φ_i consists of the three linear paths indicated by ϕ, ϕ', ϕ'', respectively. The results of the labelling procedure applied to Γ_i and these two collections of paths are indicated in the figure. The set Π_i constructed in the proof of the theorem gives the three linear paths $\theta.A_1.\phi'$, $\theta'.A_2.\phi$, $\pi_i = \phi.B.\theta.A_3.\phi''$. This is the only set of paths satisfying the conclusion of the theorem. Now consider the directed graph Γ which is obtained from Γ_i $(i = 0, 1, 2, \ldots)$ by identifying the node α_{i+1} with β_{i+1} $(i = 0, 1, 2, \ldots)$. We define Θ to be the finite linear paths of $\bigcup_{i=0}^{\infty} \Theta_i$ and Φ the finite linear paths of $\bigcup_{i=0}^{\infty} \Phi_i$ where two paths are combined when the terminal node of one is α_{i+1} and the initial node of the other is β_{i+1} $(i = 0, 1, 2, \ldots)$. The labelling procedure applied to Γ gives the same results as the labelling procedure applied to the individual Γ_i $(i = 0, 1, 2, \ldots)$. The set Π constructed in the proof of the theorem consists of the paths in $\bigcup_{i \in I} \Pi_i$ where paths are combined if the terminal node of one is α_{i+1} and the initial node of the other is β_{i+1} $(i = 0, 1, 2, \ldots)$. Thus Π contains the unending path $\pi_0 . \pi_1 . \pi_2 . \ldots$. It is not difficult to see that this is the only set of paths satisfying the conclusion of the theorem; thus unending paths are indispensable. If one defines Γ by identifying α_{i+1} with β_{i+1} $(i = 0, \pm 1, \pm 2, \ldots)$, then a doubly-infinite path results.

References

1. Banach, S. Un théorème sur les transformations biunivoques, *Fund. Math.* **6** (1924), 236–239.
2. Brualdi, R. A. An extension of Banach's mapping theorem, *Proc. Amer. Math. Soc.* **20** (1969), 520–526.
3. Brualdi, R. A. Common transversals and strong exchange systems, *J. Comb. Theory* **8** (1970), 307–329.
4. Brualdi, R. A. A general theorem concerning common transversals, *Proceedings of the Conference on Combinatorial Mathematics and its Applications at Oxford, 1969.* (To appear).
5. Knaster, B. Un théorème sur les fonctions d'ensembles, *Ann. Polonaise Math.* **6** (1927), 133.
6. Perfect, H. and Pym, J. S. An extension of Banach's mapping theorem, with applications to problems concerning distinct representatives, *Proc. Cambridge Philos. Soc.* **62** (1966), 187–192.
7. Pym, J. S. The linking of sets in graphs, *J. London Math. Soc.* **44** (1969), 542–550.
8. Pym, J. S. A proof of the linkage theorem, *J. Math. Anal. Applic.* **27** (1969) 636–638.

The Exterior Cycle Index of a Permutation Group

N. G. de Bruijn

1. Introduction

Let G be a finite group and let H be a subgroup. Let $g_1H, \ldots, g_t H$ be the right-hand cosets of H (thus $t = |G|/|H|$). The set of these cosets is denoted by G/H. If $g \in G$, then by $\zeta(g)$ we denote a permutation of G/H defined as follows: $\zeta(g)$ maps any coset $g_i H$ into $gg_i H$.

To this situation there belongs a cycle index (see (2.2)) which, in this special case, can be described as follows. Let $x_1, x_2, x_3, \ldots$ be variables. We shall define an expression $Q(G; H; x_1, x_2, \ldots)$, which is a polynomial in $x_1, x_2, \ldots$. Let (for $j = 1, 2, \ldots$) $c_j(g)$ denote the number of cycles of length j occurring in the permutation $\zeta(g)$ (whence $c_1(g) + 2c_2(g) + 3c_3(g) + \ldots = |G|/|H|$).

We define

$$Q(G; H; x_1, x_2, \ldots) = |G|^{-1} \sum_{g \in G} x_1^{c_1(g)} x_2^{c_2(g)} \ldots . \tag{1.1}$$

In particular if H consists of the unit element only, $Q(G; H)$ is the cycle index of the Cayley representation of G (see (**1**), example 5.6).

We shall specialize by taking for G the symmetric group S_D of all $|D|!$ permutations of a finite set D. Accordingly, the subgroup H becomes a group of permutations of D. We shall call

$$Q(S_D; H; x_1, x_2, \ldots) \tag{1.2}$$

the *exterior cycle index* of the permutation group H. We shall show in this paper that this exterior cycle index is completely determined by the ordinary cycle index of H.

2. Notation

If A and B are finite sets, then A^B denotes the set of all mappings of B into A; $|A|$ denotes the number of elements of A; S_A is the group of all $|A|!$ permutations of A.

$\mathscr{J}$ will denote the set of all those sequences of nonnegative integers of which all but a finite number of entries are zero. If $J \in \mathscr{J}$, then the entries of J are denoted by $p_1(J), p_2(J), \ldots$.

For $n = 1, 2, 3, \ldots$, we denote by $\mathscr{J}(n)$ the subclass of all $J \in \mathscr{J}$ for which

$$\sum_1^\infty m\, p_m(J) = n.$$

If $x_1, x_2, x_3, \ldots$ are variables, and $J \in \mathscr{J}$, then x^J is defined by

$$x^J = x_1^{p_1(J)} x_2^{p_2(J)} \ldots$$

which is essentially a finite product.

If $J \in \mathscr{J}$, then we define

$$\nu(J) = \prod_{m=1}^{\infty} \{(p_m(J))!\, m^{p_m(J)}\}.$$

If σ is a permutation of n objects, then $B(\sigma)$ stands for the sequence $b_1, b_2, b_3, \ldots$ where (for each m) b_m is the number of cycles of length m in that permutation. Obviously $B(\sigma) \in \mathscr{J}(n)$. $B(\sigma)$ is called the *type* of σ.

If $J \in \mathscr{J}$, and if σ is a permutation of type J, then for $k = 1, 2, 3, \ldots$ the type of the kth power σ^k depends on J and k only. We denote that type by $\Lambda(k, J)$. It is not hard to verify that its entries are

$$p_i(\Lambda(k, J)) = \Sigma k u^{-1} p_{ki/u}(J) \qquad (i = 1, 2, 3, \ldots), \tag{2.1}$$

where the sum runs over all divisors u of k which are relatively prime to i.

If G is a finite group, and if θ is a representation of G by permutations of a finite set D (that is, $\theta(g) \in S_D$ for each $g \in G$, and $\theta(g_1)\theta(g_2) = \theta(g_1 g_2)$), then we define the polynomial

$$P(G; \theta; x_1, x_2, \ldots) = |G|^{-1} \sum_{g \in G} x^{B(\theta(g))}. \tag{2.2}$$

(It will be recalled that according to our convention

$$x^{B(\theta(g))} = x_1^{b_1(\theta(g))} x_2^{b_2(\theta(g))} \ldots .)$$

The polynomial $P(G; \theta; x_1, x_2, \ldots)$ is called the cycle index of the pair G, θ. In cases where G is given as a group of permutations of D we usually take θ to be the trivial representation ($\theta(g) = g$) and we simply speak of the cycle index P_G of G.

Note that (1.1) is a special case of (2.2):

$$Q(G; H; x_1, x_2, \ldots) = P(G; \zeta; x_1, x_2, \ldots). \tag{2.3}$$

As usual, μ denotes Möbius's function. We recall that, if $a(n) = \Sigma_{d|n} b(d)$ for $n = 1, 2, 3, \ldots$, then

$$b(n) = \sum_{d|n} \mu(n/d)\, a(d). \tag{2.4}$$

3. The exterior cycle index

Let D be a finite set and let H be a subgroup of S_D. If $|H|\,\lambda_J$ is the number of elements of H with type J, we have for the cycle index of H

$$P(H; x_1, x_2, \ldots) = \sum_{J \in \mathscr{J}} \lambda_J\, x^J. \tag{3.1}$$

Let σ be an element of S_D. $\zeta(\sigma)$ denotes the permutation of S_D/H effected by multiplication on the left by σ (cf. section 1). That is, ζ is a representation of S_D by permutations of S_D/H. By (2.3) we have $Q(S_D; H) = P(S_D; \zeta)$.

If $\sigma \in S_D$, we shall write for the type of $\zeta(\sigma)$ the sequence

$$c_1(\sigma),\ c_2(\sigma),\ \ldots\ . \tag{3.2}$$

That is, $c_m(\sigma) = p_m\big(B(\zeta(\sigma))\big)$ for all m.

We shall obtain the numbers (3.2) by studying the numbers $c_1(\sigma^k)$ ($k = 1, 2, \ldots$).

$c_1(\sigma^k)$ is the number of right cosets that are invariant under multiplication by σ^k on the left. A permutation $\pi \in S_D$ lies in one of these cosets if and only if $\sigma^k \pi \in \pi H$. Therefore

$$|H|\,.\,c_1(\sigma^k) = (\text{number of } \pi \in S_D \text{ with } \pi^{-1}\sigma^k\pi \in H). \tag{3.3}$$

The right-hand side of (3.3) can be written as

$$\sum_{\eta \in H} (\text{number of } \pi \in S_D \text{ with } \pi^{-1}\sigma^k\pi = \eta). \tag{3.4}$$

There exists a $\pi \in S_D$ with $\pi^{-1}\sigma^k\pi = \eta$ if and only if σ^k and η have the same type, that is, if $B(\sigma^k) = B(\eta)$. If this is the case, then the number of such π is $\nu\big(B(\sigma^k)\big)$. Therefore, (3.4) equals $|H|\,.\,\omega\big(B(\sigma^k)\big)$, if we introduce as abbreviation

$$\omega(J) = \lambda_J\,.\,\nu(J). \tag{3.5}$$

It follows that

$$c_1(\sigma^k) = \omega\big(B(\sigma^k)\big). \tag{3.6}$$

We have, according to (2.1),

$$c_i(\sigma^k) = p_i\Big(B(\zeta(\sigma^k))\Big) = p_i\Big(B\big((\zeta(\sigma))^k\big)\Big)$$

$$= p_i\Big(\Lambda\big(k, B(\zeta(\sigma))\big)\Big) = \Sigma k u^{-1}\, p_{ki/u}\Big(B(\zeta(\sigma))\Big),$$

whence

$$c_i(\sigma^k) = \Sigma k u^{-1}\, c_{ki/u}(\sigma),$$

where u runs through the divisors of k that are relatively prime to i.

In particular

$$c_1(\sigma^k) = \sum_{u|k} u\, c_u(\sigma).$$

Hence by (2.4), for $m = 1, 2, 3, \ldots,$

$$c_m(\sigma) = m^{-1} \sum_{k|m} \mu(m/k)\, c_1(\sigma^k). \tag{3.7}$$

Let $E(J)$ denote the sequence $e_1(J), e_2(J), \ldots,$ where

$$e_m(J) = m^{-1} \sum_{k|m} \mu(m/k)\, \omega\big(\Lambda(k, J)\big).$$

Thus, by (3.6) and (3.7), if σ has the type J, then $\zeta(\sigma)$ has the type $E(J)$. So finally we have, since S_D has $|D|!\,/\nu(J)$ elements of type J,

$$P(S_D; \zeta; x_1, x_2, \ldots) = Q(S_D; H; x_1, x_2, \ldots)$$

$$= \sum_{J \in \mathcal{J}(|D|)} \big(\nu(J)\big)^{-1}\, x^{E(J)}. \tag{3.8}$$

In this way we have expressed the coefficients of the exterior cycle index entirely in terms of $|D|$ and P_H.

4. Simpler expressions

We shall substitute into $Q(S_D; H)$

$$x_1 = y_1\, y_2\, y_3 \ldots$$

$$x_2 = (y_2\, y_4\, y_6 \ldots)^2$$

$$x_3 = (y_3\, y_6\, y_9 \ldots)^3$$

$$\ldots .$$

We then obtain

$$Q(S_D; H; x_1, x_2, \ldots) = \sum_{J \in \mathcal{J}(|D|)} (\nu(J))^{-1} {y_1}^{\omega(\Lambda(1,J))} {y_2}^{\omega(\Lambda(2,J))} {y_3}^{\omega(\Lambda(3,J))} \ldots, \tag{4.1}$$

a formula which we might equally well have derived directly, without Möbius's inversion formula.

Substitutions of the type just described occur e.g. in Theorem 5.4 in **(1)**, and more generally in formulas (4.1), (4.6) of **(2)**. Application of Theorem 5.4 of **(1)** leads to the following result.

Let K be a group of permutations of a finite set E, let D be another finite set, and let H be a subgroup of S_D.

As in Section 1, the set of right cosets S_D/H is permuted by the left multiplications $\zeta(\sigma)$ $(\sigma \in S_D)$. Two mappings f_1, f_2 of E into S_D/H are called equivalent if there are elements $\alpha \in K$, $\sigma \in S_D$ such that $f_1 = \zeta(\sigma) f_2 \alpha$. Then the number of equivalence classes is, according to Theorem 5.4 of **(1)**,

$$P_K\left(\frac{\partial}{\partial z_1}, \frac{\partial}{\partial z_2}, \dots\right) Q(S_D; H; \exp(z_1 + z_2 + \dots), \exp 2(z_2 + z_4 + \dots), \exp 3(z_3 + z_6 + \dots), \dots)$$

evaluated at $z_1 = z_2 = \dots = 0$. Using (4.1) with $y_j = \exp(z_j)$, we obtain for the number of those classes

$$\sum_{J \in \mathscr{J}(|D|)} (\nu(J))^{-1} P_K\Big(\omega(\Lambda(1, J)), \omega(\Lambda(2, J)), \omega(\Lambda(3, J)), \dots\Big). \tag{4.2}$$

At this point we recall the combinatorial interpretation of the $\omega(\Lambda(k, J))$: if σ is any permutation of type J, then $|H|\ \omega(\Lambda(k, J))$ equals the number of $\pi \in S_D$ with $\pi^{-1}\sigma^k\pi \in H$.

5. An example

As a test of (4.1), we show a simple example. For D we take a set of 3 elements, and for H we take the group of all even permutations of D. There are two cosets: the set of even and the set of odd permutations. Multiplication on the left by some $\sigma \in S_D$ leaves the cosets invariant or interchanges them, according as σ is even or odd. Therefore the exterior cycle index is simply $\frac{1}{2}x_1{}^2 + \frac{1}{2}x_2$. The cycle index of H is $\frac{1}{3}x_1{}^3 + \frac{2}{3}x_3$.

$\mathscr{J}(|D|)$ contains 3 elements, to be abbreviated as

$$J_0 = (3, 0, 0, 0, \dots),$$
$$J_1 = (1, 1, 0, 0, \dots),$$
$$J_2 = (0, 0, 1, 0, \dots).$$

Investigating the kth powers of permutations of type J_0, J_1, J_2, respectively, we obtain

$$\Lambda(k, J_0) = J_0;$$
$$\Lambda(k, J_1) = J_0 \text{ if } k \text{ even}, \ = J_1 \text{ if } k \text{ odd};$$
$$\Lambda(k, J_2) = J_2 \text{ or } J_0 \text{ if } k \text{ is or is not a multiple of 3}.$$

We evaluate

$$\lambda(J_0) = \tfrac{1}{3}, \quad \lambda(J_1) = 0, \quad \lambda(J_2) = \tfrac{2}{3},$$
$$\nu(J_0) = 6, \quad \nu(J_1) = 2, \quad \nu(J_2) = 3,$$
$$\omega(J_0) = 2, \quad \omega(J_1) = 0, \quad \omega(J_2) = 2.$$

Hence

$$\omega(\Lambda(k, J_0)) = 2 \text{ for all } k;$$
$$\omega(\Lambda(k, J_1)) = 2 \text{ if } k \text{ even}, \quad = 0 \text{ if } k \text{ odd};$$
$$\omega(\Lambda(k, J_2)) = 2 \text{ for all } k.$$

The right-hand side of (4.1) becomes

$$\tfrac{1}{6} y_1{}^2 y_2{}^2 y_3{}^2 \dots + \tfrac{1}{2} y_2{}^2 y_4{}^2 y_6{}^2 \dots + \tfrac{1}{3} y_1{}^2 y_2{}^2 y_3{}^2 \dots$$

and, indeed, this is the same thing as $\tfrac{1}{2}x_1{}^2 + \tfrac{1}{2}x_2$.

6. An application of (4.2)

E. M. Palmer and R. W. Robinson (**4**) counted the number of orbits of a certain group of permutations. We cite (**4**).

'Let A be a permutation group of degree n acting on the set $X = \{1, 2, \dots, m\}$. Let B be another permutation group of degree n acting on $Y = \{1, 2, \dots, n\}$. Let W be the collection of m by n matrices in which the elements of each row are the n objects in Y. Thus there are $(n!)^m$ matrices in W. Two matrices in W are called column-equivalent if one can be obtained from the other by a permutation of the columns. Hence there are $(n!)^{m-1}$ column-equivalence classes.

The matrix group of A and B, denoted $[A; B]$, acts on the column-equivalence classes as follows. For each permutation α in A and each sequence $\beta_1, \beta_2, \dots, \beta_m$ of m permutations with β_i in B, there is a permutation, denoted $[\alpha; \beta_1, \beta_2, \dots, \beta_m]$ in $[A; B]$ such that the column-equivalence class to which the matrix $[w_{i,j}]$ belongs is sent by $[\alpha; \beta_1, \beta_2, \dots, \beta_m]$ to the class to which $[\beta_i\, w_{\alpha i, j}]$ belongs. That is, α first determines a permutation of the rows and then each β_i permutes the entries in the ith row.

The number of orbits determined by the matrix group $[A; B]$ is denoted $N[A; B]$.'

We can interpret $N[A; B]$ by means of the exterior cycle index of a permutation group. Actually, the $N[A; B]$ orbits are just the same as the equivalence classes described at the end of Section 4, provided we replace D by Y, H by B, E by X, K by A, left classes by right classes, and consequently, take $\zeta(\sigma)$ as a permutation of right classes instead of left classes:

$$\zeta(\sigma)\, B\sigma_i = B\sigma_i\, \sigma^{-1}.$$

For details we refer to (**3**).

We can now use (4.2) for the evaluation of $N[A; B]$:

$$N[A; B] = \sum_{J \in \mathscr{J}(Y)} (\nu(J))^{-1} P_A(r_1(J), r_2(J), \ldots). \tag{6.1}$$

In this formula, P_A is the ordinary cycle index of A, and $r_k(J)$ can be defined as follows: take any arbitrary permutation $\sigma \in S_Y$ of type J, then $|B| r_k(J)$ is the number of $\pi \in S_Y$ with $\pi^{-1} \sigma^k \pi \in B$.

The expression (6.1) and the more complicated expression given in (**4**) look very different; (6.1) is the simpler one. It seems hard to verify that the two results are identical, otherwise than by the simple remark that they count the same number of objects.

References

1. DE BRUIJN, N. G. Pólya's theory of counting. Ch. V in *Applied Combinatorial Mathematics,* E. Beckenbach ed., Wiley, New York (1964), 144–184.
2. DE BRUIJN, N. G. Enumerative combinatorial problems concerning structures. *Nieuw Archief Wiskunde* (3) **11** (1963), 142–161.
3. DE BRUIJN, N. G. Comment on a paper by E. M. Palmer and R. W. Robinson. *Internal Report, Dept. of Math. Techn. Univ. Eindhoven* (October 1967).
4. PALMER, E. M. and ROBINSON, R. W. The matrix group of two permutation groups. *Bull. Amer. Math. Soc.* **73** (1967), 204–207.

The Finite Inversive Plane with Four Points on each Circle

H. S. M. COXETER

1. Introduction

The inversive plane of order 3 is a configuration of ten points and thirty circles, with four points on each circle and twelve circles through each point (**7**, pp. 104, 257). In one aspect, suggested by the geometry of complex numbers (**6**, pp. 145–147), the ten points are represented by the nine elements of the Galois field $GF(3^2)$ and an extra symbol ∞, while the thirty circles appear as the solutions of certain equations. If $GF(3^2)$ is defined by the polynomial modulus $i^2 + 1$, its nine elements are

$$0, \pm 1, \pm i, \text{ and } \pm 1 \pm i,$$

where $1 + 1 + 1 = 0$ and $i^2 = -1$. Eighteen of the circles have equations of the form

$$(z - a)(\bar{z} - \bar{a}) = \pm 1,$$

where a can be any element of $GF(3^2)$ and $\bar{a} = a^3$. The remaining twelve have equations of the form

$$\bar{c}z + c\bar{z} = 0 \text{ or } \pm 1,$$

where $c = 1$ or i or $1 \pm i$, and ∞ is regarded as a solution of any such 'linear' equation.

The object of this note is to develop a far more symmetrical notation, in which the twelve sub-configurations of five mutually tangent circles are represented by the twelve symbols

1, 2, 3, 4, 5, 6, *a, b, c, d, e, f,*

each point is represented by a triad (of numerals or letters) and each circle by a pair (or 'duad').

2. Axioms for a Miquelian inversive plane

A *Miquelian inversive plane* is a system of geometric objects, called *points* and *circles*, with a relation of *incidence* which allows us to use such phrases as 'a point P lies on a circle α' or 'a circle α passes through a point P' or 'two circles α and β intersect in two points P and Q' or 'three points P, Q, R determine a circle $\alpha = PQR$'. The sufficiency of the following four axioms was established by Yi Chen (**1**):

I. *There exist four points not on a circle.*

II. *Any three distinct points lie on just one circle.*

III. *If a point P is on a circle α while Q is not on α, there is just one circle through Q whose only common point with α is P.*

IV (Miquel's Theorem). *If each cyclically adjacent pair of four circles have a pair of common points, forming altogether eight distinct points, and if four of these points, one from each pair, lie on a circle, then the remaining four lie on a circle.*

Two circles are said to be *intersecting*, *tangent* or *non-intersecting* according as they have two common points, one common point, or no common point. Thus the circles considered in Axiom III are tangent, with P as their point of contact.

Two intersecting circles are said to be *orthogonal* if one of them belongs to a triad of mutually tangent circles, touching one another at three distinct points A, B, C, while the other is the circle ABC. That is, two circles ABC and BCD (see Figure 3 on page 47) are orthogonal if there are two circles touching each other at A and touching BCD at B and C. When this happens, there are also two circles touching each other at D and touching ABC at B and C (cf. **9**, p. 232).

Two distinct points P and P' are said to be *inverses* (of each other) in a circle ABC if they both lie on more than one circle orthogonal to ABC (for instance, if the circles APP', BPP', CPP' are all orthogonal to ABC). In other words, the inverse of P is the second point of intersection of two circles through P orthogonal to ABC. Each point on ABC is regarded as being self-inverse. Thus the *inversion* $P \to P'$ is a one-to-one transformation of the whole inversive plane onto itself.

The definition of orthogonality can now be extended as follows. Two circles (not necessarily intersecting) are said to be *orthogonal* if one of them passes through two distinct points which are inverses in the other (**7**, p. 266). It follows that each of two orthogonal circles inverts the other one into itself.

Any two distinct circles determine a *pencil* of circles ('coaxal' circles) orthogonal to them, consisting of all the circles PP_1P_2 where P is a variable point while P_1 and P_2 are its inverses in the two given circles. In other words, any two distinct circles α and β belong to (and determine) a pencil $\alpha\beta$ ('the pencil spanned by α and β') which consists of all the circles orthogonal to any two circles orthogonal to α and β (**6**, p. 86).

The circles through two distinct points, L and L', form an *intersecting pencil* (Dembowski's 'bundle'), orthogonal to the *non-intersecting pencil* (his 'flock') for which L and L' are the *limiting points* (inverses in each member of the non-intersecting pencil).

If α and β are tangent, $\alpha\beta$ is a *tangent pencil*, and the orthogonal circles through the point of contact form another tangent pencil. (Dembowski reserves the term 'pencil' for this special case.)

3. Sections of a non-ruled quadric

It was proved by van der Waerden and Smid (**12**) that the points and circles of any Miquelian inversive plane can be represented by the points and conics on a non-ruled quadric surface in a projective 3-space, that is, by the points and secant planes of such a quadric. (By taking the quadric to be a sphere in Euclidean space, and making a stereographic projection, we obtain the familiar representation of the inversive plane by the Euclidean plane plus a single 'point at infinity.')

Referring to §2, we see that Axiom II holds because three points determine a plane, and Axiom III holds because, if P is on a conic α which is the section of the quadric by a certain plane, while Q is on the quadric but not on α, the tangent to α at P determines a unique plane through Q. As for Axiom IV, this is a special case of the theorem of the *eight associated points* (**6**, p. 259). If AA', BB', CC', DD' are the four pairs of points, of which A, B, C, D are given to lie on one circle, we should conclude that D' lies on the circle $A'B'C'$. To verify this, we regard the given quadric and the two plane pairs ($AA'B$, $CC'D$), ($AA'D$, $BB'C$) as three 'quadrics' whose complete intersection consists of the eight points A, B, C, D, A', B', C', D'. The plane pair (ABC, $A'B'C'$) passes through all these points except, possibly, D'. Therefore it passes through D' also. Since D' does not lie in the plane ABC, it must lie in the plane $A'B'C'$.

Any secant plane and its pole can be taken as axial plane and centre for a *harmonic homology* (or 'harmonic inversion') which leaves invariant all the points on the plane and, in particular, all the points on the conic which is the section of the quadric by this plane. The remaining points of the quadric are interchanged in pairs. Accordingly, such a homology represents an inversion, and orthogonal circles are represented by conjugate planes (or by their poles, which are conjugate points).

A pencil of circles is represented by a pencil of planes, that is, the set of planes through a line. This line may be a secant of the quadric, a tangent, or a non-secant. The corresponding pencil is intersecting, tangent, or non-intersecting, respectively.

4. A finite inversive plane

Following Dembowski (**7**, pp. 104, 258–264) we use the symbol $M(q)$ for the Miquelian inversive plane of order q, that is, a finite plane in which, q being a power of a prime, there are $q + 1$ points on each circle, $q(q + 1)$ circles through each point, $q^2 + 1$ points and $q(q^2 + 1)$ circles in the whole plane, $q + 1$ circles in each intersecting pencil, q in each tangent pencil, $q - 1$ in each non-intersecting pencil (**3**, p. 76). It follows that each circle intersects $q\binom{q+1}{2}$ others, touches $q^2 - 1$ others, and is disjoint from the remaining $3\binom{q}{3}$.

The corresponding non-ruled quadric lies in the finite projective space $PG(3, q)$, which contains $q^3 + q^2 + q + 1 = (q + 1)(q^2 + 1)$ points. Of these, $q^2 + 1$ form the quadric; the polar planes of the remaining $q(q^2 + 1)$ yield sections of the quadric which are conics representing the circles of $M(q)$. In other words, the $q^2 + 1$ points and $q(q^2 + 1)$ circles of $M(q)$ arise from the $q^2 + 1$ points on the quadric and the $q(q^2 + 1)$ points not on the quadric.

5. Triads, duads and synthemes

In the special case when $q = 3$, this representation provides an elegant notation (**2**, p. 285; **5**, p. 157). Using homogeneous coordinates in $PG(4, 3)$, we take the quadric to be

$$x_1^2 + x_2^2 + x_3^2 + x_4^2 + x_5^2 = 0, \qquad x_1 + x_2 + x_3 + x_4 + x_5 = 0,$$

consisting of the ten points

$$(1, 1, 1, 0, 0),\ (1, 1, 0, 1, 0),\ \ldots,\ (0, 0, 1, 1, 1)$$

which we denote by *123*, *124*, ..., *345*.

To verify that this quadric is indeed *non-ruled* we consider the tangent plane at the point *123*. This, being the polar plane of *123*, has the equation

$$x_1 + x_2 + x_3 = 0,$$

which is satisfied by (1, 1, 1, 0, 0) but not by any other of the ten points.

The same 'triad' symbols *123*, ..., *345* are naturally used for the ten points of $M(3)$. The remaining thirty points of $PG(3, 3)$, satisfying $\Sigma x = 0$ but not $\Sigma x^2 = 0$, consist of:

ten such as $(-1, 1, 0, 0, 0)$, which we denote by the 'duad' (*12*),

five such as $(-1, 1, 1, 1, 1)$, which we denote by (*16*), and

fifteen such as $(-1, -1, 1, 1, 0)$, which we denote by the 'syntheme' (*12*)(*34*)(*56*).

The same duads and synthemes are naturally used for the corresponding polar planes, harmonic homologies, circles, and inversions.

The points $1\mu\nu$ and $2\mu\nu$ (where μ and ν are any two of *3*, *4*, *5*), being collinear with the point (*12*), are interchanged by the harmonic homology (*12*) in accordance with the customary use of this symbol for the transposition of the digits *1* and *2*. Similarly, the points *123* and *145* are collinear with (*16*), and the notation can be justified by using *456* as an alternative symbol for *123* (and *236* for *145*). Finally, the permutation (*12*) (*34*) (*56*) interchanges the points *125* and *345* (or *125* and *126*) which are collinear with $(-1, -1, 1, 1, 0)$.

We now have, in $M(3)$, ten points

$$123 = 456, \ldots, 124 = 356, \ldots, 156 = 234,$$

fifteen 'negative' circles

$$(12), (13), \ldots, (56)$$

arising from points $(x_1, \ldots, x_5)$ that satisfy $\Sigma x^2 = -1$, and fifteen 'positive' circles

$$(12)\,(34)\,(56), \ldots, (14)\,(25)\,(36)$$

arising from points that satisfy $\Sigma x^2 = 1$.

6. Tutte's 8-cage

As B. H. Neumann remarked (**2**, p. 283; **5**, p. 155) the corresponding inversions, interpreted as permutations, are just the thirty odd permutations of period two in the symmetric group S_6, which is thus seen to be a subgroup of index two in the group of automorphisms of $M(3)$, whose order is $2q^2(q^4 - 1) = 1440$. The complete group, including transformations that interchange negative and positive circles, is the group of automorphisms of S_6, which is also the group of automorphisms of the extraordinary graph (Figure 1) which was named the 8-*cage* by its discoverer, W. T. Tutte (**10**, p. 460). (The number 8 is its 'girth': the smallest circuits that occur are octagons.)

In this graph, the white and black vertices represent the negative and positive circles (**11**), or the two kinds of involutory odd permutations of *1, 2, 3, 4, 5, 6*, each vertex of either colour being the product of its three neighbours (of the other colour). The graph could be constructed *ab initio* as follows. Choose an arbitrary point, colour it black, and mark it (*12*) (*34*) (*56*). Join it to three white points and mark these (*12*), (*34*), (*56*) respectively. Join (*12*) to two new black points (*12*) (*35*) (*46*) and (*12*) (*36*) (*45*), these being the remaining synthemes that involve (*12*). Then join (*12*) (*35*) (*46*) to white points (*35*), (*46*), and so on. We soon see that the smallest circuits that occur are octagons such as

(*15*), (*15*) (*26*) (*34*), (*26*), (*14*) (*26*) (*35*), (*35*), (*12*) (*35*) (*46*), (*46*), (*15*) (*23*) (*46*).

In Figure 2, the same graph appears as a map of ten octagons and a decagon on a non-orientable surface of characteristic -4. This arrangement clarifies our use of letters in naming the black vertices. Each white vertex, marked with a transposition such as (*12*), has a diametrically opposite black vertex which

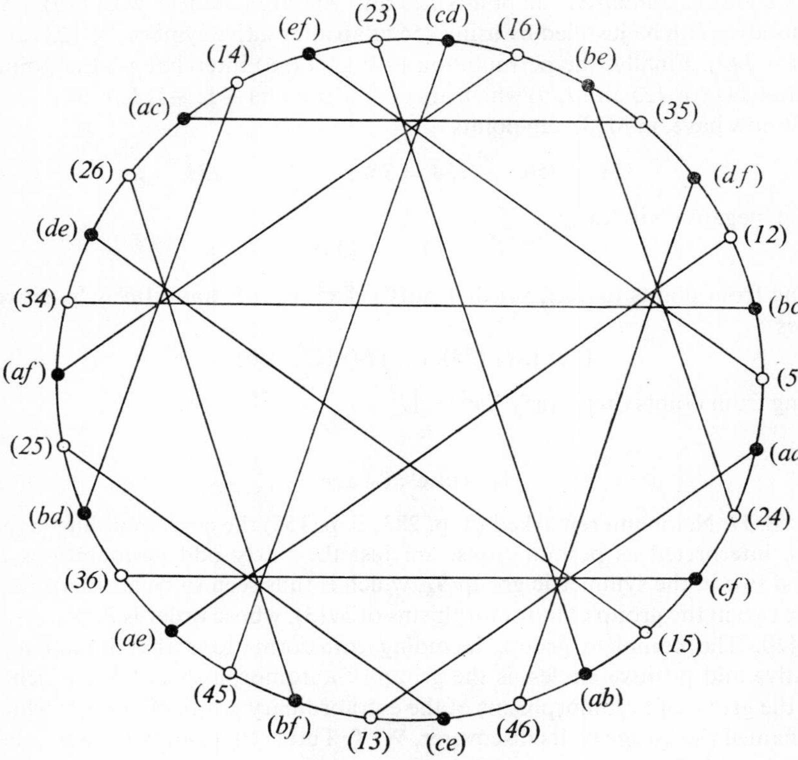

FIGURE 1

we mark with the corresponding transposition, such as (ab), of the six letters a, b, c, d, e, f. In this notation, one of the 36 involutory outer automorphisms of S_6 appears as the 'natural' permutation

$$(1a)\,(2b)\,(3c)\,(4d)\,(5e)\,(6f).$$

The graph tells us quickly how to express each permutation of numerals as a corresponding permutation of letters (or vice versa); for instance,

$$\begin{aligned}(123) = (13)\,(23) &= (ad)\,(bf)\,(ce).(ab)\,(cd)\,(ef)\\ &= (acf)\,(bed).\end{aligned}$$

In other words, the negative and positive circles, or the inversions in them, are denoted by the transpositions of numerals and of letters, respectively. To

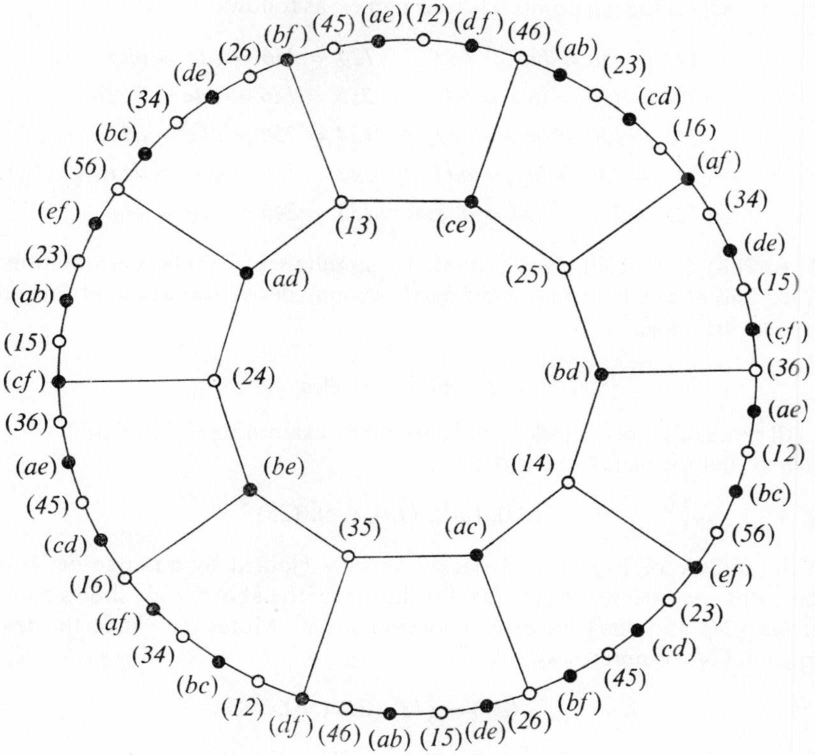

FIGURE 2

find which points lie on one of the circles, we merely have to see which points are invariant for the corresponding inversion. For instance, the circle *(12)* consists of the points *123*, *124*, *125*, *126*. The point *123* or *456* lies on the circles

(12), *(13)*, *(23)*, *(45)*, *(46)*, *(56)*,
(14) *(25)* *(36)*, *(16)* *(24)* *(35)*, *(15)* *(26)* *(34)*,
(14) *(26)* *(35)*, *(16)* *(25)* *(34)*, *(15)* *(24)* *(36)*.

In terms of letters, the last six of these twelve circles are

(bd), *(be)*, *(de)*, *(ac)*, *(af)*, *(cf)*,

suggesting that the same point should have two further names: *bde* and *acf*.

In fact, each of the ten points has four names, as follows:

$$\begin{array}{ll} 123 = 456 = bde = acf, & 124 = 356 = cde = abf, \\ 234 = 156 = ace = bdf, & 235 = 146 = ade = bcf, \\ 345 = 126 = abd = cef, & 134 = 256 = abe = cdf, \\ 145 = 236 = bce = adf, & 245 = 136 = abc = def, \\ 125 = 346 = acd = bef, & 135 = 246 = bcd = aef \end{array}$$

(**2**, p. 288; **5**, p. 160). Notice that, by simultaneous cyclic permutation of *12345* and *abcde*, leaving *6* and *f* fixed, we may derive the whole of this table from its first row.

7. Pairs of circles

All types of pairs of circles can be found by examining a '4-arc' of the graph, such as that formed by the vertices

$$(24),\ (ad),\ (13),\ (ce),\ (25)$$

in the middle of Figure 2. Adjacent vertices (joined by an edge or '1-arc') represent *non-intersecting* circles. For instance, the above table shows that the circles (*24*) and (*ad*) have no common point. Moreover, since the transposition (*24*) commutes with

$$(ad) = (13)\ (24)\ (56),$$

these non-intersecting circles are orthogonal!

Alternate vertices (joined by a V or '2-arc') represent *orthogonal intersecting* circles. For instance, (*24*) and (*13*) are orthogonal because these transpositions commute, and they intersect because both circles contain the points *245* and *246*, which are the same as *136* and *135*. Thus any vertex and its three neighbours represent four mutually orthogonal circles, one of which is disjoint from the other three while those three intersect one another in six distinct points (like three mutually orthogonal circles in the real plane).

Two vertices joined by an N or 3-arc represent *non-orthogonal intersecting* circles. For instance, (*24*) and (*ce*) are non-orthogonal because the inversion (*24*) transforms the circle

$$(ce) = (13)\ (25)\ (46)$$

into the different circle (*13*) (*45*) (*26*) = (*bf*); and they intersect because both circles contain the points *124* and *234*.

Two vertices joined by a W or 4-arc represent *tangent* circles. For instance, (*24*) and (*25*) have *245* as their *only* common point. This is the last possibility, because Tutte's graph is 5-*regular*. (This means that all 5-arcs are alike; therefore every 5-arc belongs to an octagon, and any two vertices joined by a 5-arc are also joined by a 3-arc, completing the octagon.)

Having considered all possible pairs of circles, we can assert that two non-intersecting circles are necessarily orthogonal.

The two non-intersecting circles (*24*) and (*ad*) constitute a *non-intersecting pencil*. The four circles orthogonal to them are

$$(13),\quad (56),\quad (be),\quad (cf),$$

which all pass through the two points

$$123 = 456 = bde = acf, \qquad 134 = 256 = abe = cdf$$

and thus form an *intersecting pencil*.

A typical *tangent pencil* consists of the three circles (*12*), (*13*), (*23*), touching

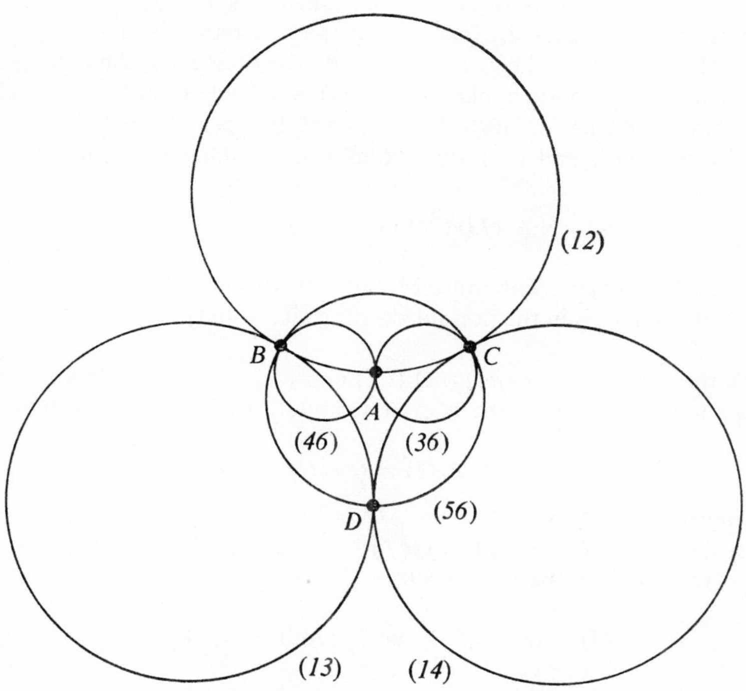

FIGURE 3

one another at the point *123* or *456*. The orthogonal tangent pencil, having the same point of contact, consists of *(45)*, *(46)*, *(56)*.

The points named in Figure 3 are

$$A = 125 = 346, \qquad B = 123 = 456,$$
$$C = 124 = 356, \qquad D = 134 = 256.$$

8. Products of inversions

In real geometry, a product of inversions is called a *homography* or an *antihomography* according as the number of inversions is even or odd (**6**, pp. 91, 146); the product of two inversions is called a *rotary*, *parabolic*, or *dilative* homography according as the inverting circles are intersecting, tangent, or non-intersecting; it is called a *Möbius involution* if the circles are orthogonal; and a product of four inversions that cannot be reduced to a product of two is called a *loxodromic* homography. Any product of three inversions can be arranged so that one of the circles is orthogonal to both the others (**4**, p. 237). The antihomography may reasonably be called *rotary*, *parabolic*, or *dilative* according as these 'others' are intersecting, tangent, or non-intersecting.

In $M(3)$, where the group generated by all inversions is S_6, the homographies and antihomographies appear as the even and odd permutations, and the various kinds can be distinguished by means of their periods, as follows.

Since circles *(13)* and *(24)* are orthogonal, the 45 even permutations of period 2, such as

$$(13)\,(24) = (bc)\,(ef),$$

are *Möbius involutions*. The same Möbius involution *(13) (24)* arises as the product of inversions in the non-intersecting circles $(ad) = (13)\,(24)\,(56)$ and *(56)*.

Since the circles $(24) = (ad)\,(be)\,(cf)$ and $(ce) = (13)\,(25)\,(46)$ are intersecting but not orthogonal, the 90 even permutations of period 4, such as

$$(13)\,(2645) = (ad)\,(bcfe),$$

are *rotary homographies*.

Since the circles $(24) = (ad)\,(be)\,(cf)$ and $(25) = (af)\,(bd)\,(ce)$ are tangent, the 80 permutations of period 3, such as

$$(245) = (abc)\,(dfe) \quad \text{and} \quad (163) = (abc)\,(def),$$

are *parabolic* homographies, each permuting triads of circles belonging to three tangent pencils.

Since non-intersecting circles are necessarily orthogonal, this simple geometry admits no dilative homographies (except the Möbius involution, which is both dilative and rotary, as we have seen).

Since $360 = 1 + 45 + 90 + 80 + 144$, the only remaining products of an even number of inversions are the 144 permutations of period 5, such as

$$(12345) = (15)\,(25)\,(35)\,(45),$$

which are thus seen to be *loxodromic* homographies.

Similarly, the 360 products of an odd number of inversions consist of

30 inversions such as (12) and $(12)\,(34)\,(56)$, of period 2;

90 rotary antihomographies such as (1234), of period 4;

240 parabolic antihomographies such as

$$(123456) = (acf)\,(bd) \quad \text{and} \quad (156)\,(24) = (abcdef),$$

of period 6.

9. Other automorphisms of $M(3)$

The remaining 720 automorphisms of $M(3)$, which transform positive circles into negative circles (and vice versa), thus leaving no circle invariant, may be obtained by expressing each product of inversions in terms of letters as well as numbers and then taking its product with

$$(1a)\,(2b)\,(3c)\,(4d)\,(5e)\,(6f).$$

In this manner,

$(15)\,(24)\,(ae)\,(bd)$	yields	$(1e)\,(2d)\,3c)\,(4b)\,(5a)\,(6f)$,	of period 2,
$(16)\,(af)\,(be)\,(cd)$	yields	$(1f)\,(2b5e)\,(3c4d)\,(6a)$,	of period 4,
$(154236)\,(aeb)\,(df)$	yields	$(1e2c3f4b)\,(5d6a)$,	of period 8,
$(12345)\,(abcde)$	yields	$(1b3d5a2c4e)\,(6f)$,	of period 10.

The permutations of periods two, eight and ten leave no point invariant. $(1e)\,(2d)\,(3c)\,(4b)\,(5a)\,(6f)$ interchanges the thirty circles in pairs: ten pairs of non-intersecting circles, and five pairs of non-orthogonal intersecting circles (represented by the five horizontal edges in Figure 1).

The automorphism of period eight cyclically permutes eight of the ten points and interchanges the remaining two: *135* and *136*. It cyclically permutes the eight circles

$$(15),\ (de),\ (26),\ (ac),\ (35),\ (df),\ (46),\ (ab),$$

represented in the graph by the octagon that appears at the bottom of Figure 2.

The one of period ten cyclically permutes the ten circles

$$(12), (bc), (34), (de), (15), (ab), (23), (cd), (45), (ae),$$

which are represented in the graph by a decagon like the central decagon in Figure 2. In fact, this central decagon itself is permuted by

$$\{(1b3d5a2c4e)\,(6f)\}^3 = (1d2e3a4b5c)\,(6f)$$

(**2**, p. 282; **5**, p. 154).

10. Five mutually tangent circles

For any three circles that are mutually tangent at three distinct points, there are, as Descartes and Steiner observed (**6**, p. 14; **8**, pp. 60–63, 524) two circles tangent to all of them. The special feature that appears in $M(3)$ is that these two circles touch each other, thus completing a symmetrical configuration of *five* mutually tangent circles. In this configuration of circles, every three determine an orthogonal circle through the three points of contact. The $\binom{5}{3} = 10$ such circles complete the set of fifteen circles of the same 'sign'. For instance, the five circles

$$(12), (13), (14), (15), (16),$$

whose symbols contain the digit *1*, are mutually tangent, their $\binom{5}{2} = 10$ points of contact

$$123, 124, \ldots, 156$$

being *all* the ten points of $M(3)$. The ten circles

$$(56), \ldots, (23),$$

which are orthogonal to them in threes, are just those whose symbols do not contain the digit *1*. Similarly, the five circles

$$(ab), (ac), (ad), (ae), (af),$$

whose symbols involve a, are mutually orthogonal.

We have seen that $M(3)$ provides a geometric interpretation for the group of automorphisms of S_6, represented by permutations of the twelve symbols

$$1, 2, 3, 4, 5, 6, \quad a, b, c, d, e, f.$$

It is natural to ask what geometric objects are represented by these twelve symbols themselves. The answer is now clear: these digits and letters represent the twelve sets of *five mutually tangent circles.*

The same group, of order 1440, can also be represented by permutations of *ten* symbols. These appear in $M(3)$ as the ten points.

11. The role of Miquel's theorem

It was proved by Witt (**12**, Satz 3) that there is only one inversive plane of order 3 (satisfying Axioms I, II, III), namely the one derived, as in §5, from a quadric in $PG(3, 3)$. There is a quaint irony in the observation that, although we have called it Miquelian and denoted it by $M(3)$, it is too meagre to satisfy Miquel's Theorem (Axiom IV) in any non-vacuous sense. Since all pairs of the ten points are alike, we lose no generality by taking the eight points mentioned in Miquel's Theorem to be all of the ten except *125* and *135*. The only circles that contain neither of these points are

$$(14), (16), (23), (45), (56),$$
$$(ab), (ce), (cf), (de), (df).$$

But these ten circles do not include three pairs of non-intersecting circles!

References

1. CHEN, Y. Der Satz von Miquel in der Möbiusebene. *Math. Ann.* **186** (1970), 81–100.
2. COXETER, H. S. M. Twelve points in *PG*(5, 3) with 95040 self-transformations. *Proc. Royal Society,* A **247** (1958), 279–293.
3. COXETER, H. S. M. The Lorentz group and the group of homographies. *Proc. Internat. Conf. Theory of Groups,* Austral. Nat. Univ. Canberra (August 1965), 73–77.
4. COXETER, H. S. M. The inversive plane and hyperbolic space. *Abh. Math. Sem. Univ. Hamburg* **29** (1966), 217–242.
5. COXETER, H. S. M. *Twelve Geometric Essays* (Carbondale, Illinois, 1968).
6. COXETER, H. S. M. *Introduction to Geometry* (2nd ed., New York, 1969).
7. DEMBOWSKI, P. *Finite Geometries* (Berlin, 1968).
8. STEINER, J. *Gesammelte Werke* **1** (Berlin, 1882).
9. SÜSS, W. Spiegelungen auf der Kugel. *Tohoku Math. J.* **27** (1926), 213–242.
10. TUTTE, W. T. A family of cubical graphs. *Proc. Cambridge Philos. Soc.* **43** (1947), 459–474.
11. TUTTE, W. T. and COXETER, H. S. M. The chords of the non-ruled quadric in *PG*(3, 3). *Canad. J. Math.* **10** (1958), 481–488.
12. VAN DER WAERDEN, B. L. and SMID, L. J. Eine Axiomatik der Kreisgeometrie und der Laguerre-Geometrie. *Math. Ann.* **110** (1935), 753–776.
13. WITT, E. Über Steinersche Systeme. *Abh. Math. Sem. Univ. Hamburg* **12** (1938), 265–275.

Intersections of Open Plane Sets

H. G. EGGLESTON

1. Introduction

Professor Rado has made many contributions to the solution of combinatorial problems, including some which have a geometrical content or significance. A problem of this type, first suggested by J. W. Green (**1**) is the following. In n-dimensional Euclidean space, G is an open bounded set and for every vector **t**, $G(\mathbf{t})$ is the transform of G under the translation **t**. Given a set of vectors X denote $\bigcap_{\mathbf{t}\in X} G(\mathbf{t})$ by G_X. Is it possible to find X, such that G_X is convex?

We exclude the case when G_X is a single point, since this is trivial, and ask whether we can select X so that G_X is a non-empty open convex set. There are a number of related problems. Firstly, if G is convex itself, then G_X is convex for any set X but we can try to specify exactly the possible open convex sets G_X. It is by no means the case that starting from G we can produce any shape of convex set; indeed, if G is a parallelepiped, then G_X is necessarily a parallelepiped so that in this case every G_X is an affine transform of G. It is not known whether the parallelepiped is the only open convex set for which this is true. At the other extreme, is there a convex open set G such that if H is any other open convex set then G_X, for some appropriate set X, is an affine transform of H? In other words, is it possible to find an open convex set G which will generate any open convex set by intersections to within affine transforms? Again the solution to this problem is not known.

I shall give here an affirmative answer to Green's question for $n = 2$. It will be clear that the method does not extend to $n = 3$. The case $n = 1$ was completely solved by E. G. Strauss (in a verbal communication).

2. A general reduction argument

It is essential that the set G should be bounded. The result is false if G is not bounded. We show next that it is sufficient to prove the result not for the whole of G but for one component of G. Let C be a component of G and suppose that X is a set of vectors such that C_X is a non-empty open convex set. G_X is a bounded set of which one component is C_X. Denote G_X by H and C_X by K. Let Y be the set of translations $\mathbf{t}$ such that $\mathbf{t} \in Y \Leftrightarrow H(\mathbf{t}) \supseteq K$. Then $H_Y \supseteq K$ and in any component L of H_Y except K itself, the largest set directly similar to K and contained in L is smaller than K. For, if this is not so, there must be a vector $\mathbf{v}$ such that $L(\mathbf{v}) \supseteq K$. Since $L \subseteq H_Y \subseteq H$, we have $H(\mathbf{v}) \supseteq K$ and $\mathbf{v} \in Y$. Hence $L(-\mathbf{v}) \subseteq H$ but then $L(-\mathbf{v} + 2\mathbf{v}) \supseteq K$ and, as above, this implies $2\mathbf{v} \in Y$. Similarly $3\mathbf{v}$, $4\mathbf{v}$ ... all belong to Y. This is impossible, for as H is bounded so is Y bounded. Thus the largest set directly similar to K contained in L is a translate of λK where $\lambda < 1$.

Since H is bounded and the components of H are disjoint we cannot find a sequence of components L_1, L_2 ... for which the corresponding sets $\lambda_1 K$, $\lambda_2 K$, ... satisfy $\lambda_n \to 1$. Thus there is a fixed number δ, $0 < \delta < 1$, such that the largest set directly similar to K in any component of H other than K itself is a translate of λK, where $\lambda < \delta$.

Let P be an interior point of K, and μ a number such that $\delta < \mu < 1$. Let J be the set directly similar to K with ratio $\mu : 1$ and centre of similitude P. Form the set Z of all the vectors $\overrightarrow{QP}$ for any $Q \in J$. Then

$$H_Z = K_Z \text{ a non-empty open convex set}$$

But $H_Z = G_{Y \cup Z}$ and we have shown that if the result is true for one component of G, then it is true of G itself.

3. The plane case

This result does not enable one to proceed to a conclusion except in the case when $n = 2$. The difficulties do not however seem to be topological. We need two lemmas.

Let G be an open bounded connected plane set. Let $S(p, r)$ be the closed disc, centre p and radius r, and let $S(r)$ be the closed disc whose centre is the origin and of radius r.

LEMMA 1. *It is possible to choose $r > 0$ and a component K of $G_{S(r)}$ such that the frontier of K is a finite number of disjoint simple closed Jordan curves.*

For any $a > 0$, $G_{S(a)}$ is an open set and, if $\mathscr{C}$ denotes complements,

$$\mathscr{C}(G_{S(a)}) = \bigcup_{p \in \mathscr{C}(G)} S(p, a).$$

Thus each point of $Fr(G_{S(a)})$ lies on a disc of radius a that does not meet $G_{S(a)}$. Let K_1 be a component of $G_{S(a)}$. Since each component of $\mathscr{C}(K_1)$ contains an open disc of radius a there are only finitely many of them (there is only one unbounded component). Of these components some may be at a positive distance apart. If there are any such, let their least distance apart be 3δ. If there are no components whose closures intersect, we write K_2 for K_1. If there are such components and δ is defined we write K_2 for $K_{1S(\delta)}$. If there are such components and δ is not defined, we write K_2 for $K_{1S(\eta)}$, where η is so small that $K_{1S(\eta)} \neq \emptyset$. Take r to be a, $a + \delta$ or $a + \eta$ as the case may be and K to be K_2, or a component of K_2.

Then each component of $Fr\,K$ is of finite length, locally connected and hence arcwise connected. Each component bounds two domains in the plane (for the components of $\mathscr{C}K$ are at a positive distance apart). Hence each component of $Fr\,K$ contains a simple closed Jordan curve.

But each component of $Fr\,K$ is a simple closed Jordan curve. For otherwise we can suppose that a component L of $Fr\,K$ contains a point p which lies on three distinct arcs τ, σ, ρ terminating at p and on the frontier of $S(p, \delta)$ for some $\delta > 0$. (Fig. 1). Moreover τ, σ, ρ will not meet except at p. They divide the interior of $S(p, \delta)$ into three domains say A, B, C. Of these two at least contain points of $\mathscr{C}K$ arbitrarily close to p. Since these points lie on closed discs lying in $\mathscr{C}K$ and of radius r, we see that one of the arcs τ, σ, ρ separates two such discs as in the figure below. Let the centres of these discs be a, b.

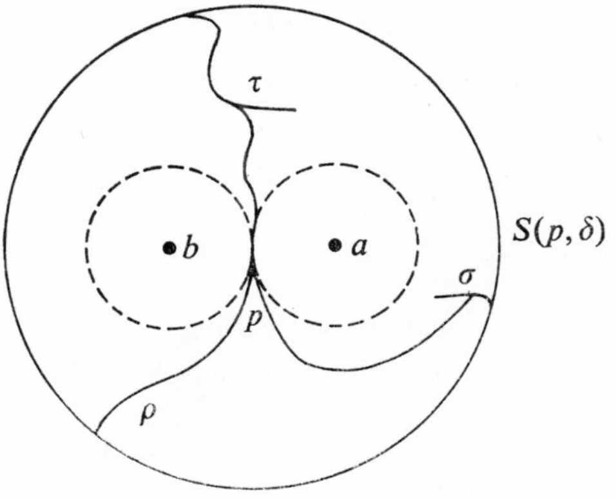

FIGURE 1

The two discs must be in the same component of $\mathscr{C}\overline{K}$ since distinct components are at a positive distance apart. We can thus join a, b in $\mathscr{C}\overline{K}$ by a polygonal line and adding segments pb, pa to this polygonal line obtain a connected subset of $\mathscr{C}K$ that separates points of τ from points ρ and σ. But there are points of K arbitrarily close to these points of τ and to these points of ρ, σ. As K is connected, this is impossible.

Thus the whole of L is a simple closed Jordan curve.

LEMMA 2. *D is a domain whose frontier is a simple closed Jordan curve. t is a point of the segment pq such that $t \notin \bar{D}$, $p \in D$, $q \in D$. For any point v not on the line pq, $B(v)$ denotes the open half-space not containing p or q and bounded by the line parallel to pq through v. Then there exists a point u on $Fr\, D$ such that, for some $\eta > 0$,*

$$S(u, \eta) \cap B(u) \subseteq D.$$

$\mathscr{C}(\bar{D})$ meets line pq in a relatively open set of which one interval contains t. Let the end-points of this interval be p_1, q_1. There are two arcs of $Fr\, D$ with end points at p_1, q_1 say α_1, α_2 which bound with the segment $p_1 q_1$ domains denoted by D_1, D_2 respectively. One of these domains contains the other, say $D_1 \supset D_2$. Of all the points of α_2 choose one, say u, that is furthest from the line pq. Then, for any $\delta > 0$,

$$S(u, \delta) \cap B(u) \cap \alpha_2 = \emptyset.$$

u is at a positive distance from α_1; thus for δ sufficiently small, say $\delta < \eta$,

$$S(u, \delta) \cap B(u) \cap \alpha_1 = \emptyset.$$

Also $S(u, \eta) \cap B(u)$ can be joined to arbitarily distant points by an arc that does not meet α_2 or the segment $p_1 q_1$. Thus

$$S(u, \eta) \cap B(u) \subseteq \mathscr{C}(D_2).$$

Since $u \in \alpha_2 \subseteq D_1$, we have $S(u, \eta) \cap B(u) \subset D_1$.

Thus

$$S(u, \eta) \cap B(u) \subseteq D_1 - \bar{D}_2 = D.$$

We can now establish Green's conjecture for the plane case. Given the open bounded set G construct, as above, a set of vectors X such that one component K of G_X satisfies Lemma 1. Let H be the convex cover of K. For $p \in Fr\, H$ let $T(p)$ denote the intersections of those open half spaces bounded by support lines to H through p which contain H.

Next select three arcs of $Fr\, H$, α, β, γ, where each is either an arc of $Fr\, K$ or is a segment that meets $Fr\, K$ only at its end points. Denote by $T(\alpha)$ the set $\bigcap_{p \in \alpha^0} T(p)$, where α^0 is the interior of α relative to $Fr\, H$, and define $T(\beta)$, $T(\gamma)$ similarly. We can, and will, choose α, β, γ, so that $T(\alpha) \cap T(\beta) \cap T(\gamma)$ is a bounded set.

If α, β, γ are all arcs of $Fr\, K$, select points a, b, c, of α^0, β^0, γ^0, respectively such that $T(a) \cap T(b) \cap T(c)$ is bounded. Then $H \cap H(a-b) \cap H(a-c) = \emptyset$.

Now for $0 < \lambda < 1$, $H \cap H(\lambda(a-b)) \cap H(\lambda(a-c))$ is an open convex set. If λ is sufficiently near to 1

$$H \cap H(\lambda(a-b)) \cap H(\lambda(a-c)) = K \cap K(\lambda(a-b)) \cap K(\lambda(a-c)).$$

Thus we have a set of vectors X such that K_X is an open convex set. If one of the arcs α, β, γ, say α, is not an arc of $Fr\,K$ we apply Lemma 2. Let X be the set of vectors of the form λa, where $0 < \lambda < \delta$, δ is a fixed positive number and a is a unit vector parallel to α. Then K_X contains a component K_1 whose frontier contains a segment parallel to α. If δ is sufficiently small and H_1 is the convex cover of K_1, $Fr\,H_1$, contains arcs that are translations of parts of β, γ say β_1, γ_1. If β_1, γ_1 are arcs of $Fr\,K_1$, we can now argue with α_1, β_1, γ_1 as we did with α, β, γ above. We find X_1 a set of vectors such that K_{1X_1} contains a convex component. By the remarks made earlier, this is sufficient.

If one of β_1, γ_1, is not an arc of $Fr\,K_1$, we apply Lemma 2 again, and if necessary apply it once more.

In any case we are led to an open convex set, and Green's conjecture is proved.

Reference

1. Green, John, W. On families of sets closed with respect to products, translations and point reflections. *Anais Acad. Brasil. Ci.* **24** (1952), 241–244.

The Least Prime in an Arithmetic Progression

P. D. T. A. Elliott and H. Halberstam

Let $P(q, h)$ denote the least prime in the arithmetic progression h mod q, $(h, q) = 1$, $1 \leqslant h \leqslant q$, $2 \leqslant q$. In 1934, S. Chowla (**1**) conjectured that $P(q, h) < c(\varepsilon)\, q^{1+\varepsilon}$ and in 1936 P. Turán (**6**) proved, assuming the grand Riemann Hypothesis, that, given $\delta > 0$, the number of arithmetic progressions mod q for which $P(q, h) < \phi(q) \log^{2+\delta} q$ is asymptotically $\phi(q)$ as $q \to \infty$. Linnik (**4**) proved, without appeal to any unproved conjecture, that $P(q,h) < q^C$, where C is an absolute positive constant.† We prove here

Theorem. *Given any $\delta > 0$, there exists a sequence Q of zero density (which may be empty) such that the number of arithmetic progressions h mod q for which $P(q, h) < \phi(q)\, (\log q)^{1+\delta}$ is asymptotically $\phi(q)$ as $q \to \infty$ through integers not in Q.*

Proof. It will be evident from what follows that we obtain a result rather more precise than that given in the statement of the Theorem.

We set off from the theorem of Davenport–Halberstam (**2**), as sharpened in Gallagher (**3**, Theorem 3), which may be stated in the following form:

If
$$\theta(x; q, h) = \sum_{\substack{p \leqslant x \\ p \equiv h \pmod q}} \log p, \qquad \text{and} \qquad A > 0,$$
then
$$\sum_{q \leqslant X} \sum_{\substack{h=1 \\ (h,q)=1}}^{q} \left\{ \theta(x; q, h) - \frac{x}{\phi(q)} \right\}^2 \ll \frac{x^2}{(\log x)^A} \tag{1}$$
provided
$$X \leqslant \frac{x}{(\log x)^{A+1}}.$$

Let X be a sufficiently large natural number, and define
$$x = KX(\log X)^{1+\frac{1}{2}\delta},$$

† According to Chen, Jing-Run *Sci. Sinica* **14** (1965), 1869–1871, C can be taken as 777.

where K is a constant so chosen that

$$X \leqslant \frac{x}{(\log x)^{1+\frac{1}{2}\delta}}.$$

Let Q_X denote the set of integers q satisfying

(i) $\frac{1}{2}X < q \leqslant X$,

(ii) $P(q, h) > \phi(q)(\log q)^{1+\delta}$ in at least $\phi(q)(\log q)^{-\delta/4}$ progressions $h(\operatorname{mod} q)$ with $1 \leqslant h \leqslant q$, $(h, q) = 1$.

Then if $q \in Q_X$,

$$P(q, h) > \phi(q)(\log q)^{1+\delta} > \tfrac{1}{2}X(\log \tfrac{1}{2}X)^{1+(2/3)\delta} > x$$

provided $X \geqslant X_0(\delta)$; hence $\theta(x; q, h) = 0$ if $q \in Q_X$. It follows from (1) with $A = \delta/2$ that

$$\sum_{q \in Q_X} \frac{x^2}{\phi^2(q)} \cdot \frac{\phi(q)}{(\log q)^{\delta/4}} \ll \frac{x^2}{(\log x)^{\delta/2}},$$

whence, if $|Q_X|$ denotes the cardinality of Q_X,

$$|Q_X| \ll \frac{X(\log X)^{\delta/4}}{(\log x)^{\delta/2}} \ll \frac{X}{(\log X)^{\delta/4}}. \tag{2}$$

To prove the theorem it suffices to take

$$Q = \bigcup_{m=1}^{\infty} Q_{2^m}$$

and to show that

$$N^{-1} \sum_{2^m \leqslant N} |Q_{2^m}| \to 0 \quad \text{as} \quad N \to \infty.$$

But (2) implies that the expression on the left is $\ll (\log N)^{-\delta/4}$, so that the proof of the Theorem is complete.

Recently H. L. Montgomery (**5**) has found, by different and deeper methods, an improvement of the results cited from (**2**) and (**3**), which allows us to assert, in place of (1), the following:

'If

$$\frac{x}{\log^2 x} < X \leqslant x,$$

then

$$\sum_{q \leqslant X} \sum_{\substack{h=1 \\ (h,q)=1}}^{q} \left\{\theta(x; q, h) - \frac{x}{\phi(q)}\right\}^2 \ll Xx \log x.\text{'} \tag{3}$$

With the help of this result we can improve our Theorem. Let $f(y)$ be a positive monotonic increasing function of y, such that $f(y) < \log y$ and $f(y)$ tends arbitrarily slowly to infinity as $y \to \infty$. If we take $x = X f^{\frac{1}{2}}(X) \log X$ in (3) and argue in essentially the same way as we did above, we find even that

$$P(q, h) < q\, f(q) \log q$$

for asymptotically $\phi(q)$ progressions $h \bmod q$, for almost all q.

References

1. Chowla, S. *J. Indian Math. Soc.* (2), **1** (1934), 1–3.
2. Davenport, H. and Halberstam, H. *Michigan Math. J.* **13** (1966), 485–489.
3. Gallagher, P. *Mathematika* **14** (1967), 21–27.
4. Linnik, Ju. V. *Mat. Sbornik* **15** (1947), 139–178.
5. Montgomery, H. L. *Michigan Math. J.* **17** (1970), 33–39.
6. Turán, P. *Acta Sci. Math. Szeged* **8** (1937), 226–235.

Polarized Partition Relations for Ordinal Numbers

P. ERDÖS, A. HAJNAL, AND E. C. MILNER*

1. Introduction

There have been several instances where some particularly well-chosen symbol has enhanced the development of a branch of mathematics, and the partition symbol

$$\alpha \to (\alpha_0, \alpha_1)^r \tag{1.1}$$

invented by Richard Rado is a case in point. By definition, (1.1) means that the following relation between the ordinal (or cardinal) numbers $\alpha, \alpha_0, \alpha_1$ holds: *If A is an ordered set of order type α* (we shall write $\operatorname{tp} A = \alpha$) *and if* $[A]^r = \{X \subset A : |X| = r\}$ *is partitioned in any way into two sets K_0 and K_1, then there are $\rho < 2$ and $A' \subset A$ such that* $\operatorname{tp} A' = \alpha_\rho$ *and* $[A']^r \subset K_\rho$. Erdös and Rado were the first to realize that a large number of seemingly unrelated problems in set theory could be reduced to a question of deciding whether or not some partition relation like (1.1) holds. In (**5**) and (**6**) they began a systematic study of these relations and laid the foundations of what they called *a partition calculus* to serve as a kind of unifying principle in set theory. Since these two pioneer papers several others have been written on the subject. In particular we refer to the long paper by Erdös, Hajnal, and Rado (**3**) which contains an almost complete analysis for partition relations involving infinite cardinal numbers. Rado's compact symbol (1.1), which reveals at a glance the whole content of a fairly complicated combinatorial statement, proved to be particularly convenient and flexible for the development of this calculus. Apart from the merit of compactness, the symbol enjoys other advantages. The negation of any statement (1.1) is conveniently expressed by replacing the arrow $\to$ by a non-arrow $\not\to$. The symbol has the following obvious monotonicity properties, if $\alpha' \geqslant \alpha$, $\beta' \leqslant \beta$ and $\gamma' \leqslant \gamma$, then (1.1) implies that

$$\alpha' \to (\beta', \gamma')^r.$$

The arrow in (1.1) separates the two kinds of monotonicity involved and this is

* Research supported by NRC grant A–5198. Part of this paper was written at the Vancouver branch of the Canadian Mathematical Congress 1969 Summer Research Institute.

helpful in recognizing which relations are *best possible*. Finally, the symbol readily lends itself to a number of interesting generalizations (see (**6**) and (**3**)).

In this paper we investigate one of these generalizations, the so-called polarized partition symbol. We consider only the simplest of such relations, namely those of the form

$$\begin{Bmatrix}\alpha\\ \beta\end{Bmatrix} \to \begin{Bmatrix}\alpha_0 & \alpha_1\\ \beta_0 & \beta_1\end{Bmatrix}^{1,1}. \tag{1.2}$$

By definition, this means that: *If A and B are ordered sets,* $\text{tp}\, A = \alpha$, $\text{tp}\, B = \beta$, *and if the cartesian product $A \times B$ is partitioned in any way into two sets K_0 and K_1, then there are $\rho < 2$ and sets $A' \subset A$, $B' \subset B$ such that* $\text{tp}\, A' = \alpha_\rho$, $\text{tp}\, B' = \beta_\rho$ *and* $A' \times B' \subset K_\rho$. If one considers instead, partitions of $[A]^r \times [B]^s$ for arbitrary integers r, s, the corresponding relation is represented by replacing the exponents 1,1 in (1.2) by r, s; these more general polarized relations clearly include the ordinary partition relations (1.1). Since we only consider relations with the exponents 1,1, for the remainder of this paper we shall omit these from (1.2) and simply write

$$\begin{Bmatrix}\alpha\\ \beta\end{Bmatrix} \to \begin{Bmatrix}\alpha_0 & \alpha_1\\ \beta_0 & \beta_1\end{Bmatrix}.$$

Note that, as for the ordinary partition symbol, the negation of (1.2) is expressed by replacing $\to$ by $\not\to$. Also, we have the same monotonicity properties: if $\alpha' \geqslant \alpha$, $\beta' \geqslant \beta$, $\alpha_\rho' \leqslant \alpha_\rho$, $\beta_\rho' \leqslant \beta_\rho$ $(\rho < 2)$, then (1.2) implies that

$$\begin{Bmatrix}\alpha'\\ \beta'\end{Bmatrix} \to \begin{Bmatrix}\alpha'_0 & \alpha_1'\\ \beta'_0 & \beta_1'\end{Bmatrix}.$$

Polarized partition relations were first introduced in (**6**), and in (**3**) a number of these relations involving cardinal numbers were established. As we already remarked, the theory for the ordinary partition relations involving cardinal numbers is fairly complete, but for polarized relations the situation is very different. There remain unsolved problems involving only the smallest transfinite cardinal numbers. For example, it is not known if the relation

$$\begin{Bmatrix}\aleph_1\\ \aleph_2\end{Bmatrix} \to \begin{Bmatrix}\aleph_1 & \aleph_1\\ \aleph_0 & \aleph_0\end{Bmatrix}$$

is true or false. In this paper we shall establish relations of the form (1.2) which involve ordinal numbers.

As a starting point for our investigation we mention the simple, but slightly surprising, negative relation

$$\lambda \not\to (\omega^n_\alpha)^1_{n<\omega} \qquad (\lambda < \omega_{\alpha+1}), \tag{1.3}$$

proved by Milner and Rado (**9**). This asserts that, if $\text{tp}\, S = \lambda < \omega_{\alpha+1}$, then S

is the union of $\aleph_0$ 'small' sets A_n $(n < \omega)$, i.e.

$$S = \bigcup_{n<\omega} A_n$$

and tp $A_n < \omega^n_\alpha$ $(n < \omega)$. If we put $B_n = A_0 \cup \ldots \cup A_n$ $(n < \omega)$, then the sets B_n are also 'small' (tp $B_n < \omega^n_\alpha$) and the union of any $\aleph_0$ of these is the whole set S. This fact may be expressed by means of a negative polarized relation

$$\begin{Bmatrix} \omega \\ \lambda \end{Bmatrix} \nrightarrow \begin{Bmatrix} 1 & \omega \\ \omega^\omega{}_\alpha & 1 \end{Bmatrix} \quad (\lambda < \omega_{\alpha+1}).$$

From (1.3), Hajnal (see (**2**)) deduced the following seemingly paradoxial theorem: *If* tp $S = \lambda < \omega_2$, *then there are* $\aleph_1$ *subsets* $F_\mu(\mu < \omega_1)$ *of* S *such that* tp $F_\mu < \omega_1{}^{\omega+2}$ (i.e. the sets are 'small') *and the union of any* $\aleph_0$ *of these* F_μ *is the whole set* S. This is equivalent to the relation

$$\begin{Bmatrix} \omega_1 \\ \lambda \end{Bmatrix} \nrightarrow \begin{Bmatrix} 1 & \omega \\ \omega_1{}^{\omega+2} & 1 \end{Bmatrix} \quad (\lambda < \omega_2). \tag{1.4}$$

In this paper we establish some analogous relations. We only consider relations (1.2) involving ordinal numbers of cardinal $\aleph_1$ and for the special case in which $\alpha = \omega_1$, $\beta = \omega_1{}^\gamma$ and $\alpha_0 = 1$ our discussion is complete. Some of our results do generalize to ordinals of higher cardinality, but new difficulties are encountered even in the case of $\aleph_2$ and a discussion of these results must be left to a later paper.

In contrast to (1.4) we show (Theorem 1) that

$$\begin{Bmatrix} \omega_1 \\ \omega_1{}^\gamma \end{Bmatrix} \rightarrow \begin{Bmatrix} 1 & \alpha \\ \xi & \beta \end{Bmatrix}, \tag{1.5}$$

where $\xi < \omega_1{}^{\omega+2} \leqslant \omega_1{}^\gamma < \omega_2$, $\alpha < \omega_1$ and $\beta < \omega_1{}^\gamma$. It follows from (1.4) that the condition $\xi < \omega_1{}^{\omega+2}$ is necessary in (1.5). Also, the trivial cardinal relation (**6**, 21.2)

$$\begin{Bmatrix} \omega_1 \\ \omega_1 \end{Bmatrix} \nrightarrow \begin{Bmatrix} 1 & \omega_1 \\ \omega_1 & 1 \end{Bmatrix} \tag{1.6}$$

shows that (1.5) is false when $\alpha = \omega_1$. In general, the condition $\beta < \omega_1{}^\gamma$ is also necessary for (1.5) since (Theorem 6)

$$\begin{Bmatrix} \omega_1 \\ \omega_1{}^\gamma \end{Bmatrix} \nrightarrow \begin{Bmatrix} 1 & \omega \\ \omega_1{}^{\omega+1}+1 & \omega_1{}^\gamma \end{Bmatrix} \tag{1.7}$$

if † $co(\omega_1{}^\gamma) = \omega_1$ and $\gamma < \omega_2$. On the other hand, if $co(\omega_1{}^\gamma) = \omega$, then it is

† We write $co(\lambda)$ to denote the least ordinal number which is cofinal with λ. Thus $co(\lambda)$ is either 1 or an initial ordinal.

possible to strengthen (1.5), i.e. (Theorem 2)

$$\begin{Bmatrix} \omega_1 \\ \omega_1^{\gamma} \end{Bmatrix} \to \begin{Bmatrix} 1 & \alpha \\ \xi & \omega_1^{\gamma} \end{Bmatrix} \tag{1.8}$$

if $\xi < \omega_1^{\omega+2} < \omega_1^{\gamma}$, $\alpha < \omega_1$ and $co\,\gamma = \omega$. Note that (1.7) is best possible since (Theorem 3)

$$\begin{Bmatrix} \omega_1 \\ \omega_1^{\gamma} \end{Bmatrix} \to \begin{Bmatrix} 1 & \alpha \\ \omega_1^{\omega+1} & \omega_1^{\gamma} \end{Bmatrix} \tag{1.9}$$

holds if $\omega + 1 \leqslant \gamma < \omega_2$.

We shall prove (Theorem 4) that

$$\begin{Bmatrix} \omega_1 \\ \omega_1^{\gamma} \end{Bmatrix} \to \begin{Bmatrix} k & \alpha \\ \omega_1^{\gamma} & \omega_1^{\gamma} \end{Bmatrix} \tag{1.10}$$

holds for $k < \omega$, $\alpha < \omega_1$ and $\gamma \leqslant \omega + 1$. This is stronger than (1.9) when $\gamma = \omega + 1$. It is not possible to replace k by ω in (1.10) since it is known (**3**, Theorem 32) that

$$\begin{Bmatrix} \omega_1 \\ \omega_1 \end{Bmatrix} \not\to \begin{Bmatrix} \omega & \omega \\ \omega_1 & \omega_1 \end{Bmatrix}. \tag{1.11}$$

However, this raises the question whether one can replace 1 by any integer k in (1.5), (1.8) and (1.9). This is not possible in the case of (1.9) since we can prove (see (1.16)) with the continuum hypothesis† that

(*)
$$\begin{Bmatrix} \omega_1 \\ \omega_1^{\gamma} \end{Bmatrix} \not\to \begin{Bmatrix} 2 & \omega \\ \omega_1^{\omega} & \omega_1^{\gamma} \end{Bmatrix} \tag{1.12}$$

if $\omega + 2 \leqslant \gamma < \omega_2$ and $co(\omega_1^{\gamma}) = \omega_1$. We do not know the status of (1.5) and (1.8) in this connection.

PROBLEM 1. Is the relation

$$\begin{Bmatrix} \omega_1 \\ \omega_1^{\omega 2} \end{Bmatrix} \to \begin{Bmatrix} 2 & \omega \\ \omega_1^{\omega} & \omega_1^{\omega 2} \end{Bmatrix}$$

true or false?

There is another problem of this kind (see §4) which we cannot settle.

† Where we use the continuum hypothesis to prove a result, we prefix the statement by (*) for easier recognition.

PROBLEM 2. Does the relation

$$\begin{Bmatrix} \omega_1 \\ {\omega_1}^{\omega+2} \end{Bmatrix} \to \begin{Bmatrix} 3 & \alpha \\ {\omega_1}^{\omega+1} & \xi \end{Bmatrix}$$

hold for $\alpha < \omega_1$ and $\xi < {\omega_1}^{\omega+2}$?

It follows as a special case of a result proved in (**2**, Theorem 1) that

$$\begin{Bmatrix} \omega_1 \\ {\omega_1}^{\gamma} \end{Bmatrix} \to \begin{Bmatrix} 1 & \omega_1 \\ \alpha & {\omega_1}^{\gamma} \end{Bmatrix} \tag{1.13}$$

if $\alpha < \omega_1, \gamma < \omega_2$ and $co({\omega_1}^{\gamma}) = \omega_1$. We also showed (**2**, Theorem 2) that

$$\begin{Bmatrix} \omega_1 \\ {\omega_1}^{\gamma} \end{Bmatrix} \not\to \begin{Bmatrix} 1 & \omega_1 \\ \omega+1 & {\omega_1}^{\gamma} \end{Bmatrix} \tag{1.14}$$

if $co({\omega_1}^{\gamma}) = \omega$. The method we used to prove (1.13) is very different from the methods used in this paper. We shall not give the details, but with the same method used in (**2**) one can also show that

$$\begin{Bmatrix} \omega_1 \\ {\omega_1}^{\gamma} \end{Bmatrix} \to \begin{Bmatrix} 1 & \omega_1 \\ \omega & {\omega_1}^{\gamma} \end{Bmatrix} \qquad (\gamma < \omega_2). \tag{1.15}$$

We mention these results because these three relations (1.13)–(1.15), together with (1.4), (1.5), (1.7), (1.8), (1.9) and (1.10) give a complete analysis of the symbol (1.2) for the case $\alpha = \omega_1, \beta = {\omega_1}^{\gamma}$ and $\alpha_0 = 1$.

In §6 we establish some strong negative results. Using the continuum hypothesis we prove (Theorem 7) that, for $\gamma < \omega_2$ and $co({\omega_1}^{\gamma}) = \omega_1$,

$$(*) \qquad \begin{Bmatrix} \omega_1 \\ \\ {\omega_1}^{\gamma} \end{Bmatrix} \not\to \begin{Bmatrix} 1 & 2 & \omega & \omega \\ & \vee & \vee & , \\ {\omega_1}^{\omega+1}+1 & {\omega_1}^{\omega} & 1 & {\omega_1}^{\gamma} \end{Bmatrix}. \tag{1.16}$$

Here we are using the partition symbol with *alternatives* (for the definition see §2). An equivalent formulation of (1.16) is the following. If tp $S = {\omega_1}^{\gamma} < \omega_2$ *and the continuum hypothesis is assumed, then there is a family of* $\aleph_1$ *sets* $F_\mu \subset S(\mu<\omega_1)$ *such that* (i) tp $F_\mu \leqslant {\omega_1}^{\omega+1}$ (i.e. 'small' sets), (ii) tp $F_\mu \cap F_\lambda < {\omega_1}^{\omega}$ if $\lambda \neq \mu$ (i.e. the intersection of any pair is 'very small'), (iii) *each point of* S *belongs to only finitely many of the sets* F_μ *and* (iv) *the union of any* $\aleph_0$ *of these sets is nearly all of* S, i.e.

$$\text{tp}\left(S - \bigcup_{\mu\in N} F_\mu\right) < {\omega_1}^{\gamma}$$

for any infinite set of indices N. Using a different kind of notation, we proved (**1**, Theorem 10.14) that

$$\begin{Bmatrix} \omega \\ \\ \lambda \end{Bmatrix} \not\to \begin{Bmatrix} 1 & \omega & \omega \\ \vee & & , \\ {\omega_1}^{\omega} & 1 & {\omega_1}^{\omega+2} \end{Bmatrix} \qquad (\lambda < \omega_2).$$

In Theorem 8 we establish the analogous result

$$\begin{Bmatrix} \omega_1 \\ \lambda \end{Bmatrix} \not\to \begin{Bmatrix} 1 & \omega & \omega \\ & \vee & , \\ {\omega_1}^{\omega+2} & 1 & {\omega_1}^{\omega+2} \end{Bmatrix} \qquad (\lambda < \omega_2).$$

This last relation is also best possible since (see §7)

$$\begin{Bmatrix} \omega_1 \\ {\omega_1}^{\gamma} \end{Bmatrix} \to \begin{Bmatrix} 1 & \omega & \omega \\ & \vee & , \\ {\omega_1}^{\gamma} & 1 & \xi \end{Bmatrix}$$

holds if $\xi < {\omega_1}^{\omega+2} < {\omega_1}^{\gamma} < \omega_2$.

2. Notation and preliminary results

Unless stated otherwise small Latin and Greek letters denote ordinal numbers. Capital letters denote sets and, in particular,

$$W_1 = \{\nu : \nu < \omega_1\}$$

is the set of countable ordinals. The obliterator sign ^ above any symbol means that that symbol is to be disregarded, e.g. $\{x_0, \ldots, \hat{x}_\lambda\} = \{x_\nu : \nu < \lambda\}$. We write $\{x_0, \ldots, \hat{x}_\lambda\}_<$ to indicate that the set $\{x_0, \ldots, \hat{x}_\lambda\}$ is ordered so that $x_\mu < x_\nu$ for $\mu < \nu < \lambda$. Similarly, $\{x_0, \ldots, \hat{x}_\lambda\}_{\neq}$ means that $x_\mu \neq x_\nu$ for $\mu < \nu < \lambda$. The order type of an ordered set S is denoted by tp S. If $X, Y \subset S$, then $X < Y$ means that $x < y$ holds for all $x \in X$ and $y \in Y$. If S is the disjoint union of sets S_ν $(\nu < \lambda)$ and $S_\mu < S_\nu$ holds for $\mu < \nu < \lambda$, then we write

$$S = S_0 \cup \ldots \cup \hat{S}_\lambda(<) \text{ or } S = \bigcup_{\nu<\lambda} S_\nu(<).$$

A subset X of S is *cofinal* with S if $X < \{\alpha\}$ is false for every $\alpha \in S$. We define $co(\lambda)$ to be the least ordinal μ such that tp $T = \mu$ for some cofinal subset T of $\{\nu : \nu < \lambda\}$.

The cardinal of S is $|S|$, and $[S]^r = \{X \subset S : |X| = r\}$ for any cardinal number r. The partition symbol

$$\alpha \to (\alpha_\nu)^r{}_{\nu<\lambda} \tag{2.1}$$

means: if tp $S = \alpha$ and $[S]^r = \bigcup_{\nu<\lambda} K_\nu$, then there are $\mu < \lambda$ and $A \subset S$ such that tp $A = \alpha_\mu$ and $[A]^r \subset K_\mu$. If $\alpha_\nu = \beta$ for all $\nu < \lambda$ we write (2.1) as

$$\alpha \to (\beta)_\lambda{}^r.$$

We need the following simple relations of the form (2.1) with $r = 1$ (see **(9)**):

$$\omega_1^n \to (\omega_1^n)_\lambda^1 \qquad \text{if } \lambda < \omega_1 \text{ and } n < \omega, \tag{2.2}$$

$$\omega_1^\rho \to (\omega_1^\rho)_l^1 \qquad \text{if } l < \omega, \tag{2.3}$$

$$\xi \nrightarrow (\omega_1^n)_{n<\omega}^1 \qquad \text{if } \xi < \omega_2. \tag{2.4}$$

These results generalize to ordinal numbers of arbitrary cardinality, but we do not use this fact.

A set mapping is a function $f: S \to \{X : X \subset S\}$ such that $x \notin f(x)$ $(x \in S)$. A *free set* in this mapping is a subset S' of S such that $x \notin f(y)$ for all $x, y \in S'$. It was shown by Erdös and Specker **(7)** that, if $S = \{\nu : \nu < \omega_\lambda\}$ and f is a set mapping on S such that $\text{tp}\,(f(x)) < \alpha\ (<\omega_\lambda)$, then there is a free set $S' \subset S$ of type ω_λ. Their proof required the generalized continuum hypothesis but Hajnal **(8)** showed how to eliminate this hypothesis. In **(2)** we pointed out a general connection between the theory of set mappings and the polarized partition relations. We need the above theorem only for the case $\lambda = 1$ and this may be expressed by the relation

$$\begin{Bmatrix} \omega_1 \\ \omega_1 \end{Bmatrix} \to \begin{Bmatrix} 1 & \omega_1 \\ \alpha & \omega_1 \end{Bmatrix} \qquad (\alpha < \omega_1). \tag{2.5}$$

The polarized partition symbol (1.2) has already been defined. In §§6,7 we use a slight extension of this by allowing alternative entries. Formally,

$$\begin{Bmatrix} \alpha \\ \beta \end{Bmatrix} \to \begin{Bmatrix} \alpha_{\nu 1} & & \alpha_{\nu 2} & & & & \alpha_{\nu k_\nu} \\ & \vee & & \vee & \dots & \vee & \\ \beta_{\nu 1} & & \beta_{\nu 2} & & & & \beta_{\nu k_\nu} \end{Bmatrix}_{\nu < \lambda}$$

means: if $\text{tp}\, A = \alpha$, $\text{tp}\, B = \beta$ and

$$A \times B = \bigcup_{\nu < \lambda} K_\nu$$

is any partition, then there are $\mu < \lambda$ and $l < k_\mu$ and sets $A' \subset A$, $B' \subset B$ such that $\text{tp}\, A' = \alpha_{\mu l}$, $\text{tp}\, B' = \beta_{\mu l}$ and $A' \times B' \subset K_\mu$.

If $K_0 \cup K_1$ is a partition of $A \times B$ then we define

$$K_\rho(a) = \{b \in B : \{a, b\} \in K_\rho\} \qquad (a \in A),$$

$$K_\rho(b) = \{a \in A : \{a, b\} \in K_\rho\} \qquad (b \in B).$$

Also, if $X \subset A \cup B$, then we write

$$K_\rho(X) = \bigcup_{x \in X} K_\rho(x) \qquad (\rho = 0 \text{ or } 1).$$

A *graph* is an ordered pair $G = (S, E)$ with $E \subset [S]^2$. The elements of E are the *edges* of G. $G = (S, E)$ is a *complete* graph if $E = [S]^2$. A *circuit* of G of length k (>2) is a sequence $x_1, x_2, \ldots, x_k$ of k distinct elements of S such that $\{x_i, x_{i+1}\} \in E$ ($1 \leqslant i \leqslant k$), where $x_{k+1} = x_1$. A graph without circuits is called a *forest*.

3. Some lemmas

We establish here some simple lemmas which will be used in the next section.

LEMMA 1. *Let* $\alpha < \omega_1$ *and let* $M_n \in [W_1]^{\aleph_1}$ $(n < \omega)$. *Then there are* $\mu_n \in M_n$ $(n < \omega)$ *such that* $\operatorname{tp}\{\mu_n : n < \omega\} \geqslant \alpha$.

Proof. It is enough to prove this in the case $\alpha = \omega^\beta$. For $\beta = 0$, the result is obvious. Now assume that $\beta > 0$ and use induction. We may write $\omega^\beta = \alpha_0 + \alpha_1 + \ldots + \hat{\alpha}_\omega$, where $\alpha_n = \omega^{\beta_n} < \omega^\beta$ $(n < \omega)$. Let $\{n : n < \omega\}$ be partitioned into $\aleph_0$ disjoint infinite sets N_i $(i < \omega)$. Let $l < \omega$ and suppose we have already chosen $\mu_n \in M_n$ for $n \in N_0 \cup \ldots \cup \hat{N}_l$. For $k \in N_l$, let

$$M'_k = \{\mu \in M_k : \mu > \mu_n \text{ for all } n \in N_0 \cup \ldots \cup \hat{N}_l\}.$$

Then M'_k is a cofinal subset of $W_1 (k \in N_l)$. Since N_l is infinite, it follows from the induction hypothesis that there are elements $\mu_n \in M'_n (n \in N_l)$ such that

$$\operatorname{tp}\{\mu_n : n \in N_l\} \geqslant \alpha_l.$$

This defines $\mu_n \in M_n$ for all $n < \omega$. By the construction,

$$\operatorname{tp}\{\mu_n : n < \omega\} = \sum_{l<\omega} \operatorname{tp}\{\mu_n : n \in N_l\} \geqslant \sum_{l<\omega} \alpha_l = \omega^\beta.$$

We frequently use the following result.

LEMMA 2. *If* $T \subset S_0 \cup S_1 \cup \ldots \cup \hat{S}_{\omega_1}(<)$ *and* $\operatorname{tp} T < \omega_1^{\omega+1}$, *then there are* $\nu < \omega_1$ *and* $n < \omega$ *such that* $\operatorname{tp}(T \cap S_\rho) < \omega_1^n$ $(\nu < \rho < \omega_1)$.

Proof. Suppose the lemma is false. For $\rho < \omega_1$ we may write $\rho = \omega\xi + n$, where $\xi = \xi(\rho) < \omega_1$ and $n = n(\rho) < \omega$. Suppose $\rho < \omega_1$ and that $\nu_\sigma < \omega_1$ has been defined for $\sigma < \rho$. By our assumption, there is $\nu_\rho < \omega_1$ such that $\nu_\sigma < \nu_\rho$ $(\sigma < \rho)$ and $\operatorname{tp}(T \cap S_{\nu_\rho}) \geqslant \omega_1^{n(\rho)}$. This defines $\nu_\rho < \omega_1$ for all $\rho < \omega_1$. From the definition we have

$$\operatorname{tp} T \geqslant \sum_{\rho<\omega_1} \operatorname{tp}(T \cap S_{\nu_\rho}) \geqslant \sum_{\rho<\omega_1} \omega_1^{n(\rho)} = \omega_1^{\omega+1},$$

a contradiction.

LEMMA 3. *Let S_n $(n < \omega)$ be $\aleph_0$ disjoint sets and suppose that* $\operatorname{tp} S_n = \omega_1^{\gamma_n}$, *where $\omega < \gamma_n < \omega_1$ and $co(\omega_1^{\gamma_n}) = \omega_1$. Let $\alpha < \omega_1$ and let $F_\mu(\mu < \omega_1)$ be $\aleph_1$ sets such that*

$$\operatorname{tp}(S_n \cap F_\mu) < \omega_1^{\omega+1} \qquad (n < \omega;\ \mu < \omega_1). \tag{3.1}$$

Then there is $A \subset W_1$ such that $\operatorname{tp} A \geqslant \alpha$ *and*

$$\operatorname{tp}\left(S_n - \bigcup_{\mu\in A} F_\mu\right) = \operatorname{tp} S_n \qquad (n < \omega). \tag{3.2}$$

Proof. By the hypothesis, there are $\gamma_{n\nu}(n < \omega;\ \nu < \omega_1)$ such that

$$\omega \leqslant \gamma_{n0} \leqslant \gamma_{n1} \leqslant \ldots \leqslant \hat{\gamma}_{n\omega_1} < \gamma_n$$

and

$$\sum_{\nu<\omega_1} \omega_1^{\gamma_{n\nu}} = \omega_1^{\gamma_n}.$$

We may write

$$S_n = \bigcup_{\nu<\omega_1} S_{n\nu}(<),$$

where $\operatorname{tp} S_{n\nu} = \omega_1^{\gamma_{n\nu}}$. By (3.1) and Lemma 2, there are $\nu(n, \mu) < \omega_1$ and $i(n, \mu) < \omega$ $(n < \omega;\ \mu < \omega_1)$ such that

$$\operatorname{tp}(S_{n\nu} \cap F_\mu) < \omega_1^{i(n,\mu)} \qquad (\nu(n, \mu) < \nu < \omega_1).$$

There are sets $M_n \in [W_1]^{\aleph_1}$ $(n < \omega)$ such that $M_0 \supset M_1 \supset \ldots$ and

$$i(n, \mu) = i(n) \qquad (\mu \in M_n).$$

By Lemma 1, there are $\mu_n \in M_n(n < \omega)$ such that $A = \{\mu_n : n < \omega\}$ has order type $\geqslant \alpha$. Choose $\lambda < \omega_1$ such that $\nu(n, \mu_m) < \lambda$ $(m, n < \omega)$ and let

$$k(n) = \max\{i(n), i(n, \mu_0), \ldots, i(n, \mu_n)\} \qquad (n < \omega).$$

Then

$$\operatorname{tp}(F_{\mu_m} \cap S_{n\nu}) < \omega_1^{k(n)} \qquad (m, n < \omega;\ \lambda < \nu < \omega_1).$$

Since $k(n) < \omega$, it follows from (2.2) and (2.3) that

$$\operatorname{tp}\left(S_{n\nu} - \bigcup_{\mu\in A} F_\mu\right) = \omega_1^{\gamma_{n\nu}} \qquad (n < \omega;\ \lambda < \nu < \omega_1)$$

and (3.2) follows.

LEMMA 4. *Let $\omega + 1 \leqslant \gamma_0 \leqslant \gamma_1 \leqslant \ldots \leqslant \hat{\gamma}_{\omega_1} < \omega_2$ and let*

$$\beta < \sum_{\nu<\omega_1} \omega_1^{\gamma_\nu} = \omega_1^{\gamma}.$$

Then there are a countable set $N \subset W_1$ and ordinals β_ν $(\nu \in N)$ such that

$$\omega + 1 \leqslant \beta_\nu \leqslant \gamma_\nu, \qquad co(\omega_1^{\beta_\nu}) = \omega_1$$

and

$$\beta < \sum_{\nu \in N} \omega_1^{\beta_\nu}. \tag{3.3}$$

Proof. By the hypothesis, there is θ such that $\omega + 1 \leqslant \theta < \gamma$ and $\beta < \omega_1^{\theta+1}$. If $\theta < \gamma_\nu$ for some $\nu < \omega_1$, then (3.3) holds with $N = \{\nu\}$ and $\beta_\nu = \theta + 1$. We may therefore assume that there is $\nu_0 < \omega_1$ such that $\gamma_\nu = \theta$ $(\nu_0 \leqslant \nu < \omega_1)$. Therefore, $\gamma = \theta + 1$ and there is $\xi < \omega_1$ such that $\beta < \omega_1^\theta \xi$. If $co(\omega_1^\theta) = \omega_1$, then (3.3) holds with $N = \{\nu : \nu_0 \leqslant \nu < \nu_0 + \xi\}$ and $\beta_\nu = \theta$. Suppose, on the other hand, that $co(\omega_1^\theta) = \omega$. Then there are $\theta_n (n < \omega)$ such that $\omega + 1 \leqslant \theta_0 < \theta_1 < \ldots < \hat{\theta}_\omega < \theta = \lim_{n<\omega} \theta_n$. In this case, (3.3) holds with

$$N = \{\nu : \nu_0 \leqslant \nu < \nu_0 + \omega\xi\} \quad \text{and} \quad \beta_{\nu_0 + \omega\rho + n} = \omega_1^{\theta_n + 1} \qquad (\rho < \xi;\, n < \omega).$$

4. Positive results

In contrast to the negative relation

$$\begin{Bmatrix} \omega_1 \\ \lambda \end{Bmatrix} \nrightarrow \begin{Bmatrix} 1 & \omega \\ \omega_1^{\omega+2} & 1 \end{Bmatrix} \qquad (\lambda < \omega_2) \tag{4.1}$$

proved in **(2)**, we shall establish the following theorem.

THEOREM 1. *If $\alpha < \omega_1, \xi < \omega_1^{\omega+2}, \beta < \omega_1^\gamma$ and $\omega + 2 \leqslant \gamma < \omega_1$, then*

$$\begin{Bmatrix} \omega_1 \\ \omega_1^\gamma \end{Bmatrix} \rightarrow \begin{Bmatrix} 1 & \alpha \\ \xi & \beta \end{Bmatrix}. \tag{4.2}$$

Proof. We first prove the result for the case $co(\omega_1^\gamma) = \omega_1$.

Let $\text{tp}\, C = \omega_1^\gamma$ and let $W_1 \times C = K_0 \cup K_1$ be a partition such that $\text{tp}\,(K_0(\mu)) < \xi$ for all $\mu \in W_1$. We have to show that there are sets $A \subset W_1$ and $B \subset C$ such that $\text{tp}\, A \geqslant \alpha$, $\text{tp}\, B \geqslant \beta$ and $A \times B \subset K_1$.

Since $co(\omega_1^\gamma) = \omega_1$, we may write

$$C = \bigcup_{\nu < \omega_1} C_\nu(<),$$

where $\text{tp}\, C_\nu = \omega_1^{\gamma_\nu}$ $(\nu < \omega_1)$ and

$$\omega + 1 \leqslant \gamma_0 \leqslant \gamma_1 \leqslant \ldots \leqslant \hat{\gamma}_{\omega_1} < \gamma.$$

There is $\eta < \omega_1$ such that $\xi < \omega_1^{\omega+1}\eta$ and the sets

$$F(\mu) = \{\nu < \omega_1 : \text{tp}\,(K_0(\mu) \cap C_\nu) \geqslant \omega_1^{\omega+1}\} \qquad (\mu < \omega_1)$$

have order type less than η. Therefore, by (2.5), there are $M, N \in [W_1]^{\aleph_1}$ such that

$$\text{tp}\,(K_0(\mu) \cap C_\nu) < \omega_1^{\omega+1} \qquad (\mu \in M;\ \nu \in N). \tag{4.3}$$

By Lemma 4 there are a countable set $N_0 \subset N$ and ordinals β_ν $(\nu \in N_0)$ such that $\omega + 1 \leqslant \beta_\nu \leqslant \gamma_\nu$ and $co(\omega_1^{\beta_\nu}) = \omega_1$ $(\nu \in N_0)$ and such that

$$\beta < \sum_{\nu \in N_0} \omega_1^{\beta_\nu}.$$

Let S_ν be a subset of C_ν of type $\omega_1^{\beta_\nu}$ $(\nu \in N_0)$. Then, by (4.3) and Lemma 3, there is a set $A \subset M$ such that tp $A \geqslant \alpha$ and

$$\text{tp}\left(S_\nu - \bigcup_{\mu \in A} K_0(\mu)\right) = \text{tp}\, S_\nu \qquad (\nu \in N_0).$$

This implies that the set

$$B = \bigcup_{\nu \in N_0} S_\nu - \bigcup_{\mu \in A} K_0(\mu)$$

has type $\geqslant \beta$ and $A \times B \subset K_1$. This proves (4.2) for the case $co(\omega_1^\gamma) = \omega_1$.

The case $co(\omega_1^\gamma) = \omega$ follows immediately from this. For, if $co\,\gamma = \omega$ and $\beta < \omega_1^\gamma$, then $\beta < \omega_1^{\delta+1}$ for some $\delta + 1 < \gamma$ and (4.2) is implied by the relation

$$\begin{Bmatrix} \omega_1 \\ \omega_1^{\delta+1} \end{Bmatrix} \rightarrow \begin{Bmatrix} 1 & \alpha \\ \xi & \beta \end{Bmatrix}.$$

The condition $\xi < \omega_1^{\omega+2}$ in Theorem 1 is necessary because of (4.1). Also, in view of the trivial relation (1.6), the condition $\alpha < \omega_1$ is necessary. The relation (4.2) is best possible in a third sense since (Theorem 6)

$$\begin{Bmatrix} \omega_1 \\ \omega_1^\gamma \end{Bmatrix} \nrightarrow \begin{Bmatrix} 1 & \omega \\ \omega_1^{\omega+1}+1 & \omega_1^\gamma \end{Bmatrix} \qquad \text{if } co(\omega_1^\gamma) = \omega_1. \tag{4.4}$$

This shows that we cannot replace β by ω_1^γ in (4.2) when $co(\omega_1^\gamma) = \omega_1$. In the next theorem we show that (4.2) can be strengthened if $co(\omega_1^\gamma) = \omega$.

THEOREM 2. *If* $\alpha < \omega_1, \xi < \omega_1^{\omega+2} < \omega_1^\gamma < \omega_2$ *and* $co(\gamma) = \omega$, *then*

$$\begin{Bmatrix} \omega_1 \\ \omega_1^\gamma \end{Bmatrix} \rightarrow \begin{Bmatrix} 1 & \alpha \\ \xi & \omega_1^\gamma \end{Bmatrix}. \tag{4.5}$$

Proof. We shall prove the result by induction on α. For $\alpha = 0$ or 1 the result is obvious. Now assume that $1 < \alpha' < \omega_1$ and that (4.5) holds for all $\alpha < \alpha'$.

Since $1 < \alpha' < \omega_1$, there are ordinals $\alpha_n < \alpha'$ $(n < \omega)$ such that

$$\alpha' = \alpha_0 + \alpha_1 + \dots .$$

Also, by the hypothesis of the theorem, there are $\gamma_n (n < \omega)$ such that

$$\omega < \gamma_0 < \gamma_1 < \dots < \gamma = \lim_{n<\omega} \gamma_n.$$

Let $\operatorname{tp} C_0 = \omega_1^{\gamma}$, $M_0 = W_1$, and let $K_0 \cup K_1$ be any partition of $M_0 \times C_0$ such that $\operatorname{tp}(K_0(\mu)) < \xi$ $(\mu \in M_0)$. We will show that there are sets $A \subset M_0$ and $B \subset C_0$ such that $\operatorname{tp} A \geqslant \alpha'$, $\operatorname{tp} B = \omega_1^{\gamma}$ and $A \times B \subset K_1$.

By the induction hypothesis, (4.5) holds for $\alpha = \alpha_0$ and hence there are sets $A_0 \subset M_0$ and $D_0 \subset C_0$ such that $\operatorname{tp} A_0 = \alpha_0$, $\operatorname{tp} D_0 = \omega_1^{\gamma}$ and $A_0 \times D_0 \subset K_1$. Let

$$D_0 = E_0 \cup C_1 \,(<),$$

where E_0 is the initial section of D_0 of type $\omega_1^{\gamma_0+2}$. We may write

$$E_0 = \bigcup_{\rho<\omega_1} E_{0\rho}(<), \qquad E_{0\rho} = \bigcup_{\sigma<\omega_1} E_{0\rho\sigma}(<),$$

where $\operatorname{tp} E_{0\rho\sigma} = \omega_1^{\gamma_0} (\rho, \sigma < \omega_1)$. There is $\eta < \omega_1$ such that $\xi < \omega_1^{\omega+1}\eta$. Therefore, since $\operatorname{tp} K_0(\mu) < \xi$ $(\mu \in M_0)$ and

$$\begin{Bmatrix} \omega_1 \\ \omega_1 \end{Bmatrix} \to \begin{Bmatrix} 1 & \omega_1 \\ \eta & 1 \end{Bmatrix} \tag{4.6}$$

by (2.5), it follows that there are $M_0' \in [M_0]^{\aleph_1}$ and $\rho_0 < \omega_1$ such that

$$\operatorname{tp}(K_0(\mu) \cap E_{0\rho_0}) < \omega_1^{\omega+1} \qquad (\mu \in M_0').$$

Therefore, by Lemma 2, for each $\mu \in M_0'$ there are $p_0(\mu) < \omega$ and $\sigma_0(\mu) < \omega_1$ such that

$$\operatorname{tp}(K_0(\mu) \cap E_{0\rho_0\sigma}) < \omega_1^{p_0(\mu)} \text{ for } \sigma_0(\mu) < \sigma < \omega_1.$$

There is a set $M_1 \in [M_0']^{\aleph_1}$ such that $A_0 < M_1$ and such that

$$p_0(\mu) = p_0 \; (\mu \in M_1).$$

More generally, suppose that $n < \omega$ and $C_n \subset C_0$, $M_n \subset M_0$ have been defined so that $\operatorname{tp} C_n = \omega_1^{\gamma}$ and $\operatorname{tp} M_n = \omega_1$. By the induction hypothesis, (4.5) holds with $\alpha = \alpha_n$ and so there are sets $A_n \subset M_n$ and $D_n \subset C_n$ such that $\operatorname{tp} A_n = \alpha_n$, $\operatorname{tp} D_n = \omega_1^{\gamma}$ and $A_n \times D_n \subset K_1$. Let E_n be the initial section of type $\omega_1^{\gamma_n+2}$ and let

$$D_n = E_n \cup C_{n+1} \,(<).$$

We may write

$$E_n = \bigcup_{\rho<\omega_1} E_{n\rho}(<) \text{ and } E_{n\rho} = \bigcup_{\sigma<\omega_1} E_{n\rho\sigma}(<), \tag{4.7}$$

where $\operatorname{tp}(E_{n\rho\sigma}) = \omega_1^{\gamma_n}$. It follows from (4.6) that there are $p_n < \omega_1$ and $M_n' \in [M_n]^{\aleph_1}$ such that

$$\operatorname{tp}(K_0(\mu) \cap E_{n\rho_n}) < \omega_1^{\omega+1} \qquad (\mu \in M_n').$$

Therefore, by Lemma 2, for each $\mu \in M_n'$ there are $p_n(\mu) < \omega$ and $\sigma_n(\mu) < \omega_1$ such that

$$\operatorname{tp}(K_0(\mu) \cap E_{n\rho_n\sigma}) < \omega_1^{p_n(\mu)} \text{ for } \sigma_n(\mu) < \sigma < \omega_1.$$

Now choose $M_{n+1} \in [M_n']^{\aleph_1}$ such that $p_n(\mu) = p_n$ $(\mu \in M_{n+1})$ and such that $A_n < M_{n+1}$.

Proceeding inductively in the above manner, we define sets $A_n \subset M_0$ and $E_n \subset C_0$ $(n < \omega)$ such that (4.7) holds, $\operatorname{tp} A_n = \alpha_n$, $\operatorname{tp} E_{n\rho\sigma} = \omega_1^{\gamma_n}$,

$$\begin{aligned} &A_0 < A_1 < \ldots, \\ &E_0 < E_1 < \ldots, \\ &A_m \times E_n \subset K_1 \qquad (m \leqslant n < \omega). \end{aligned} \tag{4.8}$$

Also, there are

$$p_n < \omega,\ \rho_n < \omega_1 \text{ and } \sigma_n(\mu) < \omega_1 \text{ for } \mu \in A_n' = A_{n+1} \cup A_{n+2} \cup \ldots,$$

such that

$$\operatorname{tp}(K_0(\mu) \cap E_{n\rho_n\sigma}) < \omega_1^{p_n} \text{ for } \sigma_n(\mu) < \sigma < \omega_1 \text{ and } \mu \in A_n'. \tag{4.9}$$

Since A_n' is countable, there is $\sigma_n < \omega_1$ such that $\sigma_n(\mu) < \sigma_n$ for all $\mu \in A_n'$. Put

$$B_n = E_{n\rho_n\sigma_n} - \bigcup_{\mu \in A_n'} K_0(\mu). \tag{4.10}$$

Since $\operatorname{tp}(E_{n\rho_n\sigma_n}) = \omega_1^{\gamma_n} > \omega_1^{\omega}$, it follows from (4.9) and (2.2) that $\operatorname{tp} B_n = \omega_1^{\gamma_n}$. Therefore, $B = B_0 \cup B_1 \cup \ldots (<)$ has type ω_1^{γ}. From (4.8) and (4.10) it follows that $A \times B \subset K_1$, where $A = A_0 \cup A_1 \cup \ldots (<)$. This completes the proof of the theorem, since $\operatorname{tp} A = \alpha_0 + \alpha_1 + \ldots = \alpha'$.

As we have already noted, the negative relation (4.4) shows that the condition placed on the cofinality type of γ in Theorem 2 is essential. The next theorem shows that we can drop this condition if we strengthen the restriction on ξ to $\xi \leqslant \omega_1^{\omega+1}$. Theorem 3 shows that (4.4) is a best possible relation.

THEOREM 3. *If* $\alpha < \omega_1$ and $\omega + 1 \leqslant \gamma < \omega_2$, *then*

$$\begin{Bmatrix} \omega_1 \\ \omega_1^{\gamma} \end{Bmatrix} \to \begin{Bmatrix} 1 & \alpha \\ \omega_1^{\omega+1} & \omega_1^{\gamma} \end{Bmatrix}. \tag{4.11}$$

Proof. In view of Theorem 2 we may assume that $co(\omega_1^{\gamma}) = \omega_1$. Let $\operatorname{tp} C = \omega_1^{\gamma}$ and let $K_0 \cup K_1$ be any partition of $W_1 \times C$ such that $\operatorname{tp}(K_0(\mu)) < \omega_1^{\omega+1}$

$(\mu < \omega_1)$. Since $co(\omega_1^{\gamma}) = \omega_1$, we may write

$$C = \bigcup_{\rho < \omega_1} C_\rho(<),$$

where tp $C_\rho = \omega_1^{\gamma_\rho}(\rho < \omega_1)$ and $\omega \leqslant \gamma_0 \leqslant \gamma_1 \leqslant \ldots \leqslant \hat{\gamma}_{\omega_1} < \gamma$. By Lemma 2, there are $\rho(\mu) < \omega_1$ and $n(\mu) < \omega$ for $\mu < \omega_1$ such that

$$\text{tp}\,(F_\mu \cap C_\rho) < \omega_1^{n(\mu)} \qquad (\rho(\mu) < \rho < \omega_1).$$

There is $M \in [W_1]^{\aleph_1}$ such that $n(\mu) = n\ (\mu \in M)$. Let A be any subset of M of order type α and chose $\rho_0 < \omega_1$ such that $\rho(\mu) < \rho_0$ for all $\mu \in A$. By (2.2) and (2.3), we have

$$\text{tp}\left(C_\rho - \bigcup_{\mu\in A} K_0(\mu)\right) = \omega_1^{\gamma_\rho} \quad (\rho_0 < \rho < \omega_1)$$

and (4.11) follows.

It is easy to prove that, for $1 \leqslant \gamma \leqslant \omega + 1$ and $\alpha < \omega_1$,

$$\begin{Bmatrix} \omega_1 \\ \omega_1^{\gamma} \end{Bmatrix} \to \begin{Bmatrix} 1 & \alpha \\ \omega_1^{\gamma} & \omega_1^{\gamma} \end{Bmatrix}.$$

In Theorem 4 we establish a stronger result.

THEOREM 4. *If* $k < \omega$, $\alpha < \omega_1$ *and* $1 \leqslant \gamma \leqslant \omega + 1$, *then*

$$\begin{Bmatrix} \omega_1 \\ \omega_1^{\gamma} \end{Bmatrix} \to \begin{Bmatrix} k & \alpha \\ \omega_1^{\gamma} & \omega_1^{\gamma} \end{Bmatrix}. \tag{4.12}$$

Proof. We shall first prove (4.12) for the case $k = 1$. If $\gamma = \omega + 1$, then this is a special case of (4.11). Suppose $\gamma \leqslant \omega$. Let tp $C = \omega_1^{\gamma}$ and let $W_1 \times C = K_0 \cup K_1$ be a partition such that tp $(K_0(\mu)) < \omega_1^{\gamma}$ $(\mu < \omega_1)$. Since $\gamma \leqslant \omega$, it follows that there are $n < \omega$ and $M \in [W_1]^{\aleph_1}$ such that tp $(K_0(\mu)) < \omega_1^{n}$ $(\mu \in M)$. Let A be any subset of M of order type α. It follows from (2.2) and (2.3) that

$$\text{tp}\left(C - \bigcup_{\mu\in A} K_0(\mu)\right) = \omega_1^{\gamma}$$

and so (4.12) holds with $k = 1$.

Now assume $k > 1$ and use induction. Let $W_1 \times C = K_0 \cup K_1$, where tp $C = \omega_1^{\gamma}$. Suppose that

$$\text{tp}\,(K_0(X)) < \omega_1^{\gamma}$$

holds for any $X \in [W_1]^k$. If tp $(K_0(\mu)) < \omega_1^{\gamma}$ for all $\mu \in W_1$, then, since (4.12) holds with $k = 1$, there are $A \subset W_1$ and $B \subset C$ such that tp $A = \alpha$, tp $B = \omega_1^\gamma$ and $A \times B \subset K_1$. Therefore, we may assume that tp $(K_0(\mu_0)) = \omega_1^\gamma$ for some $\mu_0 < \omega_1$. Also, we have

$$\text{tp}\,(K_0(\mu_0) \cap K_0(X)) < \omega_1^\gamma$$

for $X \in [W_1 - \{\mu_0\}]^{k-1}$. By the induction hypothesis (4.12) holds if k is replaced by $k-1$ and hence there are $A \subset W_1 - \{\mu_0\}$ and $B \subset K_0(\mu_0)$ such that tp $A = \alpha$, tp $B = \omega_1^\gamma$ and $A \times B \subset K_1$. This proves (4.12).

The cardinal relation (**3**, Theorem 32)

$$\begin{Bmatrix} \omega_1 \\ \omega_1 \end{Bmatrix} \nrightarrow \begin{Bmatrix} \omega_0 & \omega_0 \\ \omega_1 & \omega_1 \end{Bmatrix}$$

shows that k cannot be replaced by ω in (4.12) so the result is best possible. It is natural to ask whether Theorems 1, 2 and 3 can be strengthened by replacing 1 by k ($<\omega$) in (4.2), (4.5) and (4.11) respectively. We know this is not possible in the case of Theorem 3 since we will show (Theorem 7), with the help of the continuum hypothesis, that

$$(*) \qquad \begin{Bmatrix} \omega_1 \\ \omega_1^\gamma \end{Bmatrix} \nrightarrow \begin{Bmatrix} 2 & \omega \\ \omega_1^\omega & \omega_1^\gamma \end{Bmatrix} \quad \text{if } \omega + 1 < \gamma < \omega_2 \text{ and } co\,\omega_1^\gamma = \omega_1. \qquad (4.13)$$

However, we do not know if Theorem 2 is best possible in the sense just described. The first problem of this kind which we cannot settle is:

Problem 1. Is the relation

$$\begin{Bmatrix} \omega_1 \\ \omega_1^{\omega 2} \end{Bmatrix} \rightarrow \begin{Bmatrix} 2 & \omega \\ \omega_1^\omega & \omega_1^{\omega 2} \end{Bmatrix}$$

true or false?

We conclude this section by proving one further relation of this kind.

Theorem 5. *If* $\alpha < \omega_1$ *and* $\beta < \omega_1^{\omega+2}$, *then*

$$\begin{Bmatrix} \omega_1 \\ \omega_1^{\omega+2} \end{Bmatrix} \rightarrow \begin{Bmatrix} 2 & \alpha \\ \omega_1^{\omega+1} & \beta \end{Bmatrix}. \qquad (4.14)$$

Proof. Let tp $C = \omega_1^{\omega+2}$ and let $W_1 \times C = K_0 \cup K_1$ be any partition. There is $\eta < \omega_1$ such that $\beta < \omega_1^{\omega+1}\eta$. If tp $(K_0(\mu)) < \omega_1^{\omega+1}\eta$ for all $\mu \in W_1$, then, by Theorem 1, there are $A \subset W_1$ and $B \subset C$ such that tp $A = \alpha$, tp $B = \beta$ and $A \times B \subset K_1$. Therefore, we may assume that there is some $\mu_0 < \omega_1$ such that tp $(K(\mu_0)) = \omega_1^{\omega+1}\eta$. Since tp $(K(\mu_0) \cap K(\mu)) < \omega_1^{\omega+1}(\mu \in W_1 - \{\mu_0\})$, it follows from Lemma 3 that there are $A \subset W_1 - \{\mu_0\}$ and $B \subset K(\mu_0)$ such that tp $A = \alpha$, tp $B = \omega_1^{\omega+1}\eta$ and $A \times B \subset K_1$. This proves the result.

We do not know if 2 can be replaced by 3 in (4.14).

PROBLEM 2. Does the relation

$$\begin{Bmatrix} \omega_1 \\ \omega_1^{\omega+2} \end{Bmatrix} \to \begin{Bmatrix} 3 & \alpha \\ \omega_1^{\omega+1} & \beta \end{Bmatrix}$$

hold for $\alpha < \omega_1$ and $\beta < \omega_1^{\omega+2}$?

5. Lemmas

We need the following three lemmas in order to prove Theorem 7 in the next section. Lemma 5 is essentially the same as Lemma 10.5 of (**1**) and Lemma 6 is a known result due to Erdös, Kakutani and Tukey (**4**). We repeat the short proofs of these for the convenience of the reader.

LEMMA 5. *Let* $0 < |I| \leqslant \aleph_0$, $|M_i| = \aleph_0$ $(i \in I)$ *and let*

$$M = \bigcup_{i \in I} M_i = \{\mu_0, \mu_1, \ldots, \hat{\mu}_\omega\}_{\neq}.$$

If $\operatorname{tp} S < \omega_2$, *then there are sets* $A_\mu \subset S$ $(\mu \in M)$ *such that*

$$\text{(i)}\ \operatorname{tp} A_{\mu_n} < \omega_1^{\,n} \quad (n < \omega),$$

$$\text{(ii)}\ |\{\mu \in M : x \in A_\mu\}| < \aleph_0 \ \textit{for}\ x \in S,$$

$$\text{(iii)}\ \operatorname{tp}\Big(S - \bigcup_{\mu \in M_i} A_\mu\Big) < \omega_1^{\,\omega} \quad (i \in I).$$

Proof. Since the sets M_i $(i \in I)$ are infinite, there are mutually disjoint infinite sets $M_i' \subset M_i$ $(i \in I)$. Let $M_i' = \{\mu_{n_{ij}} : j < \omega\}_{\neq}$, where $n_{i0} < n_{i1} < \ldots$ $(i \in I)$.

By (2.4) there is a partition of S into disjoint sets C_n $(n < \omega)$ such that $\operatorname{tp} C_n < \omega_1^{\,n}$ $(n < \omega)$. Let $r < \omega$. If $r = n_{ij}$ for some pair i, j with $i \in I$ and $0 < j < \omega$, then we put

$$A_{\mu_r} = \bigcup_{n_{i,j-1} \leqslant n \leqslant n_{i,j}} C_n.$$

Otherwise, if

$$\mu_r \notin \bigcup_{i \in I} (M_i' - \{\mu_{i0}\}),$$

then we put $A_{\mu_r} = \emptyset$. In either case, $\operatorname{tp} A_{\mu_r} < \omega_1^{\,r}$ $(r < \omega)$ by (2.2), and (i) holds. If $x \in S$, then there is a unique $n < \omega$ such that $x \in C_n$. But there are only finitely many pairs i, j with $i \in I$ and $0 < j < \omega$ such that $n_{ij-1} \leqslant n \leqslant n_{ij}$ and so (ii) holds. Finally, (iii) holds since

$$S - \bigcup_{\mu \in M_i} A_\mu \subset \bigcup_{n < n_{i0}} C_n = D$$

and the order type of D is less than $\omega_1^{\,n_{i0}}$ by (2.2).

LEMMA 6. *The complete graph on W_1 is the union of $\aleph_0$ forests, i.e. there is a partition $[W_1]^2 = E_0 \cup E_1 \cup \ldots \cup \hat{E}_\omega$ such that the graph $T_i = (W_1, E_i)$ $(i<\omega)$ contains no circuit.*

Proof. For $\mu < \omega_1$ there is $t = t(\mu) \leqslant \omega$ such that $\{v : v < \mu\} = \{v_{\mu 0}, v_{\mu 1}, \ldots, \hat{v}_{\mu t}\}_{\neq}$. Thus, for $v < \mu$, there is an unique $i < t(\mu)$ such that $v = v_{\mu i}$. Put

$$E_i = \bigcup_{\mu<\omega_1} \{v_{\mu i}, \mu\}_<.$$

Then

$$[W_1]^2 = \bigcup_{i<\omega} E_i.$$

Suppose that $T_i = (W_i, E_i)$ contains a circuit. Then there are $\{v, v', \mu\}_< \subset W_1$ such that $\{v, \mu\}_< \in E_i$ and $\{v', \mu\}_< \in E_i$. But this implies the contradiction $v = v' = v_{\mu i}$.

LEMMA 7. *Let $|N_i| = \aleph_0 (i < \omega)$ and let $G_i = (S, E_i)$ $(i < \omega)$ be a graph without circuits of length 4. Then there are disjoint sets K_i $(i < \omega)$ such that*

$$\text{(i) } K_i \in [N_0 \cup N_1 \cup \ldots \cup N_i]^{\leqslant i+1},$$

$$\text{(ii) } K_i \cap N_j \neq \varnothing \qquad (j \leqslant i),$$

$$\text{(iii) } [K_i]^2 \cap E_j = \varnothing \qquad (j \leqslant i).$$

Proof. We will say that a set K has property P_{ni} $(i \leqslant n < \omega)$ if the conditions (i) and (ii) of the lemma are satisfied with $K_i = K$ and if

$$\text{(iii)}' \ [K]^2 \cap E_j = \varnothing \qquad (j \leqslant n).$$

This last condition is stronger than (iii) since $i \leqslant n$. We will prove that for fixed i and n $(i \leqslant n < \omega)$, there are infinitely many mutually disjoint sets having property P_{ni}.

If $i = 0$, this is obvious since each one-element subset of N_0 has property P_{n0}. Now assume that $0 < i \leqslant n < \omega$ and use induction on i. By assumption there are infinitely many mutually disjoint sets with property $P_{n,i-1}$ and we choose any $n + 2$ of these, say $L_0, L_1, \ldots, L_{n+1}$. We claim that, if $F \in [N_i]^t$ and $t > \frac{1}{2}(n + 2)(n + 1)^2 i^2$, then there are $x \in F$ and $\rho \leqslant n + 1$ such that $L_\rho \cup \{x\}$ has property P_{ni}. Suppose this is false. Then, for each $x \in F$ and $\rho \leqslant n + 1$ there are $j(\rho, n) \leqslant n$ and $y(\rho, x) \in L_\rho$ such that

$$\{y(\rho, x), x\}_{\neq} \in E_{j(\rho,x)}.$$

This follows since (i) and (ii) hold for $L_\rho \cup \{x\}$ and (iii)′ holds for L_ρ. There are $\rho_1(x), \rho_2(x) \leqslant n+1$ such that $\rho_1(x) \neq \rho_2(x)$ and $j(\rho_1(x), x) = j(\rho_2(x), x) = j(x)$. There are at most $\frac{1}{2}(n+2)(n+1)^2 i^2$ different vectors

$$v(x) = \big(\rho_1(x), \rho_2(x), j(x), y(\rho_1(x), x), y(\rho_2(x), x)\big)$$

and hence, there are $x_1, x_2 \in F$ such that $x_1 \neq x_2$ and $v(x_1) = v(x_2) = (\rho_1, \rho_2, j, y_1, y_2)$. Note that $\rho_1 \neq \rho_2$ and hence $y_1 \neq y_2$ since $y_1 \in L_{\rho_1}, y_2 \in L_{\rho_2}$ and L_{ρ_1}, L_{ρ_2} are disjoint. Therefore, $\{x_1, y_1, x_2, y_2\}_{\neq}$ is a circuit in G_j of length 4. This contradiction proves our claim, i.e. there are $x \in F$ and $\rho \leqslant n+1$ such that $J_0 = L_\rho \cup \{x\}$ has property P_{ni}. This argument may be repeated choosing another set $L_0', \ldots, L'_{n+1}$ of $n+2$ sets with property $P_{n,i-1}$ so that these are mutually disjoint and disjoint from J_0. As before, there are $x' \in N_i - J_0$ and $p' \leqslant n+1$ such that $J_1 = L'_{\rho'} \cup \{x'\}$ has property P_{ni}. In this way we construct infinitely many mutually disjoint sets with property P_{ni}. The assertion of the previous paragraph now follows by induction.

In particular, there are infinitely many mutually disjoint sets having property P_{ii} $(i < \omega)$. Therefore, we can choose the finite sets K_i $(i < \omega)$ so that (i), (ii) and (iii) hold and so that these are mutually disjoint.

6. Negative relations

In Theorem 6 we establish the negative polarized partition relation (4.4) discussed in §4. The condition placed upon the cofinality type of ω_1^γ is necessary by Theorem 2.

THEOREM 6. *If $\gamma < \omega_2$ and $co(\omega_1^\gamma) = \omega_1$, then*

$$\begin{Bmatrix} \omega_1 \\ \omega_1^\gamma \end{Bmatrix} \nrightarrow \begin{Bmatrix} 1 & \omega \\ \omega_1^{\omega+1}+1 & \omega_1^\gamma \end{Bmatrix}. \tag{6.1}$$

Proof. Let S be an ordered set of type ω_1^γ. Then we may write

$$S = S_0 \cup S_1 \cup \ldots \cup \hat{S}_{\omega_1}(<),$$

where $\text{tp}\, S_\nu = \omega_1^{\gamma_\nu}$ and $\gamma_0 \leqslant \gamma_1 \leqslant \ldots \leqslant \hat{\gamma}_{\omega_1} \leqslant \gamma$. By (2.4) there is a partition of S_ν,

$$S_\nu = \bigcup_{\nu<\omega} A_{\nu n},$$

with $\text{tp}\, A_{\nu n} < \omega_1^n$ $(\nu < \omega_1; n < \omega)$. For $\nu < \omega_1$, there is a mapping f_ν of $\{n : n < \omega\}$ onto $\{\mu : \mu \leqslant \nu\}$, and for each $\mu \leqslant \nu$ there is an integer $n = n(\mu, \nu)$ such that $\mu = f_\nu(n)$. Now consider the partition $W_1 \times S = K_0 \cup K_1$ in which

$$K_0(\mu) = \bigcup_{\mu \leqslant \nu < \omega_1} \bigcup_{n < n(\mu,\nu)} A_{\nu n} \tag{6.2}$$

for $\mu < \omega_1$.

By (2.2), $\text{tp}\,(K_0(\mu) \cap S_\nu) < \omega_1^{n(\mu,\nu)} < \omega_1^{\omega}$ if $\mu \leqslant \nu < \omega_1$. Therefore, since $K_0(\mu) \cap S_\nu = \emptyset$ $(\nu < \mu < \omega_1)$, we have

$$\text{tp}\, K_0(\mu) \leqslant \omega_1^{\omega+1}. \tag{6.3}$$

Let $N \in [W_1]^{\aleph_0}$. Then N contains an increasing sequence of ordinals μ_i $(i < \omega)$. Let

$$\lambda = \lim_{i<\omega} \mu_i.$$

For $\nu \geqslant \lambda$, the integers $n\,(\mu_i, \nu)$ $(i < \omega)$ are all distinct and therefore, by (6.2),

$$S_\nu \subset \bigcup_{i<\omega} K_0(\mu_i) \qquad (\lambda \leqslant \nu < \omega_1).$$

Therefore

$$\bigcap_{\mu \in N} K_1(\mu) \subset S_0 \cup S_1 \cup \ldots \cup \hat{S}_\lambda,$$

and

$$\text{tp}\left\{\bigcap_{\mu \in N} K_1(\mu)\right\} < \omega_1^{\gamma}. \tag{6.4}$$

The theorem follows from (6.3) and (6.4).

We now establish a much stronger result than (6.1) by using the continuum hypothesis. Note that (6.5) implies (4.13).

(*) THEOREM 7. *If* $\omega + 1 < \gamma < \omega_2$ *and* $co(\omega_1^{\gamma}) = \omega_1$, *then*

$$\begin{pmatrix}\omega_1 \\ \omega_1^{\gamma}\end{pmatrix} \nrightarrow \begin{pmatrix} 1 & & 2 & & \omega & & \omega \\ & \vee & & \vee & & , & \\ \omega_1^{\omega+1}+1 & & \omega_1^{\omega} & & 1 & & \omega_1^{\gamma}\end{pmatrix}. \tag{6.5}$$

Proof. Let $\text{tp}\, S = \omega_1^{\gamma}$. In order to prove (6.5) it is enough to construct sets $F_\mu \subset S$ $(\mu < \omega_1)$ such that

(i) $\text{tp}\, F_\mu \leqslant \omega_1^{\omega+1}$ $(\mu < \omega_1)$,

(ii) $\text{tp}\,(F_\mu \cap F_\lambda) < \omega_1^{\omega}$ $(\mu < \lambda < \omega_1)$,

(iii) $\{\mu < \omega_1 : x \in F_\mu\}$ is finite for each $x \in S$, and

(iv) $\text{tp}\left(S - \bigcup_{\mu \in N} F_\mu\right) < \omega_1^{\gamma}$ whenever $N \in [W_1]^{\aleph_0}$.

Let $S = S_0 \cup S_1 \cup \ldots \cup \hat{S}_{\omega_1}(<)$, where $\text{tp}\, S_\nu = \omega_1^{\gamma_\nu} < \omega_1^{\gamma}$. By Lemma 5, for each $\nu < \omega_1$ there are sets $A_{\nu n} \subset S_\nu$ $(n < \omega)$ such that

$$\operatorname{tp} A_{\nu n} < \omega_1^{\,n} \qquad (n < \omega), \tag{6.6}$$

$$\{n < \omega : x \in A_{\nu n}\} \text{ is finite for } x \in S_\nu, \tag{6.7}$$

$$\operatorname{tp}\left(S_\nu - \bigcup_{n_0 < n < \omega} A_{\nu n}\right) < \omega_1^{\,\omega}. \tag{6.8}$$

By the continuum hypothesis, $[W_1]^{\aleph_0} = \{M_0, M_1, ..., M_{\omega_1}\}_{\neq}$. For $\nu < \omega_1$, let $\{M_0, M_1, ..., M_\nu\}_{\neq} = \{N_{\nu 0}, N_{\nu 1}, ..., \hat{N}_{\nu\omega}\}$ (the sets $N_{\nu n}$ $(n < \omega)$ are not necessarily different). By Lemma 6, there is a partition of $[W_1]^2$ into $\aleph_0$ sets,

$$[W_1]^2 = E_0 \cup E_1 \cup ... \cup \hat{E}_\omega,$$

such that each graph $T_i = (W_1, E_i)$ $(i < \omega)$ is a forest. By Lemma 7, there are disjoint sets $K_{\nu n}$ $(n < \omega)$ such that

$$K_{\nu n} \subset [N_{\nu 0} \cup ... \cup N_{\nu n}]^{\leqslant n+1}, \tag{6.9}$$

$$K_{\nu n} \cap N_{\nu j} \neq \emptyset \qquad (j \leqslant n), \tag{6.10}$$

$$[K_{\nu n}]^2 \cap E_j = \emptyset \qquad (j \leqslant n). \tag{6.11}$$

We shall define the sets $F_\mu (\mu < \omega_1)$ by describing the intersections $F_\mu \cap S_\nu$ $(\mu, \nu < \omega_1)$. Let $\mu, \nu < \omega_1$ be fixed. Since the sets $K_{\nu n}$ $(n < \omega)$ are mutually disjoint, there is at most one integer n such that $\mu \in K_{\nu n}$. If $\mu \in K_{\nu n}$, then we define $F_\mu \cap S_\nu = A_{\nu n}$. If, on the other hand,

$$\mu \notin \bigcup_{n<\omega} K_{\nu n},$$

then we put $F_\mu \cap S_\nu = \emptyset$. This defines the sets F_μ $(\mu < \omega_1)$ and we have to verify that (i)–(iv) hold.

Clearly (i) holds since $\operatorname{tp}(F_\mu \cap S_\nu) < \omega_1^{\,\omega}$ $(\mu, \nu < \omega_1)$. Let $\mu < \lambda < \omega_1$. There is a unique integer l such that $\{\mu, \lambda\}_<$ is an edge of T_l, i.e. such that $\{\mu, \lambda\} \in E_l$. Therefore, by (6.11), if $\nu < \omega_1$ and $l \leqslant n < \omega$, then μ and λ are not both elements of $K_{\nu n}$. It follows from this and the way $F_\mu \cap S_\nu$ and $F_\lambda \cap S_\nu$ are defined, that

$$F_\mu \cap F_\lambda \cap S_\nu \subset A_{\nu 0} \cup ... \cup \hat{A}_{\nu l}$$

for all $\nu < \omega_1$. Therefore, $\operatorname{tp}(F_\mu \cap F_\lambda \cap S_\nu) < \omega_1^{\,l}$ by (6.6) and (2.2). Thus, $\operatorname{tp}(F_\mu \cap F_\lambda) \leqslant \omega_1^{\,l+1} < \omega_1^{\,\omega}$ and (ii) holds.

If $x \in S$, then there is a unique $\nu < \omega_1$ such that $x \in S_\nu$. By (6.7), there is a finite set of integers $N(x)$ such that $x \notin A_{\nu n}$ if $n \notin N(x)$. From the definition of the sets $F_\mu \cap S_\nu$, it follows that $x \notin F_\mu$ unless

$$\mu \in \bigcup_{n \in N(x)} K_{\nu n}.$$

This proves that (iii) holds since the sets $K_{\nu n}$ are finite.

Finally, let $N \in [W_1]^{\aleph_0}$. Then $N = M_\sigma$ for some $\sigma < \omega_1$. Let $\sigma \leqslant \nu < \omega_1$. Then there is an integer $j(\sigma, \nu)$ such that $N = N_{\nu, j(\sigma,\nu)}$. By (6.10) there is an element

$$\mu_n \in K_{\nu n} \cap N_{\nu, j(\sigma,\nu)}$$

for $j(\sigma, \nu) \leqslant n < \omega$. Therefore, by the definition of F_{μ_n},

$$A_{\nu n} \subset F_{\mu_n} \subset \bigcup_{\mu \in N} F_\mu \qquad (j(\sigma, \nu) \leqslant n < \omega).$$

Therefore, by (6.8),

$$\operatorname{tp}\left(S_\nu - \bigcup_{\mu \in N} F_\mu \right) < \omega_1^{\omega} \qquad (\sigma \leqslant \nu < \omega_1).$$

It follows that

$$\operatorname{tp}\left(S - \bigcup_{\mu \in N} F_\mu \right) \leqslant \sum_{\nu < \sigma} \omega_1^{\gamma_\sigma} + \omega_1^{\omega+1} < \omega_1^{\gamma}.$$

This proves (iv) and completes the proof of Theorem 7.

We proved in (**1**, Theorem 10.14) with the continuum hypothesis that

$$(*) \qquad \begin{Bmatrix} \omega \\ \lambda \end{Bmatrix} \nrightarrow \begin{Bmatrix} 1 & & \omega & & \omega \\ & \vee & & , & \\ \omega_1^{\omega} & & 1 & & \omega_1^{\omega+2} \end{Bmatrix} \qquad (6.12)$$

holds for all $\lambda < \omega_2$. This result is best possible in the sense that none of the entries on the right side of (6.12) can be decreased (see §7). We shall use (6.12) to establish an analogous result for (ω_1, λ)-systems.

(*) THEOREM 8. *If* $\lambda < \omega_2$, *then*

$$\begin{Bmatrix} \omega_1 \\ \lambda \end{Bmatrix} \nrightarrow \begin{Bmatrix} 1 & & \omega & & \omega \\ & \vee & & , & \\ \omega_1^{\omega+2} & & 1 & & \omega_1^{\omega+2} \end{Bmatrix}. \qquad (6.13)$$

Proof. It is enough to prove (6.13) for the case when $\lambda = \omega_1^{\gamma}, \gamma < \omega_2$.

For $\gamma < \omega + 2$, the result is immediately obvious. We shall, therefore, assume that $\gamma \geqslant \omega + 2$ and use induction on γ.

Let $\operatorname{tp} S = \omega_1^{\gamma}$. We shall construct sets $F_\mu \subset S$ $(\mu < \omega_1)$ such that

(i) $\operatorname{tp} F_\mu < \omega_1^{\omega+2} \quad (\mu < \omega_1)$,

(ii) $|\{\mu < \omega_1 : x \in F_\mu\}| < \aleph_0 \quad (x \in S)$,

and

(iii) $\operatorname{tp}\left(S - \bigcup_{\mu \in N} F_\mu \right) < \omega_1^{\omega+2}$ whenever $N \in [W_1]^{\aleph_0}$.

Case 1. $co(\gamma) = \omega$. In this case $S = S_0 \cup \dots \hat{S}_\omega(<)$, where $\text{tp}\, S_n = \omega_1^{\gamma_n} < \omega_1^{\gamma}$. By the induction hypothesis, there are sets $F_{n\mu} \subset S_n$ $(\mu < \omega_1 ; n < \omega)$ such that, for $n < \omega$,

$$\text{tp}\, F_{n\mu} < \omega_1^{\omega+2} \qquad (\mu < \omega_1),$$

$$|\{\mu < \omega_1 : x \in F_{n\mu}\}| < \aleph_0 \qquad (x \in S_n),$$

$$\text{tp}\left(S_n - \bigcup_{\mu \in N} F_{n\mu}\right) < \omega_1^{\omega+2} \text{ for } N \in [W_1]^{\aleph_0}.$$

It is easy to verify that the sets $F_\mu = \bigcup_{n<\omega} F_{n\mu}$ satisfy all the conditions (i), (ii) and (iii).

The next case is less trivial.

Case 2. $co(\omega_1^{\gamma}) = \omega_1$.

In this case,

$$S = \bigcup_{\nu<\omega_1} S_\nu(<),$$

where $\text{tp}\, S_\nu = \omega_1^{\gamma_\nu} < \omega_1^{\gamma}$ $(\nu < \omega_1)$. Therefore, by the induction hypothesis, there are sets $F^1_{\nu\mu} \subset S_\nu$ $(\mu < \omega_1 ; \nu < \omega_1)$ such that

$$\text{tp}\, F^1_{\nu\mu} < \omega_1^{\omega+2} \qquad (\mu, \nu < \omega_1), \tag{6.14}$$

$$|\{\mu < \omega_1 : x \in F^1_{\nu\mu}\}| < \aleph_0 \qquad (x \in S_\nu ; \nu < \omega_1), \tag{6.15}$$

$$\text{tp}\left(S_\nu - \bigcup_{\mu \in N} F^1_{\nu\mu}\right) < \omega_1^{\omega+2} \qquad (N \in [W_1]^{\aleph_0} ; \nu < \omega_1). \tag{6.16}$$

By the continuum hypothesis, $[W_1]^{\aleph_0} = \{N_0, N_1, \dots, \hat{N}_{\omega_1}\}_{\neq}$. From Lemma 5 it follows that for each $\nu < \omega_1$, there are $\aleph_0$ sets $F^2_{\nu\mu} \subset S_\nu$ $(\mu \in N_0 \cup \dots \cup N_\nu)$ such that

$$\text{tp}\, F^2_{\nu\mu} < \omega_1^{\omega} \qquad (\mu \in N_0 \cup \dots \cup N_\nu ; \nu < \omega_1), \tag{6.17}$$

$$|\{\mu \in N_0 \cup \dots \cup N_\nu : x \in F^2_{\nu\mu}\}| < \aleph_0 \qquad (x \in S_\nu ; \nu < \omega_1), \tag{6.18}$$

$$\text{tp}\left(S_\nu - \bigcup_{\mu \in N_\rho} F^2_{\nu\mu}\right) < \omega_1^{\omega} \qquad (\rho \leqslant \nu < \omega_1). \tag{6.19}$$

By (6.12)†, there are sets $F^3_{\nu\mu} \subset S_\nu$ $(\mu \leqslant \nu < \omega_1)$ such that

$$\text{tp}\, F^3_{\nu\mu} < \omega_1^{\omega} \qquad (\mu \leqslant \nu < \omega_1), \tag{6.20}$$

$$|\{\mu \leqslant \nu : x \in F^3_{\nu\mu}\}| < \aleph_0 \qquad (x \in S_\nu ; \nu < \omega_1), \tag{6.21}$$

$$\text{tp}\left(S_\nu - \bigcup_{\mu \in N} F^3_{\nu\mu}\right) < \omega_1^{\omega+2} \qquad (N \in [\{0, 1, \dots, \nu\}]^{\aleph_0} ; \nu < \omega_1). \tag{6.22}$$

† Note that we can only properly apply (6.12) when $\omega \leqslant \nu < \omega_1$. However, for $\nu < \omega$, if we put $F^3{}_{\nu\mu} = \emptyset$ $(\mu \leqslant \nu)$, then (6.20), (6.21) and (6.22) are all satisfied, the last vacuously.

Now define the sets F_μ $(\mu < \omega_1)$ by putting

$$F_\mu = \bigcup_{\nu<\mu} F^1_{\nu\mu} \cup \left(\bigcup_{\nu<\omega_1} \bigcup_{\mu \in N_0 \cup \dots \cup N_\nu} F^2_{\nu\mu} \right) \cup \bigcup_{\mu \leqslant \nu < \omega_1} F^3_{\nu\mu}.$$

We shall verify that (i), (ii) and (iii) hold.

By (6.14) and (6.17) we have that

$$\operatorname{tp}(F_\mu \cap S_\nu) < \omega_1^{\omega+2} \qquad (\nu < \mu),$$

and by (6.17) and (6.20)

$$\operatorname{tp}(F_\mu \cap S_\nu) < \omega_1^{\omega} \qquad (\mu \leqslant \nu).$$

This implies that $\operatorname{tp} F_\mu < \omega_1^{\omega+2} (\mu < \omega_1)$, i.e. (i) holds.

Let $x \in S$. Then there is a unique $\nu < \omega_1$ such that $x \in S_\nu$. By (6.15), (6.18) and (6.21) it follows that x is a member of only finitely many of the sets $F^\rho_{\nu\mu} (\rho = 1, 2 \text{ or } 3)$ and hence (ii) holds.

Let $N \in [W_1]^{\aleph_0}$. Then there is $\rho < \omega_1$ such that $N_\rho = \{\mu_0, \mu_1, \dots, \hat{\mu}_\omega\}_< \subset N$. Let $\lambda = \lim_{n<\omega} \mu_n$. If $\nu < \lambda$, then $N' = \{\mu_n : n < \omega; \nu < \mu_n\}$ is infinite and therefore, by (6.16),

$$\operatorname{tp}\left(S_\nu - \bigcup_{\mu \in N} F_\mu\right) \leqslant \operatorname{tp}\left(S_\nu - \bigcup_{\mu \in N'} F^1_{\nu\mu}\right) < \omega_1^{\omega+2}. \tag{6.23}$$

If $\rho \leqslant \nu < \omega_1$, then by (6.19),

$$\operatorname{tp}\left(S_\nu - \bigcup_{\mu \in N} F_\mu\right) \leqslant \operatorname{tp}\left(S_\nu - \bigcup_{\mu \in N_\rho} F^2_{\nu\mu}\right) < \omega_1^{\omega}. \tag{6.24}$$

Also, if $\lambda \leqslant \nu < \rho$, then $N_\rho \in [\{0, 1, 2, \dots, \nu\}]^{\aleph_0}$ and

$$\operatorname{tp}\left(S_\nu - \bigcup_{\mu \in N} F_\mu\right) \leqslant \operatorname{tp}\left(S_\nu - \bigcup_{\mu \in N_\rho} F^3_{\nu\mu}\right) < \omega_1^{\omega+2} \tag{6.25}$$

by (6.22). Let $\pi = \max\{\lambda, \rho\}$. Then (6.23), (6.24) and (6.25) show that

$$\operatorname{tp}\left(S_\nu - \bigcup_{\mu \in N} F_\mu\right) < \omega_1^{\omega+2} \qquad (\mu < \pi)$$

and

$$\operatorname{tp}\left(S_\nu - \bigcup_{\mu \in N} F_\mu\right) < \omega_1^{\omega}. \qquad (\pi \leqslant \nu < \omega_1).$$

Thus (iii) holds.

Theorem 8 now follows by induction on γ.

7. Conclusion

We conclude by showing that $\omega_1^{\omega+2}$ in (6.13) cannot be replaced by anything smaller, i.e.

$$\begin{Bmatrix} \omega_1 \\ \\ \omega_1^{\gamma} \end{Bmatrix} \to \begin{Bmatrix} 1 & & \omega & & \omega \\ & \vee & & , & \\ \omega_1^{\gamma} & & 1 & & \xi \end{Bmatrix} \tag{7.1}$$

holds if $\xi < \omega_1^{\omega+2} \leqslant \omega_1^{\gamma} < \omega_2$. We remark that the situation is rather different with regard to the relation (6.12). For we have proved (**1**, Theorem 10.13) that

$$\begin{Bmatrix} \omega \\ \\ \omega_1^{\gamma} \end{Bmatrix} \to \begin{Bmatrix} 1 & & \omega & & \omega \\ & \vee & & , & \\ \omega_1^{\gamma} & & 1 & & \xi \end{Bmatrix} \tag{7.2}$$

holds for $\xi < \omega_1^{\omega+2} \leqslant \omega_1^{\gamma} < \omega_2$ *provided* that

$$co(\gamma) \neq \omega \text{ and } co(\gamma - 1) \neq \omega. \tag{7.3}$$

Here $\gamma - 1 = \gamma'$ if $\gamma = \gamma' + 1$ and $\gamma - 1 = \gamma$ if γ is a limit ordinal. If (7.3) holds, then (7.2) is stronger than (7.1). However, if (7.3) is false, then (7.2) is also false (see Theorems 10.11 and 10.12 of (**1**)).

Proof of (7.1). In view of the remarks above, we can assume that (7.3) is false, i.e. either $co(\gamma) = \omega$ or $co(\gamma - 1) = \omega$.

Let $\text{tp}\, S = \omega_1^{\gamma}$ and let $W_1 \times S = K_0 \cup K_1$ be a partition such that (i) $\text{tp}\,(K_0(\mu)) < \omega_1^{\gamma} (\mu < \omega_1)$ and (ii) $\text{tp}\,(K_0(x)) < \omega$ for $x \in S$. We have to show that there are sets $A \subset W_1$ and $B \subset S$ such that $\text{tp}\, A \geqslant \omega$, $\text{tp}\, B \geqslant \xi$ and $A \times B \subset K_1$.

Case 1. $co(\gamma) = \omega$. In this case we may write $S = S_0 \cup S_1 \cup \ldots \cup \hat{S}_{\omega}(<)$, where $\text{tp}\, S_n = \omega_1^{\gamma_n + 2}$ and $\omega \leqslant \gamma_0 < \gamma_1 < \ldots < \hat{\gamma}_{\omega} < \gamma$. For each $\mu < \omega_1$ there is an integer $n(\mu)$ such that

$$\text{tp}\,(K_0(\mu) \cap S_{n(\mu)}) < \omega_1^{\gamma_{n(\mu)}+2}.$$

There is $M \subset W_1$ such that $\text{tp}\, M = \omega$ and $n(\mu) = n\ (\mu \in M)$. Since (7.2) holds with γ replaced by $\gamma_n + 2$, it follows that there are $A \subset M$ and $B \subset S_{n(\mu)}$ such that $\text{tp}\, A = \omega$, $\text{tp}\, B = \xi$ and $A \times B \subset K_1$.

Case 2. $\gamma = \gamma' + 1$ and $co(\gamma') = \omega$. We may write $S = S_0 \cup \ldots \cup \hat{S}_{\omega_1}(<)$, where $\text{tp}\, S_{\nu} = \omega_1^{\gamma} (\nu < \omega_1)$. Let $\gamma_n (n < \omega)$ be a sequence of ordinals such that

$$\omega \leqslant \gamma_0 < \gamma_1 < \ldots < \hat{\gamma}_{\omega} < \gamma' = \lim_{n<\omega} \gamma_n.$$

For $\mu < \omega_1$ there are $n(\mu) < \omega$ and $\nu(\mu) < \omega_1$ such that

$$\text{tp}\,(F_\mu \cap S_\nu) < \omega_1^{\gamma_{n(\mu)}} \qquad (\nu(\mu) < \nu < \omega_1).$$

There is $M \subset W_1$ such that $\text{tp}\, M = \omega$ and $n(\mu) = n\ (\mu \in M)$. Choose $\nu_0 < \omega_1$ so that $\nu(\mu) < \nu_0\ (\mu \in M)$ and let S' be a subset of S_ν of order type $\omega_1^{\gamma_n+2}$. As in Case 1, there are $A \subset M$ and $B \subset S'$ such that $\text{tp}\, A = \omega$, $\text{tp}\, B = \xi$ and $A \times B \subset K_1$.

References

1. Erdös, P., Hajnal, A. and Milner, E. C. On the complete subgraphs of graphs defined by systems of sets. *Acta Math. Acad. Sci. Hung.* **17** (1966), 159–229.
2. Erdös, P., Hajnal, A. and Milner, E. C. Set mappings and polarized partition relations. To appear in the *Proceedings of the Balatonfüred Combinatorial Conference (1969).*
3. Erdös, P., Hajnal, A. and Rado, R. Partition relations for cardinal numbers. *Acta Math. Acad. Sci. Hung.* **16** (1965), 93–196.
4. Erdös, P. and Kakutani, S. On non-denumerable graphs. *Bull. Amer. Math. Soc.* **49** (1943), 457–461.
5. Erdös, P. and Rado, R. Combinatorial theorems on classifications of subsets of a given set. *Proc. London Math. Soc.* (3) **2** (1952), 417–439.
6. Erdös, P. and Rado, R. A partition calculus in set theory. *Bull. Amer. Math. Soc.* **62** (1956), 427–489.
7. Erdös, P. and Specker, E. On a theorem in the theory of relations and a solution of a problem of Knaster. *Colloq. Math.* **8** (1961), 19–21.
8. Hajnal, A. Proof of a conjecture of Ruziewicz. *Fund. Math.* **50** (1961), 123–128.
9. Milner, E. C. and Rado, R. The pigeon-hole principle for ordinal numbers. *Proc. London Math. Soc.* (3), **15** (1965), 750–768.

On Some Applications of Graph Theory, II

P. ERDÖS, A. MÉIR, VERA T. SÓS, AND P. TURÁN

1. In the first paper of this sequence we dealt with applications of graphs in the Michigan sense; in this paper we are dealing with m-graphs, i.e. structures in which the fundamental elements beside the vertices are not edges $P_\mu P_\nu$ $(1 \leqslant \mu < \nu \leqslant n)$ but m-tuples

$$P_{\mu_1} P_{\mu_2} \dots P_{\mu_m} \qquad (= \text{'}m\text{-edges'}),$$
$$1 \leqslant \mu_1 < \mu_2 < \dots < \mu_m \leqslant n.$$

For $m = 2$ we get the graphs. n is again the order of the m-graph; the meaning of m-subgraphs, complete m-graphs is obvious. We shall deal especially with the case $m = 3$, i.e. with the case of trigraphs, though the geometrical problems we are dealing with have natural analogues (and also problems of new type) for higher dimensions, and these involve m-graphs with general m's.

Let A_1, A_2, A_3 be three distinct points of the plane and let

$$f(A_1, A_2, A_3), \qquad g(A_1, A_2, A_3)$$

two non-negative triangle functions which are continuous functions of the vertices. Such choices of f and g are e.g.

$$f = \text{perimeter of the } \Delta A_1 A_2 A_3$$

$$g = \text{radius of the inscribed circle of } \Delta A_1 A_2 A_3 \tag{1.1}$$

or

$$f = g = \text{area of } \Delta A_1 A_2 A_3 \tag{1.2}$$

or

$$f = g = \text{perimeter of } \Delta A_1 A_2 A_3. \tag{1.3}$$

Let D be a constant such that

$$f(A_1, A_2, A_3) \leqslant 1 \text{ implies } g(A_1, A_2, A_3) \leqslant D; \tag{1.4}$$

here $D = +\infty$ is also admitted. We shall deal with finite sets of points $A_1, A_2, \ldots, A_k$ in the plane subjected to the restriction

$$\max f(A_{i_1}, A_{i_2}, A_{i_3}) = 1 \tag{1.5}$$

where the max refers to

$$1 \leqslant i_1 < i_2 < i_3 \leqslant k;$$

we shall call them normalized point sets. Suppose that, for a certain integer $l \geqslant 3$, there is constant $D_l < D$ such that for all normalized point sets

$$(A_1, A_2, \ldots, A_l)$$

$$\min g(A_{i_1}, A_{i_2}, A_{i_3}) \leqslant D_l \tag{1.6}$$

(where the min refers to $1 \leqslant i_1 < i_2 < i_3 \leqslant l$) holds. Then we are going to prove the

THEOREM I. *If $n \geqslant l$, then for all normalized point sets $(P_1, P_2, \ldots, P_n)$ at least*

$$\binom{l}{3}^{-1}\binom{n}{3}$$

triangles $P_{i_1} P_{i_2} P_{i_3}$ $(1 \leqslant i_1 < i_2 < i_3 \leqslant n)$ satisfy the inequality

$$g(P_{i_1}, P_{i_2}, P_{i_3}) \leqslant D_l. \tag{1.7}$$

In other words, in all normalized point sets $(P_1, P_2, \ldots, P_n)$, at least $\binom{l}{3}^{-1}$th part of all $P_{i_1} P_{i_2} P_{i_3}$ triangles satisfies (1.7).

In very general cases (to which (1.1), (1.2) and (1.3) belong)

$$\max \min_{1 \leqslant i_1 < i_2 < i_3 \leqslant l} g(A_{i_1}, A_{i_2}, A_{i_3})$$

exists, even for all $l \geqslant 3$; here the maximum refers of course to all normalized systems of l points in the plane. These can be called—by analogy with paper I of this sequence of papers or with the lecture of one of us in Proceedings† of the Combinatorial Colloquium in Calgary held June 1–14, 1969—the 'packing constants' δ_l of the problem; in such cases D_l in (1.7) can be replaced of course by δ_l. As it was shown l.c. in the case of problems concerning distances, the packing constants defined *there* lead to several *best possible* inequalities. This is not so much the case with triangle problems though, as will be indicated in some cases later, our graph–theoretical method can also lead to best possible results here. Nevertheless this method is perhaps the only one available at

† In course of publication.

present which yields estimates in *general* problems of the combinatorial geometry of triangles; and it is possible that the use of more appropriate theorems on trigraphs will considerably improve present results. If physicists should ever introduce potentials depending on the interaction of three (not two) particles, then results of the above type would gain an additional interest.

In the case of $l = 5$ the value $\binom{l}{3}^{-1}$ is $\frac{1}{10}$. A better result in this case is given by the

THEOREM II. *Suppose the inequality*

$$\min_{1 \leqslant i_1 < i_2 < i_3 \leqslant 5} g(A_{i_1}, A_{i_2}, A_{i_3}) \leqslant D_5 (< D) \tag{1.8}$$

holds for all normalized point sets $(A_1, A_2, A_3, A_4, A_5)$. *Then for all* $n \geqslant 7$ *and normalized point sets* $(P_1, P_2, \ldots, P_n)$ *at least*

$$\frac{1}{7}\binom{n}{3}$$

triangles $P_{i_1}P_{i_2}P_{i_3}$ $(1 \leqslant i_1 < i_2 < i_3 \leqslant n)$ *satisfy the inequality*

$$g(P_{i_1}, P_{i_2}, P_{i_3}) \leqslant D_5. \tag{1.9}$$

In other words, for $n \geqslant 7$ the inequality (1.9) holds with a probability $\geqslant \frac{1}{7}$ in all normalized point sets $(P_1, P_2, \ldots, P_n)$.

2. In order to give Theorem II effective geometrical applications, let us consider first the case (1.2). Then $\delta_3 = 1$ and choosing the four vertices of a square, we obtain $\delta_4 = 1$. As we shall see in the Appendix

$$\delta_5 = \frac{\sqrt{5} - 1}{2}; \tag{2.1}$$

thus Theorem II gives the

COROLLARY I. *Having on the plane* $n \geqslant 7$ *points* $P_1, \ldots, P_n$ *so that the maximal area of all* $P_{i_1}P_{i_2}P_{i_3}$ *triangles is* 1, *then at least* $\frac{1}{7}\binom{n}{3}$ *such triangles have an area* $\leqslant \frac{\sqrt{5}-1}{2}$.

In other words if, for $n \geqslant 7$, the maximal area of

$$\Delta P_{i_1} P_{i_2} P_{i_3} \qquad (1 \leqslant_{i_1} <_{i_2} <_{i_3} \leqslant_n)$$

is 1, then the inequality

$$\text{area } \Delta P_{i_1} P_{i_2} P_{i_3} \leqslant \frac{\sqrt{5}-1}{2} \tag{2.2}$$

holds with a probability $\geqslant \frac{1}{7}$. Since this does not depend on n, a trivial passage to the limit gives the corresponding theorem for bounded closed measurable point sets in the plane with a plausible interpretation of the probability.

Putting m points 'near' to each vertices of a square (m large) we see at once (with $n = 4m$) that in the Corollary I the constant $\frac{1}{7}$ certainly cannot be replaced by any constant $> \frac{5}{8}$; the same example shows that the 'bad' triangles, ($4m^3$ in number, with area $> (\sqrt{5}-1)/2$) are actually 'very bad', i.e. with area $> 1-\varepsilon$. We conjectured that this is best possible in the following sense. There exists a constant

$$0 < \theta_1 < 1$$

with the following property. Having $n = 4m$ points $P_1, \ldots, P_n$ on the plane such that

$$\max_{1 \leqslant i_1 < i_2 < i_3 \leqslant n} \text{area } \Delta P_{i_1} P_{i_2} P_{i_3} = 1,$$

then, taking any $(4m^3 + 1)$ triangles $P_{i_1} P_{i_2} P_{i_3}$ out of these, one of them at least has an area

$$\leqslant \theta_1. \tag{2.3}$$

This special problem was solved by a special argument by B. Bollobás;† he did not specify the value of θ_1 (though this would be of interest).

On putting m points near to each vertex of a regular hexagon (m large) one can see after a little reflection that in the Corollary I the constant $\frac{1}{7}$ cannot be replaced by $\frac{11}{18}$. In order to push the constant down from $\frac{11}{18}$ it would be reasonable to study the distribution of triangle areas generated by the point system of a regular n-gon.

What does Theorem II give in the case (1.3)? Whereas in this case we have again $\delta_3 = \delta_4 = 1$, we can only show that $\delta_5 < 1$. Hence this theorem gives the

COROLLARY II. *There is a constant $\delta^* < 1$ such that, if the points $P_1, P_2, \ldots, P_n$ $(n \geqslant 7)$ have the property*

$$\max_{1 \leqslant i_1 < i_2 < i_3 \leqslant n} \text{perimeter of } \Delta P_{i_1} P_{i_2} P_{i_3} = 1,$$

then at least $\frac{1}{7}\binom{n}{3}$ triangles have perimeter $\leqslant \delta^*$.

† Oral communication.

It would be of interest to determine δ^*; probably it is

$$2\frac{1+\cos\frac{1}{5}\pi}{1+4\cos\frac{1}{5}\pi} \sim 0{\cdot}85 \tag{2.4}$$

which occurs in the case of a regular pentagon. Again, as before, Corollary II implies that we may assert with a probability $\geqslant \frac{1}{7}$ that the perimeter of a random triangle with vertices in a given bounded closed measurable point set does not exceed the δ^*-th part of the maximal possible perimeter value of such triangles.

3. Concerning possible improvements of our theorem, we make the following observation. The applications of graph theory in the first paper were partly based on the following theorem (see (**1**)). If $3 \leqslant l \leqslant n$ and

$$n \equiv h \bmod (l-1), \qquad 0 \leqslant h \leqslant l-2, \tag{3.1}$$

then the maximal number of edges in a graph of order n and not containing complete subgraphs of order l is

$$\frac{l-2}{2(l-1)}(n^2-h^2)+\binom{h}{2}, \tag{3.2}$$

equality being attained if and only if the vertices are distributed into $(l-1)$ disjoint classes 'possibly uniformly' so that two vertices are connected by an edge if and only if they belong to different classes. The problem to generalize the theorem (3.1)–(3.2) to m-graphs was already raised in the same paper; the partial reason for the imperfection of our theorems is the fact that such a generalization does not exist up to now for $3 \leqslant m < l \leqslant n$, even asymptotically. A conjecture in this direction asserts for the case

$$(m-1)/(l-1) \tag{3.3}$$

that an 'extremal m-graph' can be obtained by distributing the vertices into

$$\frac{l-1}{m-1} \tag{3.4}$$

disjoint classes 'possibly uniformly' and taking all m-edges with *not all* vertices in the same class. If this were true our proof of Theorem I would for $\varepsilon > 0$ and $n > n_0(\varepsilon)$ yield the quantity

$$\left(\frac{2}{l-1}\right)^2 - \varepsilon \tag{3.5}$$

in the place of $\binom{l}{3}^{-1}$. Hence the constant $\frac{1}{7}$ would be replaced by $(\frac{1}{4}-\varepsilon)$ in

Corollaries I and II. However, in the last case if A and B are two points with $\overline{AB} = \frac{1}{2}$ and if k points (k large) are taken close to A and B, then the maximal perimeter of the triangles is 1 while the number of such triangles whose perimeter is less than δ^* is

$$2\binom{k}{3}.$$

Moreover

$$\frac{2\binom{k}{3}}{\binom{2k}{3}} \to \tfrac{1}{4} \qquad \text{for } k \to \infty.$$

Hence if the m-graph conjecture (3.3)–(3.4)–(3.5) is correct then the graph-theoretical approach can lead to results, which are in a sense best possible in triangle problems too. As to this particular problem, B. Bollobás† succeeded in proving by a special method without conjectures that there is a constant $\delta^{**} < 1$ such that for arbitrarily small $\varepsilon > 0$ and $n > n_0(\varepsilon)$ having n points $P_1, P_2, \ldots, P_n$ on the plane such that

$$\max_{1 \leqslant i_1 < i_2 < i_3 \leqslant n} \text{perimeter of } \Delta P_{i_1} P_{i_2} P_{i_3} = 1,$$

at least $(\frac{1}{4} - \varepsilon)\binom{n}{3}$ of these triangles have a perimeter $\leqslant \delta^{**}$. Again, nobody knows at present which one is greater, δ^* or δ^{**}.

Not having the theorem corresponding to (3.1)–(3.2), we could use only the strongest existing theorem in the required direction due to Gy. Katona, T. Nemetz, M. Simonovits (see (**2**)) according to which in an m-graph of order n the existence of more than

$$\left\{1 - \frac{1}{\binom{l}{m}}\right\}\binom{n}{m} \tag{3.6}$$

m-edges implies the existence of a complete m-subgraph of order l if only $3 \leqslant m < l \leqslant n$. But for $m = 3, l = 5$ we shall need a slightly stronger result; we shall use the

LEMMA. *If in a trigraph of order* $n \geqslant 7$ *we have more than*

$$\frac{6}{7}\binom{n}{3} \tag{3.7}$$

triedges, then the trigraph contains a complete subtrigraph of order 5.

†Oral communication.

4. We shall prove only Theorem I; the proof of Theorem II goes through analogously with (3.7) in place of (3.6).

Let $l \geqslant 3$ be fixed and let our (normalized) point set P consist of the points $P_1, P_2, \ldots, P_n$ in the plane ($n \geqslant l$). We attach to this point set P the trigraph G with the vertices $P_1', P_2', \ldots, P_n'$ so that the triedge $P_{i_1}' P_{i_2}' P_{i_3}'$ occurs in G if and only if

$$g(P_{i_1}', P_{i_2}', P_{i_3}') > D_l. \tag{4.1}$$

Suppose that the number of our triangles with the property (4.1) is greater than

$$\left\{1 - \frac{1}{\binom{l}{3}}\right\} \binom{n}{3} \overset{\text{def}}{=} U. \tag{4.2}$$

Then the trigraph G would contain more than U triedges and hence, owing to (3.6), it would contain a complete trisubgraph of order l. But this means again the existence of l points in P such that *all* triangles from these points satisfy (4.1). But this contradicts (1.6). Hence (4.1) holds for U triangles at most, and thus the inequality (1.7) holds for at least

$$\frac{1}{\binom{l}{3}} \binom{n}{3}.$$

triangles.

5. We have to prove the lemma. Denoting the maximal number of triedges in a trigraph of order n not containing a complete trisubgraph of order 5 by $N(n)$, we see at once that $N(6) \leqslant 18$ (since if the triedge $P_4 P_5 P_6$ were the *only* missing one then $(P_1, P_2, P_3, P_4, P_5)$ would be a complete pentagon). The inequality $N(6) \geqslant 18$ is clear by removing from the complete trigraph of order 6 the triedges $P_1 P_2 P_3$ and $P_4 P_5 P_6$ and evidently this is the *only* type of trigraphs of order 6 with $N(6) = 18$. As to $N(7)$, we assert that

$$N(7) = 30. \tag{5.1}$$

That $N(7) \geqslant 30$ is again evident by considering the trigraph obtained by omitting from the complete trigraph of order 7 all triedges from (P_1, P_2, P_3, P_4) and the triedge (P_5, P_6, P_7). Let N_i stand for the number of triangles in the trigraph obtained from our given graph of order 7 by omitting P_i. Then from $N(6) = 18$ we have on one hand

$$\sum_{i=1}^{7} N_i \leqslant 7 \cdot 18 = 126 \tag{5.2}$$

and on the other hand

$$\sum_{i=1}^{7} N_i = 4N(7) \tag{5.3}$$

since any fixed triedge occurs in exactly four N_i's. Hence

$$N(7) \leqslant 31$$

and, if $N(7) = 31$, we have

$$\sum_{i=1}^{7} N_i = 124,$$

i.e.

$$N_7 \overset{\text{def}}{=} \max_i N_i \geqslant 18$$

and hence

$$N_7 = 18. \tag{5.4}$$

But then the structure of N_7 is given above and the number of triedges containing P_7 as a vertex is 13, i.e. from the $\binom{6}{2} = 15$ triedges only two are missing. This gives altogether six configurations and one can check easily that each contains a complete trisubgraph of order 5 which is a contradiction, and hence (5.1) is true. But, as remarked in (**2**),

$$N(n) \Big/ \binom{n}{3}$$

is monotonically non-increasing; hence we have for $n \geqslant 7$

$$\frac{N(n)}{\binom{n}{3}} \leqslant \frac{N(7)}{\binom{7}{3}} = \frac{6}{7},$$

as required.

Appendix

6. We shall show that if P_1, P_2, P_3, P_4 and P_5 are 5 points in the plane so that

$$\max_{1 \leqslant i_1 < i_2 < i_3 \leqslant 5} \text{area } \Delta P_{i_1} P_{i_2} P_{i_3} = 1,$$

then

$$V \overset{\text{def}}{=} \min_{1 \leqslant i_1 < i_2 < i_3 \leqslant 5} \text{area } \Delta P_{i_1} P_{i_2} P_{i_3} \leqslant \frac{\sqrt{5}-1}{2}. \tag{6.1}$$

This inequality is best possible as is shown by the regular pentagon. (Somewhat longer proof would also show that *all* cases of equality are given by affine regular pentagons but we shall not go into details of this.)

Case I. The smallest convex polygon K of the P_ν's has at most four vertices. If K is a triangle, we have at once $V \leqslant \frac{1}{5}$; if K is a quadrilateral then the area of K is $\leqslant 2$ and hence

$$V \leqslant \tfrac{2}{4} = \tfrac{1}{2} < \frac{\sqrt{5}-1}{2}.$$

Hence we may suppose that our five points form a convex pentagon. Let $\Delta P_1 P_2 P_3$ be one of its triangles with

$$\text{area } \Delta P_1 P_2 P_3 = 1. \tag{6.2}$$

Case II. Two sides of $\Delta P_1 P_2 P_3$ *are on the perimeter of the convex polygon*. Let the point Q be such that

$$P_3 Q \,||\, P_1 P_2 \qquad P_2 Q \,||\, P_1 P_3 \tag{6.3}$$

i.e.

$$\text{area } \Delta P_2 P_3 Q = 1.$$

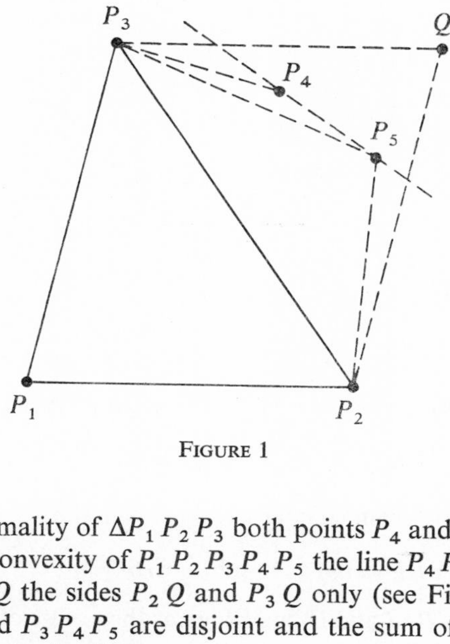

FIGURE 1

Owing to the maximality of $\Delta P_1 P_2 P_3$ both points P_4 and P_5 are in $\Delta P_2 P_3 Q$ and owing to the convexity of $P_1 P_2 P_3 P_4 P_5$ the line $P_4 P_5$ does meet within the triangle $P_2 P_3 Q$ the sides $P_2 Q$ and $P_3 Q$ only (see Fig. 1). Since the triangles $P_2 P_3 P_5$ and $P_3 P_4 P_5$ are disjoint and the sum of their areas is $\leqslant 1$ owing to (6.3), we have in this case

$$V \leqslant \tfrac{1}{2} < \frac{\sqrt{5}-1}{2}.$$

Case III. Only one side $\Delta P_1 P_2 P_3$ is on the smallest convex polygon; without loss of generality let this be $P_1 P_2$.

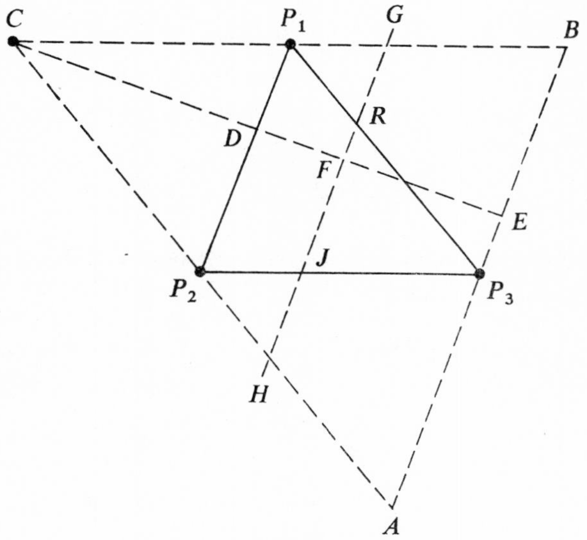

FIGURE 2

Let (see Fig. 2)

$$P_1 B \,||\, P_2 P_3 \qquad P_2 A \,||\, P_1 P_3$$

i.e.

$$\overline{AP_3} = \overline{P_3 B}.$$

Owing to (6.2) and the definition of Case III

$$P_4 \in \Delta P_1 P_3 B, \qquad P_5 \in \Delta P_2 P_3 A. \tag{6.4}$$

Let C be the point of intersection of $P_1 B$ and $P_2 A$ further

$$CD \perp P_1 P_2, \qquad \overline{CD} = \tfrac{1}{2}\overline{CE} = m. \tag{6.5}$$

Let $0 < \theta < 1$ to be determined later and F be such that

$$\overline{DF} = \theta m \qquad \text{and} \qquad GF \,||\, P_1 P_2. \tag{6.6}$$

Let finally the points R, J and H be defined as the points of intersection of GF with $P_1 P_3$, $P_2 P_3$ and CA respectively. If P_4 is between the parallels $P_1 P_2$ and GF, then

$$\begin{aligned} \text{area } \Delta P_1 P_2 P_4 &\leqslant \text{area } \Delta P_1 P_2 G \\ &= \theta \text{ area } \Delta P_1 P_2 P_3 = \theta \end{aligned} \tag{6.7}$$

and analogously with P_5 instead of P_4. Hence we have to investigate only the case when

$$P_4 \in BGRP_3 \quad \text{and} \quad P_5 \in P_3\, JHA. \tag{6.8}$$

In this case let us investigate the area of $\Delta P_3 P_4 P_5$. If P_4 is not on the broken line BGR then, shifting it along $P_3 P_4$, the area of $\Delta P_3 P_4 P_5$ is increased; and analogously for P_5; hence we may suppose that

$$\begin{aligned} &P_4 \text{ is on the broken line } BGR \\ &P_5 \text{ is on the broken line } AHJ. \end{aligned} \tag{6.9}$$

Suppose that P_4 is on the segment BG, but not at G. We move P_4 parallel to $P_3 P_5$ to a position P_4' inside $BGRP_3$; this process preserves the area of $\Delta P_3 P_4 P_5$. P_4' may be chosen to lie on $P_3\, G$. If, next, P_4 is moved along $P_3\, G$ from P_4' to G, the area of $\Delta P_3 P_4 P_5$ is increased. Performing an analogous operation on P_5, we see that

$$\text{area } \Delta P_3 P_4 P_5 \leqslant \text{area } \Delta P_3 GH. \tag{6.10}$$

But

$$\overline{GH} = (1 + \theta)\, \overline{P_1 P_2}, \qquad \overline{FE} = (1 - \theta)\, \overline{DE}$$

and thus from (6.2)

$$\text{area } \Delta P_3 GH = (1 - \theta^2) \quad \text{area } \Delta P_1 P_2 P_3 = 1 - \theta^2. \tag{6.11}$$

Hence, in the Case *III*, (6.7) and (6.10)—(6.11) give

$$V \leqslant \max\, (\theta, 1 - \theta^2)$$

for all $0 < \theta < 1$. Choosing θ so that

$$\theta = 1 - \theta^2,$$

(6.1) is proved.

References

1. TURÁN, P. Egy gráfelméleti szélsöértékfeladatról. *Matematikai Lapok* **48** (1941), 436–452 (With German abstract).
2. KATONA, GY, NEMETZ, T. and SIMONOVITS, M. Egy Turán-féle gráfproblémáról. *Matematikai Lapok* **15** (1964), 228–238 (With Russian and English abstracts).

Notes on Landau's Proof of Picard's 'Great' Theorem

T. ESTERMANN

The object of this paper is to supply a proof of Picard's 'great' theorem which differs in the following respects from that given in Chapter 7 of Landau's book 'Darstellung und Begründung einiger neuerer Ergebnisse der Funktionentheorie', New York, 1946.

1. I replace Landau's Hilfssatz by my Theorem 2, which, with $\frac{1}{8}$ instead of $\frac{1}{6}$, would be equivalent to the particular case $a = |f'(0)|$, $M = 2|f'(0)|$ of the Hilfssatz. Landau uses only this particular case, and therefore makes matters unnecessarily complicated by stating and proving the Hilfssatz in all its generality. The fact that my constant $\frac{1}{6}$ is better than $\frac{1}{8}$ is of no consequence here. My proof of my Theorem 2 is fundamentally different from Landau's proof of his Hilfssatz.

2. I avoid the unnecessary sequences $\{2^{-k}M(1 - 2^{-k})\}$ and $\{x_n\}$, which Landau uses in the proof of his Satz 1 and in his §26 respectively.

3. I avoid the substitution of e^t for x, which Landau also uses in his §26. This is necessary only if we want to deduce Picard's 'great' theorem from the refinement of Schottky's theorem (Landau's Satz 6), but I do not see why we should want to do that, and I am not even convinced that Schottky's theorem and its refinement are worth having. They seem to have been arbitrarily singled out from the infinitely many particular cases of the following more general theorem, which can be proved just as easily. I express it in an imitation of Landau's style to make comparison easier.

THEOREM. *To every ω and every η there is a $\Psi^*(\omega, \eta)$, so that, if S is a simply connected domain, $T \subset S, z_0 \in T, F(z)$ regular, $\neq 0$ and $\neq 1$ for $z \in S$, $|F(z_0)| \leqslant \omega$, d the distance between T and the complement of S, and every point of T can be joined to z_0 by a curve contained in T of length $\leqslant \eta\, d$, then $|F(z)| < \Psi^*(\omega, \eta)$ for $z \in T$.*

To deduce Landau's Satz 6, one need only take (in the notation explained below) $\eta = \theta/(1 - \theta)$, $S = D(0, 1)$, $T = D(0, \theta)'$, $z_0 = 0$, $d = 1 - \theta$ and

$\Psi(\omega, \theta) = \Psi^*(\omega, \eta)$. I use another particular case of the above theorem (with f instead of F), obtained by substituting $\frac{1}{3}$ for ω, π for η, T for S, C for T, w for z_0 and $|w|$ for d.

Notation. For any function f and any set of numbers S, $f(S)$ is the set of the values assumed by $f(z)$ with $z \in S$, i.e. $w \in f(S)$ if and only if there is a number z such that $z \in S$ and $w = f(z)$.

$D(w, r)$ is the disc with centre w and radius r, i.e. the set of those numbers z for which $|z - w| < r$—the phrase 'a disc of radius 0' means 'the empty set'—and $D(w, r)'$ is the set of those numbers z for which $|z - w| \leqslant r$.

$C(w, r)$ is the circle with centre w and radius r, described in the positive sense.

$\{s, t\}$ is the line segment from s to t.

dist $(z, \text{comp } S)$ is the distance of z from the complement of S.

THEOREM 1. *Let r be positive, f regular in $D(z_0, r)'$, $u \geqslant 0$, and*

$$|f(z) - f(z_0)| \geqslant u \qquad (|z - z_0| = r). \tag{1}$$

Then

$$D\{f(z_0), u\} \subset f\{D(z_0, r)\}. \tag{2}$$

Proof. Let $w \in D\{f(z_0), u\}$, i.e.

$$|w - f(z_0)| < u. \tag{3}$$

Let $g(z) = f(z) - f(z_0)$ and

$$h(z) = f(z) - w. \tag{4}$$

Then g and h are regular in $D(z_0, r)'$, and, by (3) and (1),

$$|g(z) - h(z)| < |g(z)| \qquad (|z - z_0| = r).$$

Hence, by Rouché's theorem, h has as many zeros as g in $D(z_0, r)$, and therefore at least one, since $g(z_0) = 0$. From this and (4) it follows that

$$w \in f\{D(z_0, r)\}.$$

Since this holds for every point w of $D\{f(z_0), u\}$, we have (2).

THEOREM 2. *Let R be positive, f regular in $D(z_0, R)'$, and*

$$|f'(z)| \leqslant 2|f'(z_0)| \qquad (|z - z_0| = R). \tag{5}$$

Then

$$D\{f(z_0), \tfrac{1}{6}|f'(z_0)|R\} \subset f\{D(z_0, R)\}. \tag{6}$$

Proof. By Cauchy's formula,

$$f'(w) - f'(z_0) = \frac{1}{2\pi i} \int_{C(z_0,R)} f'(t) \left(\frac{1}{t - w} - \frac{1}{t - z_0} \right) dt \quad (|w - z_0| < R).$$

Also, if $|t - z_0| = R$ and $|w - z_0| \leqslant \frac{1}{4}R$, then $|t - w| \geqslant \frac{3}{4}R$, and hence, by (5),

$$\left| f'(t)\left(\frac{1}{t-w} - \frac{1}{t-z_0}\right)\right| = \left|\frac{f'(t)\,(w-z_0)}{(t-w)\,(t-z_0)}\right| \leqslant \tfrac{8}{3}|f'(z_0)|R^{-2}|w-z_0|.$$

Since the length of $C(z_0, R)$ is $2\pi R$, it follows that

$$|f'(w) - f'(z_0)| \leqslant \tfrac{8}{3}|f'(z_0)|R^{-1}|w - z_0| \qquad (|w - z_0| \leqslant \tfrac{1}{4}R). \tag{7}$$

Now let $|z - z_0| = \frac{1}{4}R$. Then, by (7),

$$\begin{aligned}
&\tfrac{1}{4}|f'(z_0)|R - |f(z) - f(z_0)| \\
&\leqslant |f(z) - f(z_0) - f'(z_0)(z - z_0)| \\
&= \left|\int_{\{z_0, z\}} \{f'(w) - f'(z_0)\}\, dw\right| \\
&= \left|\int_0^1 [f'\{z_0 + (z - z_0)t\} - f'(z_0)]\,(z - z_0)\, dt\right| \\
&\leqslant \int_0^1 |f'\{z_0 + (z - z_0)t\} - f'(z_0)|\,|z - z_0|\, dt \\
&\leqslant \tfrac{8}{3}|f'(z_0)|R^{-1}|z - z_0|^2 \int_0^1 t\, dt \\
&= \tfrac{1}{12}|f'(z_0)|R.
\end{aligned}$$

Thus

$$|f(z) - f(z_0)| \geqslant \tfrac{1}{6}|f'(z_0)|R \qquad (|z - z_0| = \tfrac{1}{4}R).$$

From this and Theorem 1 it follows that

$$D\{f(z_0), \tfrac{1}{6}|f'(z_0)|R\} \subset f\{D(z_0, \tfrac{1}{4}R)\},$$

which implies (6).

THEOREM 3. *Let S be a non-empty closed bounded set, let f be regular in S, and let*

$$g(z) = |f'(z)| \operatorname{dist}(z, \operatorname{comp} S). \tag{8}$$

Then every point w of S has the property that $f(S)$ contains a disc of radius $\frac{1}{12}g(w)$.

Proof. It is clearly sufficient to show that the point (or one of the points) of S at which g is greatest has the said property. Such a point exists since g is continuous on S. Let z_0 be such a point, and let

$$R = \tfrac{1}{2}\operatorname{dist}(z_0, \operatorname{comp} S). \tag{9}$$

The case $R = 0$ is trivial. Suppose, therefore, $R > 0$. Then $g(z) \leqslant g(z_0)$ $(|z - z_0| = R)$. From this, (8) and (9) we obtain (5), and it is trivial that the other hypotheses of Theorem 2 are satisfied. The result now follows from (6), (8) and (9).

THEOREM 4. *Let T be a set of complex numbers, but not the set of all complex numbers, t an interior point of T, f regular in T, and suppose $f(T)$ does not contain any disc of radius* 1. *Then*

$$|f'(t)| \leqslant 12/\text{dist}\,(t, \text{comp}\, T).$$

Proof. Suppose $|f'(t)| > 12/\text{dist}(t, \text{comp}\, T)$. Then, using Theorem 3 with $S = D\{t, 12/|f'(t)|\}'$ and $w = t$, we obtain a contradiction.

THEOREM 5. *Let T be a star domain, $w \in T$, f regular in T, $0 \notin f(T)$, $1 \notin f(T)$ and*

$$1 - f(w) = -\exp\{\pi i \cosh(2a)\}. \tag{10}$$

Then there is a function j, regular in T, such that

$$1 - f(z) = -\exp[\pi i \cosh\{2j(z)\}] \qquad (z \in T), \tag{11}$$

$$j(w) = a, \tag{12}$$

and $j(T)$ does not contain any disc of radius 1.

This is essentially Landau's Satz 2.

THEOREM 6. *Let r be positive, and $g(z)$ regular and bounded for $0 < |z - z_0| < r$. Then $\exists \lim_{z \to z_0} g(z)$.*

This is well known.

Let U be the set of those numbers z for which $0 < |z| < 1$. Then Picard's 'great' theorem is equivalent to the following:

THEOREM 7. *Let f be regular in U,*

$$0 \notin f(U) \tag{13}$$

and

$$1 \notin f(U). \tag{14}$$

Then f has not an essential singularity at 0.

Proof. We note that any function g, regular in U, has an essential singularity at 0 if and only if neither $\lim_{z \to 0} g(z)$ nor $\lim_{z \to 0} \{1/g(z)\}$ exists.

We therefore have to prove that at least one of the formulae

$$\exists \lim_{z\to 0} f(z) \tag{15}$$

and

$$\exists \lim_{z\to 0} \{1/f(z)\} \tag{16}$$

holds. Suppose that (16) does not hold, i.e. that

$$\nexists \lim_{z\to 0} \{1/f(z)\}. \tag{17}$$

Then we have to prove (15).

Let

$$c_1 = \max_{|z|=\frac{1}{2}} |f(z)|, c_2 = 1 + \exp(\pi \cosh 78), c = \max(c_1, c_2). \tag{18}$$

We shall show that

$$|f(z)| \leqslant c \qquad (0 < |z| < \tfrac{1}{2}). \tag{19}$$

To this end, let z_1 be any number such that

$$0 < |z_1| < \tfrac{1}{2}. \tag{20}$$

Since f is regular in U, it follows from (13) and (20) that $1/f(z)$ is regular for $0 < |z| < |z_1|$. Hence, by Theorem 6 and (17), $1/f(z)$ is unbounded for $0 < |z| < |z_1|$, which implies that there is a number w such that

$$0 < |w| < |z_1| \tag{21}$$

and $|1/f(w)| > 3$, i.e.

$$|f(w)| < \tfrac{1}{3}. \tag{22}$$

Now let $|s| = |w|$ and $s \neq w$. If $\mathrm{im}(s/w) \geqslant 0$, let $z_2 = -iw/|w|$, and if $\mathrm{im}(s/w) < 0$, let $z_2 = iw/|w|$. Let T consist of those points of U that are not on $\{0, z_2\}$. Then one and only one of the two arcs of the circle $|z| = |w|$ that lead from w to s is contained in T. Call that arc C.

Let

$$a_1 = \frac{1}{\pi i}\log\{1 - f(w)\}, \quad a_2 = a_1 + \sqrt{(2a_1 + a_1{}^2)}, \quad a = \tfrac{1}{2}\log(1 + a_2), \tag{23}$$

the logarithms and the square root having their principal values. Then it is easily seen that the hypotheses of Theorem 5 are satisfied. Hence, choosing j as indicated in that theorem, we have (11) and (12); and if, moreover, t is a point of C, then the hypotheses of Theorem 4 are satisfied with j instead of f, and dist$(t, \text{comp } T) = |w|$. Hence

$$|j'(t)| \leqslant 12/|w| \qquad (t \text{ on } C). \tag{24}$$

It is trivial that

$$j(s) - j(w) = \int_C j'(t)\, dt,$$

and that the length of C is at most $\pi|w|$. Hence, by (24),

$$|j(s) - j(w)| \leqslant 12\pi. \tag{25}$$

By (22) and (23),

$$|\log\{1 - f(w)\}| \leqslant -\log\{1 - |f(w)|\} < -\log(1 - \tfrac{1}{3}) = \log\tfrac{3}{2} < \tfrac{1}{2},$$

$$|a_1| < \tfrac{1}{6}, \qquad |a_2| \leqslant \tfrac{1}{6} + \surd(\tfrac{1}{3} + \tfrac{1}{36}) < \tfrac{5}{6},$$

$$|a| < -\tfrac{1}{2}\log(1 - |a_2|) < \tfrac{1}{2}\log 6 < 1.$$

Hence, by (25) and (12),

$$|j(s)| \leqslant 12\pi + 1 < 39.$$

From this, (11) and (18), it follows that $|f(s)| \leqslant 1 + \exp(\pi \cosh 78) \leqslant c$. This has been proved for every number s for which $|s| = |w|$ and $s \neq w$, and follows from (22) for $s = w$. Thus

$$|f(z)| \leqslant c \qquad (|z| = |w|). \tag{26}$$

Now let S be the set of those numbers z for which $|w| \leqslant |z| \leqslant \frac{1}{2}$. Then S is closed and bounded, f is regular in S, and, by (18) and (26), $|f(z)| \leqslant c$ for every boundary point z of S. Hence, by the maximum modulus theorem,

$$|f(z)| \leqslant c \qquad (z \in S).$$

Now, by (21) and (20), $z_1 \in S$. Hence $|f(z_1)| \leqslant c$. This holds for every number z_1 for which (20) holds, and so (19) is proved. From (19) and Theorem 6 we obtain (15), which was to be proved.

Disjoint Common Partial Transversals of Two Families of Sets

D. R. FULKERSON

1. Introduction

Let $\mathfrak{A} = (A_i : i \in I)$ and $\mathfrak{B} = (B_j : j \in J)$ be two families of subsets of a finite set E, the cardinalities $|I|$ and $|J|$ of the index sets I and J being assumed finite also. A subset P of E, with $|P| = p$, is a *partial transversal* (of size p) of the family $\mathfrak{A}$ if there is a one-one mapping ϕ from P into I such that $e \in A_{\phi(e)}$ for all $e \in P$. If P is a partial transversal of $\mathfrak{A}$ and also of $\mathfrak{B}$, then P is a *common partial transversal* of $\mathfrak{A}$ and $\mathfrak{B}$. A partial transversal of $\mathfrak{A}$ of size $p = |I|$ is a *transversal* of $\mathfrak{A}$; and, if $|I| = |J|$, a common partial transversal of $\mathfrak{A}$ and $\mathfrak{B}$ of size $p = |I|$ is a *common transversal* of $\mathfrak{A}$ and $\mathfrak{B}$.

In this note we show how the theory of flows in networks (**3**) can be used to solve a packing problem for common partial transversals, of prescribed size p, of the families $\mathfrak{A}$ and $\mathfrak{B}$. Specifically, we answer the question: What are necessary and sufficient conditions in order that there exist k mutually disjoint common partial transversals, each of size p, of the two families $\mathfrak{A}$ and $\mathfrak{B}$?

2. A packing theorem

For the case $k = 1$ and $p = |I| = |J|$, the following theorem is known (**3**, **4**).

THEOREM 2.1. *The finite families $\mathfrak{A} = (A_i : i \in I)$ and $\mathfrak{B} = (B_j : j \in J)$ of subsets of the finite set E, with $|I| = |J|$, have a common transversal if and only if*

$$|I'| + |J'| - |I| \leqslant \left| \bigcup_{i \in I'} A_i \cap \bigcup_{j \in J'} B_j \right| \tag{2.1}$$

holds for all $I' \subseteq I$, $J' \subseteq J$.

The inequalities (2.1) can be generalized in a simple way to provide an answer to the question posed above. This generalization is described below in Theorem 2.2 (ii); an equivalent set of conditions is provided by (iii) of Theorem 2.2. To state (iii), we use the notation, for $E' \subseteq E$:

$$\#(\mathfrak{A}, E') = |\{i \in I \mid e \in A_i \text{ for some } e \in E'\}|. \tag{2.2}$$

In words, $\#(\mathfrak{A}, E')$ is the number of members of the family $\mathfrak{A}$ represented by elements of E'.

THEOREM 2.2. *Let* $\mathfrak{A} = (A_i : i \in I)$ *and* $\mathfrak{B} = (B_j : j \in J)$ *be finite families of subsets of the finite set E. Then the following statements are equivalent.*

(i) *There exist k mutually disjoint common partial transversals, each of size p, of* $\mathfrak{A}$ *and* $\mathfrak{B}$.

(ii) *The inequality*

$$k[p-(|I - I'| + |J - J'|)] \leqslant \left| \bigcup_{i \in I'} A_i \cap \bigcup_{j \in J'} B_j \right| \tag{2.3}$$

holds for all $I' \subseteq I, \quad J' \subseteq J$.

(iii) *The inequality*

$$k[p-(\#(\mathfrak{A}, E') + \#(\mathfrak{B}, E''))] \leqslant |E - (E' \cup E'')| \tag{2.4}$$

holds for all $E' \subseteq E, \quad E'' \subseteq E$.

We defer the proof of Theorem 2.2 to Section 4, following the discussion in Section 3 of a certain decomposition theorem for network flows that will be needed in the proof. Here we note only that it is enough to state (2.4) for all disjoint subsets E', E'' of E, since this yields an equivalent set of conditions.

3. Flows and matching flows

Let f be an integral flow from a set S of sources to a set T of sinks in a (directed) network having node set N. Thus S and T are disjoint subsets of N, and

$$f(x, N) - f(N, x) = \begin{cases} a(x), & x \in S, \\ -b(x), & x \in T, \\ 0, & x \in N-(S \cup T), \end{cases} \tag{3.1}$$

$$f(x, y) \geqslant 0, \qquad (x, y) \in N \times N. \tag{3.2}$$

Here $a(x)$, $x \in S$, and $b(x)$, $x \in T$, are nonnegative integers, and $v = a(S) = b(T)$ is the size (or amount) of the flow f. (We are using the notation of (**3**), e.g.

$$f(x, N) = \sum_{y \in N} f(x, y), \quad \text{and} \quad a(S) = \sum_{x \in S} a(x).)$$

If $a(x) = 0$ or 1 for all $x \in S$, and $b(x) = 0$ or 1 for all $x \in T$, we say that f is a *matching flow* from S to T. An integral flow from S to T of amount v can be decomposed into a sum of an integral cyclic flow, or circulation, (all right-hand sides zero in (3.1)), and v unit chain-flows, where each chain begins at a node of S and ends in a node of T (**3**). In particular, if f is a matching flow, the chain-flows in such a decomposition induce a matching between those nodes $x \in S$ such that $a(x) = 1$ and those nodes $x \in T$ such that $b(x) = 1$, by pairing first and last members of each chain. (Several different matchings can result in this way, since the decomposition of f need not be unique.) This justifies calling f a matching flow.

For the proof of Theorem 2.2, we shall be interested in decomposing an arbitrary integral flow from S to T into a sum of matching flows, each of the same size.

THEOREM 3.1. *Let f be an integral flow from S to T of size $v = a(S) = b(T)$, and let*

$$m = \max\left(\max_{x \in S} a(x), \quad \max_{x \in T} b(x)\right). \tag{3.3}$$

Then f decomposes into a sum of k matching flows, each of size p, if and only if $v = kp$ and $m \leqslant k$.

Proof. Necessity is clear. To prove sufficiency, we can proceed as follows. Decompose f into the sum of a cyclic flow and v unit chain-flows from S to T. Use the chains in this decomposition to construct a bipartite graph G having node parts S and T by inserting an edge in G joining first and last nodes in each chain. In general, G will have multiple edges joining the same vertices, but in any event, G has $v = kp$ edges and the maximum valence in G is m. By a theorem of Dulmage and Mendelsohn (**1**), G has a matching consisting of $[v/m]$ edges that hits all nodes of valence m, i.e. each node of valence m is incident with some edge of the matching. (This theorem can also be derived using flows in networks (**2**).) One can use this fact and induction on k to show that G decomposes into a sum of k matchings, each containing p edges, as follows. The case $k = 1$ is trivial. Assume the assertion for $k - 1$ and consider k. If $m < k$, then G has a matching M containing

$$p = \frac{v}{k} \leqslant \left[\frac{v}{m}\right]$$

edges. Moreover, the graph $G - M$ has $kp - p = p(k - 1)$ edges and maximum valence at most $k - 1$. If $m = k$, then G has a matching M containing $[v/m] = p$ edges that hits all nodes of valence k, and thus again $G - M$ has $p(k - 1)$ edges and maximum valence $k - 1$. Hence, by the induction assumption, G decomposes into a sum of k matchings, each having p edges. It follows that f decomposes into a sum of k matching flows, each of size p.

4. Proof of Theorem 2.2

Using the families $\mathfrak{A}$ and $\mathfrak{B}$, construct the flow network with source s and sink t shown below:

Nodes	Directed Edges	Edge capacity function c
s, t	$(s, x_i),\quad i \in I$	k
$S = \{x_i \mid i \in I\}$	$(x_i, y_e) \leftrightarrow e \in A_i$	∞
$R = \{y_e \mid e \in E\}$	$(y_e, y_e'),\quad e \in E$	1
$R' = \{y_e' \mid e \in E\}$	$(y_e', z_j) \leftrightarrow e \in B_j$	∞
$T = \{z_j \mid j \in J\}$	$(z_j, t),\quad j \in J$	k

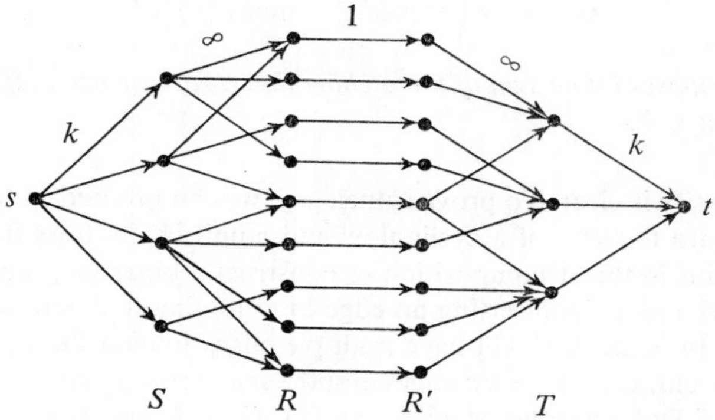

It follows from Theorem 3.1 that the families $\mathfrak{A}$ and $\mathfrak{B}$ have k mutually disjoint common partial transversals of size p if and only if there is an integral flow from s to t in this network of size $v = kp$ that satisfies the capacity constraints $f \leqslant c$ on all edges. By the max-flow min-cut theorem and the integrity theorem for network flows, such a flow exists if and only if all cuts separating s and t have capacities at least kp, i.e. if and only if

$$kp \leqslant c(X, N-X) \tag{4.1}$$

for all $X \subseteq N$ such that $s \in X$, $t \in N-X$. Let

$$\begin{aligned} S \cap X &= U, & S \cap (N-X) &= \overline{U}. \\ R \cap X &= V, & R \cap (N-X) &= \overline{V}. \\ R' \cap X &= V', & R' \cap (N-X) &= \overline{V}'. \\ T \cap X &= W, & T \cap (N-X) &= \overline{W}. \end{aligned}$$

Then

$$c(X, N-X) = c(s, U) + c(U, \overline{V}) + c(V, \overline{V}') + c(V', \overline{W}) + c(W, t). \tag{4.2}$$

The inequality (4.1) holds automatically unless the sets of edges $(U, \overline{V})$ and $(V', \overline{W})$ are empty. Let

$$B(\overline{V}) = \{x_i \in S \mid (x_i, y_e) \text{ is an edge for some } y_e \in \overline{V}\}$$
$$A(V') = \{z_j \in T \mid (y_e', z_j) \text{ is an edge for some } y_e' \in V'\}.$$

Then $(U, \overline{V})$ is empty if and only if $B(\overline{V}) \subseteq \overline{U}$, and $(V', \overline{W})$ is empty if and only if $A(V') \subseteq W$. Thus (4.2) is, if anything, decreased by taking $\overline{U} = B(\overline{V})$, $W = A(V')$. Consequently (4.1) holds if and only if

$$kp \leqslant k|B(\overline{V})| + k|A(V')| + c(V, \overline{V}') \tag{4.3}$$

holds for all $V \subseteq R$, $V' \subseteq R'$. Translating (4.3) into the notation of Section 2 yields (2.4) as a necessary and sufficient condition for the existence of k mutually disjoint common partial transversals, each of size p, of $\mathfrak{A}$ and $\mathfrak{B}$.

Condition (2.3) can be derived from (4.1) in a similar way.

A corollary of Theorem 2.2 is the following formula for the maximum number $k(p)$ of mutually disjoint common partial transversals, of size p, of two families $\mathfrak{A}$ and $\mathfrak{B}$:

$$k(p) = \min_{\substack{E' \subseteq E \\ E'' \subseteq E}} \left[\frac{|E - (E' \cup E'')|}{p - \#(\mathfrak{A}, E') - \#(\mathfrak{B}, E'')} \right], \tag{4.4}$$

where the minimum in (4.4) is taken over all disjoint subsets E', E'' of E such that the denominator is positive.

Theorem 2.2 can be viewed as a generalization of the main result in (**5**), which gives necessary and sufficient conditions in order that a p by n (0, 1)-matrix $A = (a_{ij})$, with $p \leqslant n$, can be written as a sum

$$A = P_1 + \ldots + P_k + R, \tag{4.5}$$

where each P_i has exactly one 1 in each row and at most one 1 in each column. To see this, let $I = \{1, \ldots, p\}$, $J = \{1, \ldots, n\}$, and define $E = \{(i, j) \in I \times J \mid a_{ij} = 1\}$, $A_i = E \cap (\{i\} \times J)$, $i \in I$, $B_j = E \cap (I \times \{j\})$, $j \in J$. Then a permutation matrix P in the decomposition (4.5) corresponds to a common partial transversal of size p of the families $\mathfrak{A} = (A_i : i \in I)$ and $\mathfrak{B} = (B_j : j \in J)$, and Theorem 2.2 reduces to the result of (**5**) mentioned above.

Theorem 2.2 also gives some information on the following maximum packing problem. Let A be the (0, 1)-incidence matrix of all common partial transversals of size p of two families $\mathfrak{A}$ and $\mathfrak{B}$ of subsets of E, where the rows of A correspond to the common partial transversals and the columns of A correspond to members of E. Associate a weight $w(e) \geqslant 0$ with each $e \in E$, and ask for a solution vector y to the linear program

$$\begin{aligned} yA &\leqslant w \\ y &\geqslant 0 \\ \max\ & 1 \cdot y, \end{aligned} \tag{4.6}$$

where $1 = (1, \ldots, 1)$. If $w(e) = 1$ all $e \in E$, and if we restrict y to be a $(0, 1)$-vector in (4.6), then the formula (4.4) is applicable. That is, $k(p)$ in (4.4) is then equal to max $1 \cdot y$ in (4.6). The case $w(e) = 0$ or 1 can be treated in this fashion also. Knowing how to solve the linear program (4.6) is tantamount to knowing the blocking matrix B for the incidence matrix A (**6**). But the general maximum packing problem (4.6) does not seem to be amenable to the network flow approach used in this note.

References

1. DULMAGE, A. L. and MENDELSOHN, N. S. Some graphical properties of matrices with nonnegative entries. *Aequationes Mathematicae* **2** (1969), 150–162.
2. FOLKMAN, JON and FULKERSON, D. R. Edge colorings in bipartite graphs. RM–5061–PR, 1966 (to appear in the *Proceedings of the Chapel Hill Conference on Combinatorial Mathematics*).
3. FORD, L. R. Jr. and FULKERSON, D. R. *Flows in Networks* (Princeton University Press, Princeton, New Jersey, 1962).
4. FORD, L. R. Jr. and FULKERSON, D. R. Network flow and systems of representatives. *Canad. J. Math.* **10** (1958), 78–85.
5. FULKERSON, D. R. The maximum number of disjoint permutations contained in a matrix of zeros and ones. *Canad. J. Math.* **16** (1964), 729–735.
6. FULKERSON, D. R. Blocking polyhedra. *Proceedings of the Advanced Seminar in Graph Theory* (University of Wisconsin, 1969). To appear.

Affine Generalized Quadrilaterals

MARSHALL HALL, JR.*

1. Introduction

Feit and Higman (**2**) have defined a generalized n-gon as a system N of points and lines together with incidences of certain points on certain lines such that each line contains $1 + s$ points and each point is on $1 + t$ lines. Furthermore a chain of length m, $e = e_0, e_1, \ldots, e_m = f$ is a sequence in which e_i is incident with e_{i+1}, $i = 0, \ldots, m - 1$. The chain is irreducible if $e_i \neq e_{i+2}$, $i = 0, \ldots, m - 2$. We put $\lambda(e,f) = m$ if this is the shortest chain joining e and f. We call a chain closed if $e_m = e_0$ Then N is a generalized n-gon if $\lambda(e,f) \leqslant n$ for every e and f of N and if N does not contain a closed irreducible chain of length $2m$ with $m < n$.

In this paper a construction is given for generalized quadrilaterals (4-gons above) with $s = q - 1$, $t = q + 1$ where $q = 2^e$, $e \geqslant 2$. Feit and Higman remark that in known examples of generalized n-gons s and t are powers of the same prime. Thus this construction provides examples in which s and t are not powers of the same prime.

In a finite projective Desarguesian plane $P(2, q)$, $q = 2^e$, there exists a set $\mathcal{O}$ of $q + 2$ points with no three on a line, which we call an ovoid or a complete oval. Such a set does not exist if q is odd (**3**). If $P_i = (x_i, y_i, z_i)$, $i = 1, \ldots, q + 2$ are representatives of the $q + 2$ points of $\mathcal{O}$, then in the affine three dimensional geometry $A(3, q)$ the points $tP_i = (tx_i, ty_i, tz_i)$, $t \in GF(q)$ form an additive group of order q. The q^3 points (x, y, z), $x, y, z \in GF(q)$, of $A(3, q)$ are the points of the generalized quadrilateral and the $(q + 2)q^2$ cosets of the $q + 2$ groups tP_i form the lines of the generalized quadrilateral.

2. Construction of the generalized quadrilateral $GQ(q)$

Let $\pi = P(2, q)$ be the Desarguesian projective plane over the field $GF(q)$ where $q = 2^e$ and $e \geqslant 2$. We shall use the terms *ovoid* (following Dembowski

* This research was supported in part by ONR Contract N00014–67–A0094–0010.

(**1**) or *complete oval* (following Segre (**6**)) to describe a set $\mathcal{O}$ of $q+2$ points of π with the property that no three points of $\mathcal{O}$ lie on a line.

Suppose that π is a projective plane of order n (i.e. having exactly $n+1$ points on each line). Then an oval S in π is a set of $n+1$ points, $S = \{P_1, \ldots, P_{n+1}\}$ such that no three points of S lie on a line. Through P_i there are the n lines $P_i P_j$, $j \neq i$, and exactly one further line, T_i, the tangent to S at P_i which intersects S in the single point P_i. It has been shown by Qvist (**3**) that if n is odd, then no three different tangents go through a point, whereas if n is even all $n+1$ tangents go through the same point P^*, called the nucleus of the oval S. Hence when n is even the $n+2$ points $\{P^*, P_1, \ldots, P_{n+1}\}$ form a complete oval. Hence for a complete oval of $n+2$ points to exist it is necessary that n be even.

In a Desarguesian projective plane $P(2, q)$, $q = p^e$ if p is odd, it has been shown by Segre (**4**) that an oval of $q+1$ points must consist of the points of a non-degenerate conic. When $q = 2^e$ the points of a non-degenerate conic form an oval S of $q+1$ points, and S together with its nucleus P^* form a complete oval or ovoid of $q+2$ points. But in general there are other complete ovals. Segre (**5**) has shown that if $2 \leqslant k \leqslant e-2$ and $(e, k) = 1$, then in $P(2, q)$ the q points $(x, x^{2^k}, 1)$, $x \in GF(q)$, together with $(0, 1, 0)$ and $(1, 0, 0)$ form a complete oval $\mathcal{O}$ which does not contain a conic.

Let the Desarguesian plane $P(2, q)$, $q = 2^e$, $e \geqslant 2$, be represented by homogeneous coordinates so that a point P is represented by (tx, ty, tz) where $(x, y, z) \neq (0, 0, 0)$ is fixed, $x, y, z \in GF(q)$ and t ranges over $GF(q)$, except that $t \neq 0$. Hence a point P of $P(2, q)$ corresponds to a line through the origin of the three dimensional affine geometry $A(3, q)$, whose points are (tx, ty, tz), where $(x, y, z) \neq (0, 0, 0)$ is fixed and t ranges over $GF(q)$ including $t = 0$. Such a line is a subgroup of dimension one of the vectors (x, y, z) under addition.

THEOREM 2.1. *A generalized quadrilateral* $GQ(q)$, $q = 2^e$, $e \geqslant 2$ *is defined by*:

(1) q^3 *points* (x, y, z) *of* $A(3, q)$, $x, y, z \in GF(q)$.

(2) $q^2(q+2)$ *lines where a line L is a coset* $\{X_0 + tP_i\}$ *of one of the additive subgroups* $\{tP_i\}$, $i = 1, \ldots, q+2$, *t ranging over* $GF(q)$ *and*

$$P_i = (x_i, y_i, z_i), \qquad i = 1, \ldots, q+2$$

are the $q+2$ *points of a complete oval in the projective plane* $P(2, q)$.

(3) *A point P is incident with a line L if P is included in the set of points defining L.*

Here a line contains $1 + s = q$ *points and a point is on* $1 + t = q + 2$ *lines so that* $s = q - 1$, $t = q + 1$.

Proof. Each line $\{tP_i\}$, $i = 1, \ldots q+2$, $t \in GF(q)$, contains q points of $A(3, q)$, and so also does each of q^2 cosets $\{X_0 + tP_i\}$. If $\{X_0 + tP_i\}$ and $\{X_1 + uP_j\}$, $i \neq j$, contained more than one point in common we would have

$$Y_1 = X_0 + t_1 P_i = X_1 + u_1 P_j \quad \text{and} \quad Y_2 = X_0 + t_2 P_i = X_1 + u_2 P_j.$$

Subtracting $(t_1 - t_2) P_i = (u_1 - u_2) P_j$ and as P_i and P_j represent different points in $P(2, q)$ this is possible only if $t_1 = t_2$, $u_1 = u_2$ so that $Y_1 = Y_2$. Hence distinct lines contain at most one point in common. Hence the $q^2(q+2)$ lines defined are all distinct, and a point P is contained in exactly $q+2$ cosets, one for each P_i, $i = 1, \ldots, q+2$.

Following Feit and Higman (**2**), let us define $\lambda(e,f)$ as the length n of the shortest chain $e = e_0, e_1, \ldots, e_n = f$ joining e to f where e_i are points or lines of our system $GQ(q)$ and e_i is incident with e_{i+1}, $i = 0, \ldots, n-1$.

LEMMA: *If e is a point and f is a line, then $\lambda(e,f) = 1$ or 3. If e is a point and f is a point, then $\lambda(e,f) = 0, 2,$ or 4. If e and f are lines, then $\lambda(e,f) = 0, 2, 4$.*

Proof: Since $GQ(q)$ consists of the points of $A(3, q)$ and all the cosets of $q+2$ subgroups of the additive group, clearly $GQ(q)$ has the additive group A of $A(3, q)$ as automorphisms. Hence in proving the lemma it is sufficient to take $e = (0, 0, 0)$. The lines $\{tP_i\}$, $i = 1, \ldots, q+2$ are the lines containing e and for such a line f, $\lambda(e,f) = 1$. In a line $\{X_0 + tP_i\}$, $t \in GF(q)$, which is a coset and not the subgroup $\{tP_i\}$ then $X_0 = (x_0, y_0, z_0)$ and $P_i = (x_i, y_i, z_i)$ represent different points in $P(2, q)$. But in $P(2, q)$ the $q+1$ lines $P_i P_j$, $j \neq i$, are the complete pencil of lines through P_i and so one of these, say $P_i P_j$ contains X_0. This means that for appropriate $t_0, u_0 \in GF(q)$ we have $X_0 = u_0 P_j + t_0 P_i$. Hence the coset $\{X_0 + tP_i\}$ is the same as the coset $\{u_0 P_j + tP_i\}$, t ranging over $GF(q)$. Hence with $e_0 = (0, 0, 0)$, $e_1 = \{uP_j\}$, $e_2 = u_0 P_j = (u_0 x_j, u_0 y_j, u_0 z_j)$ and $e_3 = \{u_0 P_j + tP_i\} = f$ we have a chain $e = e_0, e_1, e_2, e_3 = f$ with e_i incident with e_{i+1}, $i = 0, 1, 2$ and here $\lambda(e,f) = 3$. If f is a point of the form $u_0 P_j$, then $e = e_0, e_1, e_2 = f$ and $\lambda(e,f) = 2$. If f is a point $X_0 = (x_0, y_0, z_0)$ not of this form then we have seen that for a P_i and appropriate P_j, u_0, t_0 we have $X_0 = u_0 P_j + t_0 P_i$. Thus writing $X_0 = f = e_4$, we have a chain $e = e_0$, $e_1, e_2, e_3, e_4 = f$ using e_0, e_1, e_2, e_3 as above and so $\lambda(e,f) = 4$.

If e is an arbitrary line, without loss of generality we may take $e = \{tP_i\}$. If f is a line $\{uP_j\}$ we may take $e_1 = (0, 0, 0)$ and $e = e_0, e_1, e_2 = f$ is a chain so that $\lambda(e,f) = 2$. If f is a line of the form $\{X_0 + tP_i\} = \{u_0 P_j + tP_i\}$ we may take $e_1 = (0, 0, 0)$, $e_2 = \{u_0 P_j\}$ and $e_4 = f = \{u_0 P_j + tP_i\}$ so that $\lambda(e,f) \leqslant 4$. If f is a line of the form $\{X_0 + tP_j\}$, $j \neq i$, then $f = \{u_0 P_k + tP_j\}$, and we take $e_1 = (0, 0, 0)$, $e_2 = \{uP_k\}$, $e_3 = u_0 P_k$, $e_4 = f = \{u_0 P_k + tP_j\}$ and again $\lambda(e,f) \leqslant 4$.

To complete the proof that our system $GQ(q)$ is a generalized quadrangle we must show that there is no closed irreducible chain of length 6 or that there are no triangles. If there were a triangle, without loss of generality we may assume that one of the vertices is $e_0 = (0, 0, 0)$. Suppose there is a closed irreducible chain $e_0, e_1, e_2, e_3, e_4, e_5, e_6 = e_0$. Here $e_1 = \{tP_i\}$ for some P_i and $e_5 = \{uP_j\}$ for some j and, as the chain is irreducible, $i \neq j$. Then $e_2 = t_0 P_i$, $e_4 = u_0 P_j$ and by irreducibility $t_0 \neq 0, u_0 \neq 0$. Then $e_3 = \{X_0 + rP_k\}$ must be a line containing $t_0 P_i$ and $u_0 P_j$. Hence $t_0 P_i = X_0 + r_1 P_k$, $u_0 P_j = X_0 + r_2 P_k$, and subtracting $t_0 P_i - u_0 P_j = (r_1 - r_2) P_k$. Now $t_0 \neq 0$ and $u_0 \neq 0$ so that we cannot have $P_k = P_i$ or P_j. But this relation means that in the projective plane $P(2, q)$ the three points P_i, P_j, P_k are on a line, contrary to the choice of $P_1, \ldots, P_{q+2}$ as the points of a complete oval.

This completes the proof that our construction does yield a generalized quadrilateral. Note that this construction does not require that q be even, but that q must be even for the existence of the complete oval.

Note Added in Proof

Essentially the same construction has been found independently by G. Szekeres.

References

1. Dembowski, P. *Finite Geometries* (Ergebnisse der Mathematik und ihrer Grenzgebiete, Band 44, Springer, 1968).
2. Feit, W. and Higman, G. The nonexistence of certain generalized polygons. *Journal of Algebra* **1** (1964), 114–131.
3. Qvist, B. Some remarks concerning curves of the second degree in a finite plane. *Ann. Acad. Sci. Fenn.* No. 134 (1952), 1–27.
4. Segre, B. Ovals in a finite projective plane. *Can. J. Math.* **7** (1955), 414–416.
5. Segre, B. Sui k-archi nei piani finiti di caratteristica due. *Rev. Math. Pures Appl.* **2** (1957), 289–300.
6. Segre, B. Introduction to Galois geometries. *Atti del Accad. Naz. dei Lincei* (Cl. Sc. fis. mat.) *Memorie* **VIII** (1967), 137–236.

On the 2-Classgroup of Cubic Fields

H. HEILBRONN

Let k_2 be a quadratic numberfield of discriminant d_2. It is well known (2) that there exists a cubic numberfield k_3 of discriminant $d_3 = d_2$ if and only if the class-number of k_2 is divisible by 3. The object of this paper is to prove the following analogue.

Let k_3 be a cubic numberfield of discriminant d_3. Then there exists a quartic numberfield k_4 of discriminant $d_4 = d_3$ such that the normal closure $\bar{k}_4$ of k_4 over Q contains k_3 if and only if the class-number h_3 of k_3 (in the narrow sense) is even. More precisely, I shall prove the

THEOREM. *Let $g = g(k_3) = \frac{1}{3}$ or 1 for cyclic or non-cyclic k_3 respectively. Let h_3^* denote the number of elements in the ideal class-group of k_3 of order 2. Then there exist $g(h_3^* - 1)$ quadruplets of conjugate quartic fields k_4 such that $d_4 = d_3$, $k_3 \subset \bar{k}_4$.*

Proof. We first deal with the case when k_3 is not cyclic. Let k_6 denote the normal closure of k_3. Then it follows from class-field theory, or from the theory of relative quadratic fields (3, Kap. VIII) that k_3 has exactly $h_3^* - 1$ unramified quadratic extensions, say $k_{6,j} = k_3(a_j^{\frac{1}{2}})$, where $1 \leqslant j \leqslant h_3^* - 1$. Because $k_{6,j}$ is unramified over k_3, the ideal (a_j) is the square of an ideal in k_3 and it can be assumed that $a_j \equiv 1 \pmod 4$. a_j cannot be chosen in Q because then all rational primes dividing a_j would become squares of ideals in k_3, which no rational prime can do in k_3. The case $a_j = -1$ will be excluded in a moment.

Let a_j', a_j'' denote the conjugates of a_j over Q. Then

$$a_j\, a_j'\, a_j'' = N_{k_3/Q}(a_j) = \pm N_{k_3/Q}((a_j)) = \pm A_j^2,$$

where $A_j \in Q^*$. And our congruence relation $a_j \equiv 1 \pmod 4$ ensures that $a_j\, a_j'\, a_j'' = A_j^2$. Hence $k_{24,j} = k_6(a_j^{\frac{1}{2}}, a_j'^{\frac{1}{2}})$ is normal over k_6, and therefore over Q.

We shall now construct the Galois group $\mathrm{Gal}(k_{24,j}/Q)$ which will turn out to be isomorphic to S_4. To each permutation of $a_j^{\frac{1}{2}}, a_j'^{\frac{1}{2}}, a_j''^{\frac{1}{2}}$ in this order we assign the corresponding element in S_3 written as the group of permutations on the figures 1, 2, 3 in this order. To the automorphism

$$a_j^{\frac{1}{2}} \to a_j^{\frac{1}{2}}, \qquad a_j'^{\frac{1}{2}} \to -a_j'^{\frac{1}{2}}, \qquad a_j''^{\frac{1}{2}} \to -a_j''^{\frac{1}{2}}$$

we assign the permutation (14) (23). These assignments fix the isomorphism between $\mathrm{Gal}(k_{24,j}/Q)$ and S_4. Let V_4 be the subgroup of S_4 generated by the 2-cycles (14) and (23); it is clear that $V_4 = \mathrm{Gal}(k_{24,j}/k_{6,j})$. Further, let W_8 be the subgroup of S_4 generated by V_4 and the substitution (13) (24); it is clear that $W_8 = \mathrm{Gal}(k_{24,j}/k_3)$ as the automorphism $(13)(24) = (12)^{-1}(14)(23)(12)$ transforms a_j into itself. Finally, let $k_{4,j}$ be defined as the extension $Q(a_j^{\frac{1}{2}} + a_j'^{\frac{1}{2}} + a_j''^{\frac{1}{2}})$. Then $S_3 = \mathrm{Gal}(k_{24,j}/k_{4,j})$.

The field $k_{4,j}$ is, apart from conjugacy, the only quartic subfield of $k_{24,j}$. In $k_{24,j}$ there exist only 3 quadratic extensions of k_3, namely $k_{6,j}$, k_6, $k_3((da_j)^{\frac{1}{2}})$. Of these only the first is unramified over k_3. Hence, if $j \neq i$, $k_{24,j} \neq k_{24,i}$, and so $k_{4,j} \neq k_{4,i}$.

It remains to show that $d_3 = d_{4,j}$ for all j. Direct computation would be very tedious, but the Artin L-series provide a quick proof. We write down the character table of S_4.

C	$\sigma(C)$	$n(C)$	χ_1	χ_2	χ_3	χ_4	χ_5	$\psi(W_8)$	$\psi(V_4)$	$\psi(S_3)$
ident.	1	1	1	1	2	3	3	3	6	4
(12) (34)	2	3	1	1	2	−1	−1	3	2	0
(123)	3	8	1	1	−1	0	0	0	0	1
(12)	2	6	1	−1	0	1	−1	1	2	2
(1234)	4	6	1	−1	0	−1	1	1	0	0

Here C denotes the conjugacy class; $\sigma(C)$ the order of C; $n(C)$ the cardinality of C; $\chi_1, \ldots, \chi_5$ the simple characters of S_4; and $\psi(W_8)$, $\psi(V_4)$, $\psi(S_3)$ the characters of S_4 induced by the principal characters of W_8, V_4, and S_3 respectively. One verifies at once that $\psi(W_8) = \chi_1 + \chi_3$, $\psi(V_4) = \chi_1 + \chi_3 + \chi_4$, $\psi(S_3) = \chi_1 + \chi_4$. Writing $\zeta(s)$, $\zeta_3(s)$, $\zeta_{6,j}(s)$, $\zeta_{4,j}(s)$ for the Dedekind ζ-functions of Q, k_3, $k_{6,j}$ and $k_{4,j}$ respectively, these relations yield (**1**, Chapter VIII, 3)

$$\zeta(s)\,\zeta_{6,j}(s) = \zeta_3(s)\,\zeta_{4,j}(s);$$

and the functional equation of these ζ–functions gives

$$d_{6,j} = d_3\, d_{4,j}.$$

Because $k_{6,j}$ is unramified over k_3, we have $d_{6,j} = d_3{}^2$; and it follows that $d_3 = d_{4,j}$.

Conversely, if k_3 and $k_{4,j}$ are given such that $k_3 \subset \bar{k}_{4,j}$, then $k_{6,j}$ can be determined as the field such that $\text{Gal}(\bar{k}_{4,j}/k_{6,j}) = V_4$; from the previous calculations it follows that $k_{6,j}$ is unramified over k_3 as $d_3 = d_{4,j}$.

It remains to prove the theorem when k_3 is cyclic. a_j can be determined as before. a_j must again be irrational; because otherwise the field $k_{6,j}$ would be in the union of the absolutely abelian fields k_3 and $Q(a_j^{\frac{1}{2}})$ and its discriminant $d_{6,j}$ would equal $d_3^2 \text{disc}^3(Q(a_j^{\frac{1}{2}})) \neq d_3^2$. But now the fields $k_3(a_j'^{\frac{1}{2}})$ and $k_3(a_j''^{\frac{1}{2}})$ are also unramified extensions of k_3 itself, which accounts for the factor $g = \frac{1}{3}$ in our theorem. To justify this argument we have, of course, to show that $k_{6,j}$ is different from its conjugates. Otherwise $k_{6,j}$ would be abelian over Q and we could choose a_j in Q, a possibility that was excluded above.

One sees as in the first case that $a_j a_j' a_j'' = A_j^2, A_j \in Q^*$. Calling $k_{12,j}$ the normal closure of $k_{6,j}$ over Q, it follows that $\text{Gal}(k_{12,j}/Q) = A_4$; $\text{Gal}(k_{12,j}/k_{6,j}) = V_2$, the subgroup of A_4 generated by the permutation (14) (23); $\text{Gal}(k_{12,j}/k_3) = W_4$, the subgroup of order 4 of A_4. Calling again $k_{4,j} = Q(a_j^{\frac{1}{2}} + a_j'^{\frac{1}{2}} + a_j''^{\frac{1}{2}})$, it follows that $\text{Gal}(k_{12,j}/k_{4,j}) = A_3$, the subgroup of A_4 generated by the cycle (123).

Our character table now becomes:

C	$\sigma(C)$	$n(C)$	χ_1	χ_2	χ_3	χ_4	$\psi(W_4)$	$\psi(V_2)$	$\psi(A_3)$
ident.	1	1	1	1	1	3	3	6	4
(12) (34)	2	3	1	1	1	-1	3	2	0
(123)	3	4	1	ρ	ρ^2	0	0	0	1
(132)	3	4	1	ρ^2	ρ	0	0	0	1

where ρ denotes a 3rd root of 1. One sees at once that $\psi(W_4) = \chi_1 + \chi_2 + \chi_3$, $\psi(V_2) = \chi_1 + \chi_2 + \chi_3 + \chi_4$, $\psi(A_3) = \chi_1 + \chi_4$.

Hence, again with the obvious notation,

$$\zeta(s)\,\zeta_{6,j}(s) = \zeta_3(s)\,\zeta_{4,j}(s),$$

and the relation

$$d_3 = d_{4,j}$$

follows as before. The converse argument works similarly.

References

1. Cassels, J. W. S. and Fröhlich, A. (editors). *Algebraic Number Theory* (Academic Press, 1967).
2. Hasse, H. Arithmetische Theorie der kubischen Zahlkörper auf klassenkörpertheoretischer Grundlage. *Math. Zeitschrift* **31** (1930), 565–582.
3. Hecke, E. *Theorie der algebraischen Zahlen* (Akademische Verlagsgesellschaft, 1923).

Discrepancy and Riemann Integration

EDMUND HLAWKA

Let E^s be the unit cube $0 \leqslant \xi_i < 1$ $(i = 1, \ldots, s)$, $\bar{E}^s$ the closed cube $0 \leqslant \xi_i \leqslant 1$ $(i = 1, \ldots, s)$. If $\omega = (x_i)$, $i \in N$ is a sequence in E^s, then ω is called† u.d.(mod 1), if for all intervals $J \subset E^s$

$$\lim_{N\to\infty} \mu_N(\chi(J)) = \mu(\chi(J)). \tag{1}$$

where

$$\mu_N(\chi(J)) = \frac{1}{N}\sum_{i=1}^{N} \chi(J; x_i), \quad \mu(\chi(J)) = \int_{E^s} \chi(J; x)\, dx = \mathrm{Vol}\,(J)$$

($\chi(J)$ is the indicator function of J). More generally, the sequence ω is called u.d.(mod 1) with density ρ, if we have, instead of (1),

$$\lim \mu_N(\chi(J)) = \int_{E^s} \chi\rho\, dx = \mu(\chi; \rho). \tag{1'}$$

It is supposed, that ρ is Riemann-integrable on $\bar{E}^s$ with $\int \rho\, dx = 1$ and non-negative.

It is well known that as a consequence of (1) for any periodic, Riemann-integrable function f of period one

$$\lim \mu_N(f) = \lim \frac{1}{N}\sum_{i=1}^{N} f(x_i) = \int_{E^s} f\, dx = \mu(f). \tag{2}$$

In the case (1′) we have instead of $\mu(f)$ the integral $\int f\rho\, dx = \mu(f, \rho)$. The discrepancy $D_N(\omega; \rho)$ of the sequence ω is defined as

$$\sup_J |\mu_N(\chi(J)) - \mu(\chi(J); \rho)|. \tag{3}$$

† Uniformly distributed.

If $\rho \equiv 1$ (the classical case), we write $D_N(\omega)$. Now we ask: is it possible to estimate

$$D_N(f, \omega, \rho) = |\mu_N(f) - \mu(f, \rho)| \tag{4}$$

from above with the help of D_N? If f is of bounded variation $V(f)$ in the sense of Hardy–Krause on $\bar{E}^s$, then it is known, that

$$D_N(f, \omega, \rho) \leqslant V(f)\, D_N(\omega; \rho).$$

Now we will give an estimate of $D_N(f)$ for general f. The result is simplest in the case $\rho \equiv 1$.

THEOREM 1†

$$D_N(f, \omega) \leqslant (1 + 2^{2s-1}) \sum (f, [D^{-1/s}]^{-1}) \tag{5}$$

Here

$$\sum(f, k) = \sup_{n(p) \leqslant k} \sigma(f\,; p),$$

where we consider all partitions p of $\bar{E}^s$ in intervals with norm $n(p) \leqslant k$ and $\sigma(f\,;p)$ is the mean oscillation of f for the partition p. The norm $n(p)$ is the largest length of all the edges of the intervals in p. (Usually the norm $n'(p)$ is the largest diameter of the intervals in p but we have $n(p) \leqslant n'(p) \leqslant \sqrt{s}\, n(p)$). For arbitrary ρ see (14).

If ω is u.d.(mod 1), then $D_N \to 0$; f is integrable; therefore the right side of (5) tends to zero, as it should do.

For the proof of (5), we will first consider the case $s = 1$, because here the details of the proof are much simpler. Let $p(L)$ be the partition of $E^1 = E$ in the intervals $J(z)$:

$$\frac{z-1}{L} \leqslant \xi < \frac{z}{L}$$

(L natural number; $z = 1, \ldots, L$), therefore $n(p(L)) = L^{-1}$. Further let

$$G(z) = \sup_{J(z)} f, \qquad g(z) = \inf_{J(z)} f$$

and

$$\Phi_2 = \sum_{z=1}^{L} G(z)\chi(J(z)), \quad \Phi_1 = \sum_{z=1}^{L} g(z)\chi(J(z)),$$

† The result was announced in 'Asymptotic Distribution Modulo 1'. Nuffic International summer session in Breukelen 1962 (P. Nordhoff N.V. Groningen) p. 87, formula (9).

then we have

$$\Phi_1 \leqslant f \leqslant \Phi_2 \quad \text{and} \quad \mu(\Phi_1) \leqslant \mu(f) \leqslant \mu(\Phi_2),$$
$$\mu_N(\Phi_1) \leqslant \mu_N(f) \leqslant \mu_N(\Phi_2);$$

further

$$\mu(\Phi_2) - \mu(\Phi_1) = \sigma(f; p(L)),$$

if $\rho \equiv 1$, which we suppose. It is now clear that

$$\mu(f) - \mu_N(f) \leqslant \sigma(f) + \mu(\Phi_1) - \mu_N(\Phi_1)$$

and

$$\mu(f) - \mu_N(f) \geqslant -\sigma(f) + \mu(\Phi_2) - \mu_N(\Phi_2);$$

therefore

$$D_N(f) \leqslant \max_i D_N(\Phi_i) + \sigma(f; p(L)). \tag{6}$$

It is enough to estimate $D_N(\Phi_2)$. We have

$$\mu_N(\Phi_2) = \frac{1}{N} \sum_{i=1}^{N} \Phi_2(x_i) = \sum_z G(z) \frac{1}{N} \sum_{i=1}^{N} \chi(J(z); x_i).$$

Now we set for $z = 1, \ldots, L$.

$$S(z) = \frac{z}{L} - \frac{1}{N} \sum_{i=1}^{N} \sum_{r=1}^{z} \chi(J(r); x_i).$$

We define $S(z) = 0$ for $z \leqslant 0$ and $z > L$ (z integer). Now $\sum_{r=1}^{z} \chi(J(r))$ is the indicator function of the interval $J'(z) : 0 \leqslant \xi < z/L$; therefore

$$S(z) = \frac{z}{L} - \frac{1}{N} \sum_{i=1}^{N} \chi(J'(z); x_i).$$

For $z = L$, $S(z) = 0$, because $J'(L) = E$.

We have $S(z) - S(z-1) = \dfrac{1}{L} - \dfrac{1}{N} \sum_{i=1}^{N} \chi(J(z); x_i)$; therefore

$$S = \mu(\Phi_2) - \mu_N(\Phi_2) = \sum_{z=1}^{L} G(z) \left(\frac{1}{L} - \frac{1}{N} \sum_{i=1}^{N} \chi(J(z); x_i) \right)$$
$$= \sum_{z=1}^{L} G(z) \big(S(z) - S(z-1)\big)$$
$$= G(L)\, S(L) + \sum_{z=1}^{L-1} \big(G(z) - G(z+1)\big)\, S(z).$$

After the definition of D_N, we have $|S(z)| \leqslant D_N$; therefore

$$|S| \leqslant D_N \sum_{z=1}^{L-1} |G(z+1) - G(z)|. \tag{7}$$

Now we set $L = 2M$ (M natural number) and we have

$$\sum_{z=1}^{L-1} = \sum_{l=1}^{M} |G(2l) - G(2l-1)| + \sum_{l=1}^{M-1} |G(2l+1) - G(2l)| = \Sigma_1 + \Sigma_2.$$

Now consider in p the union of $J(2l-1)$, $J(2l)$ ($l = 1, \ldots, M$), which is the interval $J_1''(l)$:

$$\frac{2(l-1)}{L} \leqslant \xi < \frac{2l}{L}.$$

Then we get a partition p_1'' of $\bar{E}$ with norm $n(p_1'') = 2/L$. If

$$\sup_{J_1''(l)} f = G_1''(l), \qquad \inf_{J_1''(l)} f = g_1''(l),$$

then we have

$$G(2l) - G(2l-1) \leqslant G''(l) - g''(l);$$

therefore

$$\sum\nolimits_1 \leqslant M\,\sigma\left(p_1''; \frac{1}{M}\right).$$

If we consider in p the union of $J(2l)$, $J(2l+1)$ ($l = 1, \ldots, M-1$), which is the interval $J_2''(l)$:

$$\frac{2l-1}{L} \leqslant \xi < \frac{2l+1}{L},$$

then the intervals $J_2''(l)$ ($l = 1, \ldots M-1$), with the intervals $J(1)$ and $J(l)$, define a partition p_2'' of $\bar{E}$, with norm $2/L$ (all intervals of p_2' have the length $2/L$, except the first and the last, which have the length $1/L$). We have in Σ_2

$$G(2l+1) - G(2l) \leqslant G_2''(l) - g_2''(l)$$

(G'', g'' defined similarly as above) and therefore

$$\Sigma_2 \leqslant M\sigma\left(p_2''; \frac{1}{M}\right)$$

and

$$|S| \leqslant M\,D_N\left(\sigma\left(p_1''; \frac{1}{M}\right) + \sigma\left(p_2''; \frac{1}{M}\right)\right); \tag{8}$$

therefore

$$D_N(f) \leqslant (2\,M\,D_N + 1) \sum \left(f, \frac{1}{M}\right).$$

Now we take $M = [D_N^{-1}]$ and we have the result for $s = 1$.

Now let us consider the case for general ρ. We have only to define

$$S(z) = \int \rho\chi(J'(z); x)\, dx - \frac{1}{N} \sum_{i=1}^{N} \chi(J'(z); x_i).$$

Then we get (8) again. Further we have to consider

$$\mu(\Phi_2) - \mu(\Phi_1) = \sum_{z=1}^{L} (G(z) - g(z)) \int \chi(J(z); x)\, dx.$$

We define

$$K = L \sup_z \int \chi(J(z); x)\, dx, \quad \text{then} \quad \mu(\Phi_2) - \mu(\Phi_1) \leqslant K\sigma\left(p(L); \frac{1}{L}\right)$$

and we have with $L = 2[D_N^{-1}]$

$$D_N(f, \omega, \rho) \leqslant (2 + K) \sum (f, [D_N^{-1}]^{-1}). \tag{5'}$$

Now let us consider the multidimensional case. At first we make some formal remarks. Let F be a real-valued function defined on Z^s and let us assume that $F = 0$ outside some bounded set in Z^s. By e we denote a point in Z^s, whose coordinates e_i have only the values 0 or 1. There exist 2^s such points.

Now we define the following functions on Z^s:

$$\Delta F = \sum_e F(z + e)(-1)^{\sigma(e)}, \qquad \Delta' F = \sum_e F(z - e)(-1)^{\sigma(e)}$$

$(\sigma(e) = e_1 + \ldots + e_s)$. It is clear that Δ, Δ' are linear operators. If $F_1, \ldots, F_s$ are real-valued functions on Z and $F = F_1 \times \ldots \times F_s$, then

$$\Delta F = \prod_{j=1}^{s} (F_j(z_j) - F_j(z_j + 1)), \qquad \Delta' F = \prod_j (F_j(z_j) - F_j(z_j - 1))$$

because

$$\Delta F = \sum_e \prod_{j=1}^{s} F_j(z_j + e_j)(-1)^{e_j} = \prod_{j=1}^{s} \sum_{e_j = 0,1} F_j(z_j + e_j)(-1)^{e_j}.$$

We have the Abel transformation

$$\sum_z F(z)\, \Delta H(z) = \sum_z H(z)\, \Delta' F(z) \tag{9}$$

because

$$\sum_z F(z)\, \Delta H(z) = \sum_e (-1)^{\sigma(e)} \sum_z F(z) H(z + e) = \sum_e (-1)^{\sigma(e)} \sum_z F(z - e) H(z).$$

Now let us consider again a partition $p(L)$ of E^s in the intervals $J_s(z)$:

$$\frac{z_i - 1}{L} \leqslant \xi_i < \frac{z_i}{L} \qquad (i = 1, \ldots, s) \quad (1 \leqslant z_i \leqslant L),$$

where $z = (z_1, \ldots, z_s)$. The set of $z = (z_1, \ldots, z_s)$ with $1 \leqslant z_i \leqslant L$ we denote $Z(L)$. The norm $n(p(L))$ is L^{-1}. By $J'_s(z)$ we denote the interval

$$0 \leqslant \xi_i < \frac{z_i}{L} \qquad (i = 1, \ldots, s).$$

We define $\chi(J_s(z)) = 0$ if $z \notin Z(L)$ and similarly for $J'(z)$. Now we have $\chi(J_s(z); \xi) = \chi(J_1(z_1); \xi_1) \ldots \chi(J_1(z_s); \xi_s)$ because $\xi \in J_s$ if and only if

$$\frac{z_i - 1}{L} \leqslant \xi_i < \frac{z_i}{L}.$$

The same is true for J'. Now for each $\xi \in E^s$ we have with $F(z) = \chi(J_s(z); \xi)$

$$\Delta' \chi(J'_s(z); \xi) = \chi(J_s(z); \xi) \tag{10}$$

because

$$\Delta' \chi(J'_s(z); \xi) = \prod_{i=1}^{s} \chi(J'_1(z_i); \xi_i) - \chi(J'_1(z_i - 1); \xi_i) = \prod_{i=1}^{s} \chi(J_1(z_i); \xi_i).$$

This point has now been settled, and we can use the same methods as in the case $s = 1$.

We set

$$G(z) = \sup_{J(z)} f, \qquad g(z) = \inf_{J(z)} f, \qquad (G(z) = g(z) = 0 \text{ if } z \notin Z(L))$$

$$\Phi_1 = \sum_z g(z)\chi(J(z)), \qquad \Phi_2 = \sum_z G(z)\chi(J(z))$$

and we have again (6). Now

$$S = \mu(\Phi_2) - \mu_N(\Phi_2) = \sum_z G(z)\Big(\mu(J(z)) - \mu_N(J(z))\Big).$$

Because of (10) we have $\mu(J(z)) = \Delta'\mu(J'(z))$, $\mu_N(J(z)) = \Delta'\mu_N(J'(z))$; therefore by (9),

$$S = \sum_z G(z)\Big(\Delta'\big(\mu(J'(z)) - \mu_N(J'(z))\big)\Big) = \sum_z \Delta G(z)\big(\mu(J'(z)) - \mu_N(J'(z))\big). \tag{11}$$

On the right-hand side of (11) it is enough to consider only the z with $z \in Z(L)$.

For $z_L = (L, \ldots, L)$ we have $\mu(J'(z)) = \mu_N(J'(z)) = 1$; therefore it is enough to consider the $z \in Z'(L) = Z(L) - \{z_L\}$. We have therefore

$$|S| \leqslant D_N \sum_{z \in Z'(L)} |\Delta G(z)| = D_N \Sigma'.$$

Now we set $L = 2M$ and we divide $Z'(L)$ in 2^s classes $Z''(L)$, where in each class $z \equiv z' \pmod 2$; this means $z_i \equiv z_i' \pmod 2$ $(i = 1, \ldots, s)$. Therefore we have

$$\sum' = \sum_{Z''} \sum_{z \in Z''}' .$$

We write

$$\sum_{z \in Z''}' = \sum''.$$

Now we have

$$\sum'' = \sum_{z \in Z'(L) \cap Z''} \left| \sum_e (-1)^{\sigma(e)} G(z + e) \right| . \tag{12}$$

It is impossible for $z, z' \in Z''$ that $z + e = z' + e'$ because then $e \equiv e' \pmod 2$, which is only the case for $e = e'$, except $z = z'$, $e = e'$. In

$$\sum'''(z) = \sum_e (-1)^{\sigma(e)} G(z + e)$$

we have only to consider the e for which $z + e$ belongs to $Z(L)$. This e we denote by d, the whole set by D and their number by $A(z)$. It is clear that $0 \in D$, because $z \in Z'(L) \subset Z(L)$. We have further

$$\sum'''(z) = \sum_{d, \sigma(d) \equiv 0(2)} G(z + d) - \sum_{d, \sigma(d) \equiv 1(2)} G(z + d).$$

We have

$$\sum_{\sigma(d) \equiv 0(2)} 1 = \sum_{\sigma(d) \equiv 1(2)} 1,$$

because

$$\sum_d (-1)^{\sigma(d)} = \prod_{i=1}^{s} \sum_{d_i} (-1)^{d_i}.$$

Now there exists always a $d \neq (0, \ldots, 0)$ in D, because of $z \in Z'(L)$ there exists a coordinate of z, let us say z_j, with $z_j < L$ and then the point $e = (e_1, \ldots, e_s)$ with $e_j = 1$ and $e_i = 0$ for $i \neq j$ is such a d. Therefore for $i = j$ we have

$$\sum_{d_j} (-1)^{d_j} = 1 + (-1) = 0.$$

Therefore $A(z)$ is even.

Now we consider $J''(z) = \bigcup_{d \in D} J(z+d) = \bigcup_{e} J(z+e) \cap \bar{E}^s$.

$J''(z)$ is the intersection of the cube

$$\frac{z_j - 1}{L} \leqslant \xi_j < \frac{z_j + 1}{L} \qquad (j = 1, \ldots, s)$$

with E^s. We have $\mu(J''(z)) = A(z)L^{-s}$. We set

$$G''(z) = \sup_{J''(z)} f, \qquad g''(z) = \inf_{J''(z)} f;$$

then we have

$$|\Sigma'''(z)| \leqslant \frac{A(z)}{2}(G''(z) - g''(z)); \tag{13}$$

therefore

$$\sum{}'' \leqslant \tfrac{1}{2} \sum_{z \in Z''} A(z)(G''(z) - g''(z)) = \frac{L^s}{2} \sum_{z \in Z'(L) \cap Z''} (G''(z) - g''(z))\, \mu(J''(z));$$

therefore

$$\sum{}'' \leqslant \frac{L^s}{2} \sum_{z \in Z''}{}' (G''(z) - g''(z))\, \mu(J''(z))$$

where we consider all z, for which $J''(z) \cap E^s \neq \emptyset$. The set of all these $J''(z)$ defines a partition p'' of E^s, where the edges of $J''(z)$ have only the value L^{-1} or $2L^{-1}$. The value of L^{-1} is only possible if $J''(z) \not\subset E^s$. Now let us denote $\mathscr{P}$ the set of all p of the above form and let

$$\Sigma^*\left(f, \frac{1}{M}\right) = \sup_{p \in \mathscr{P}} \sigma(p, n(p)),$$

then we have

$$\Sigma'' \leqslant \tfrac{1}{2} L^s\, \Sigma^*(f).$$

Now we have 2^s such sums Σ'' and therefore

$$\Sigma' \leqslant 2^{s-1} L^s\, \Sigma^*(f, M^{-1})$$

and further

$$|S| \leqslant 2^{s-1} L^s D_N\, \Sigma^*(f)$$

and for $\rho = 1$

$$'D_N(f) \leqslant (2^{2s-1} M^s D_N + 1) \sum{}^*\left(f, \frac{1}{M}\right). \tag{14}$$

We take $M = [D_N^{-1}]^{1/s}$ and we have the result, even in a somewhat stronger form.

In the general case, defining again

$$K = \sup_{J'(z)} \frac{\int \rho(x)\,\chi(J'(z); x)\,dx}{\mu\big(\chi(J'(z))\big)},$$

we get

$$D_N(f; \omega, \rho) \leqslant (2^{2s-1} + K) \sum{}^* \left(f, \frac{1}{M}\right) \tag{15}$$

with the same M as above.

A final remark: If we assume that f is continuous we get with the help of (15) with the same M

$$D_N(f) \leqslant (2^{2s-1} + 1)\,\omega\left(\frac{1}{M}\right) \tag{14'}$$

where ω is the modulus of continuity of f. We can also take (for $s = 1$ this has been done by Koksma) $M = [N^s]$; then we get

$$D_N(f) \leqslant (2^{2s} + 1)\,N\,D_N\,\omega\,([N^{1/s}]^{-1}); \tag{14''}$$

but (14″) is not as generally applicable as (14).

On Vertices near a Vertex of a Graph

ALAN J. HOFFMAN*

1. Introduction

Let G be a graph (on a finite number of vertices, undirected, with at most one edge joining a pair of vertices, and no edge joining a vertex to itself). The adjacency matrix of G denoted by $A(G)$, is the (0, 1) matrix (a_{ij}) given by:

$$a_{ij} = \begin{cases} 1 & \text{if } i \text{ and } j \text{ are adjacent vertices,} \\ 0 & \text{otherwise.} \end{cases}$$

Since $A = A(G)$ is a real symmetric matrix, A has real eigenvalues. We denote the algebraically least of these by $\lambda^1(G)$. Note that, since trace $A = 0$, $\lambda^1(G) \leqslant 0$. In fact it is easy to see that, if G has at least one edge, $\lambda^1(G) \leqslant -1$.

We denote the set of vertices of G by $V(G)$, the set of edges of G by $E(G)$. If $S \subset V(G)$, $S \neq \emptyset$, we denote by $\langle S \rangle$ the graph with $V\langle S \rangle = S$, $E\langle S \rangle =$ the set of edges of G both of whose endpoints are in S. We say $H \subset G$ if $V(H) \subset V(G)$, and $H = \langle V(H) \rangle$.

A *clique* is a set of vertices each pair of which is adjacent. The *cliquomatic number* of G, denoted by $\kappa(G)$, is the smallest number of cliques in G whose union is $V(G)$. If $0 \in V(G)$, G^0 is the set of vertices of G each of which is adjacent to 0. More generally, if $S \subset V(G)$, G^s is the set of vertices of G each of which is adjacent to all vertices in S.

The purpose of this note is to prove two facts about vertices near (at distance 1 or 2 from) a given vertex of G; namely that the size of certain configurations among the near vertices is bounded by a function of $\lambda^1(G)$.

THEOREM 1. *There exists a function f such that, if $0 \in V(G)$, $\kappa(G^0) \leqslant f(\lambda^1(G))$.*

THEOREM 2. *There exists a function g such that, if $0 \in V(G)$,*

$$|\{i \mid i \text{ is not adjacent to } 0, |V(G^{\{0,i\}})| > g(\lambda^1(G))\}| < g(\lambda^1(G)).$$

* This research was supported in part by the Office of Naval Research under Contract No. Nonr 3775(00).

Theorem 1 is part of a study of the relation of colouring numbers, cliquomatic numbers, etc. of graphs to eigenvalues (see (**2**) and (**3**) for other results). Theorem 2 will be used by Sims in a paper dealing with partial geometries, strongly regular graphs and rank 3 permutation groups.

One can prove Theorems 1 and 2 directly, or as corollaries of a general theorem (**1**) characterizing those (infinite) families of graphs with uniform lower bound on $\lambda^1(G)$. To illustrate both methods, we will prove Theorem 1 directly, and Theorem 2 as a consequence of the characterization theorem.

2. Preliminaries

The graph K_t is a clique on t vertices, together with all $t(t-1)/2$ edges. The graph $K_{1,t}$ is a graph on $t+1$ vertices, of which one is adjacent to the other t, each of which is not adjacent to any other vertex of $K_{1,t}$. The graph

$$K_{t+1}(K_t)\,K_{2t}$$

is a graph on $2t+1$ vertices, consisting of a clique K_{t+1} and a clique K_{2t}, with t vertices common to both graphs. The graph $K_{t+1}(K_t)G_{2t}$ is a graph on $2t+1$ vertices, consisting of a clique K_{t+1}, a graph G_{2t} on $2t$ vertices, with t vertices common to both graphs.

LEMMA 1. *If* $H \subset G$, $\lambda^1(H) \geqslant \lambda^1(G)$.

LEMMA 2. *If* $\alpha \neq 0, -1$ *is an eigenvalue of* $A(G)$, $x = (x_1, \ldots, x_n)$ *a corresponding eigenvector and if i and j are vertices of G such that* $V(G^i) - \{j\} = V(G^j) - \{i\}$, *then* $x_i = x_j$.

LEMMA 3. $\lambda^1(K_{1,t}) \to -\infty$ as $t \to \infty$.

LEMMA 4. $\lambda^1(K_{t+1}(K_t)K_{2t}) \to -\infty$ as $t \to \infty$.

LEMMA 5. $\lambda^1(K_{t+1}(K_t)G_{2t}) \to -\infty$ as $t \to \infty$.

Lemma 1 is simply a restatement of the fact that the least eigenvalue of a principal submatrix of a real symmetric matrix is not less than the least eigenvalue of the whole matrix. Lemma 2 is an exercise in the solution of two linear equations in two unknowns. To prove Lemmas 3 and 4, observe that $K_{1,2}$ is a subgraph of each graph, hence Lemma 2 applies. It is easy to see that $\lambda^1(K_{1,t}) = -\sqrt{t}$, proving Lemma 3. To prove Lemma 4 requires estimating roots of a cubic equation whose parameters depend on t. To prove Lemma 5, let $\alpha = \lambda^1(K_{t+1}(K_t)\,K_{2t})$ and w a corresponding eigenvector of norm 1. Note that, if i and j are vertices adjacent in $K_{t+1}(K_t)\,K_{2t}$ which are not adjacent in

$K_{t+1}(K_t)G_{2t}$, then $w_i = w_j$. It follows that letting $A = A(K_{t+1}(K_t)\,K_{2t})$, $\tilde{A} = A(K_{t+1}(K_t)G_{2t})$, then

$$\alpha = (Aw, w) \geqslant (\tilde{A}w, w) \geqslant \lambda^1(K_{t+1}(K_t)\,G_{2t}).$$

3. Proof of Theorem 1

For any graph G, let $\bar{G}$ be the complementary graph (i.e., $V(\bar{G}) = V(G)$, i and j are adjacent in $\bar{G}$ if and only if i and j are not adjacent in G). Define $I(G)$ to be largest integer k such that $\bar{K}_k \subset G$.

Lemma 6. *There exists a function $f(d,\lambda)$ such that, if $0 \in V(G)$, $\lambda^1(G) \geqslant \lambda$, $I(G^0) \leqslant d$, then*

$$\kappa(G^0) \leqslant f(d, \lambda). \tag{3.1}$$

Proof by induction: If $d = 1, f(1, \lambda) = 1$. Assume (3.1) proved for $d - 1$. Let $1 \in V(G^0)$, and let C_1 be the set of vertices of G^0 not adjacent to 1. Clearly, $I(\langle C_1 \rangle) < d$, and (by Lemma 1), $\lambda^1(\langle \{0\} \cup C_1 \rangle) \geqslant \lambda^1(G) \geqslant \lambda$. Hence by the induction hypothesis.

$$\kappa(\langle C_1 \rangle) \leqslant f(d - 1, \lambda). \tag{3.2}$$

Let $2 \in V(G^0) - C_1$, and let C_2 consist of all vertices in $V(G^0) - C_1$ which are not adjacent to 2. Clearly, $I(\langle C_2 \rangle) < d$, $\lambda^1(\langle \{0\} \cup C_2 \rangle) \geqslant \lambda$, so

$$\kappa(\langle C_2 \rangle) \leqslant f(d - 1, \lambda). \tag{3.3}$$

Note that $2 \in V(G^{\{0,1\}})$.

Now let $s = s(\lambda)$ be defined by

$$K_{s+1}(K_{2s})\,G_{2s} \not\subset G. \tag{3.4}$$

Such an s exists by Lemmas 1 and 5. If we cannot continue our construction of $C_1, C_2, \ldots,$ to $s - 1$ steps, then

$$\kappa(G_0) < 1 + (s - 1)f(d - 1, \lambda),$$

proving (3.1.) So assume it can be carried out to construct $C_1, C_2, \ldots, C_{s-1}$. Consider the set V of vertices in G^0 not yet accounted for. Each vertex in V is adjacent to $0, 1, \ldots, s - 1$. If there were a vertex $v \in V$ not adjacent to as many as s other vertices in V, then these $s + 1$ vertices, together with the clique $\{0, 1, \ldots, s - 1\}$ would violate (3.4). Hence $\langle \bar{V} \rangle$ has the property that each vertex has valence at most $s - 1$. By Brooks's theorem, $\kappa(\langle V \rangle) \leqslant s$. Therefore,

$$f(d, \lambda) \leqslant s + (s - 1)f(d - 1, \lambda)$$

satisfies (3.1).

To prove the theorem, observe that there exists a function $r(\lambda)$ such that $K_{1,r(\lambda)} \nsubseteq G$ if $\lambda^1(G) \geqslant \lambda$ (Lemmas 1 and 3). Set $f(\lambda) = f(r(\lambda), \lambda)$, and Theorem 1 follows from Lemma 6.

4. Proof of Theorem 2

We shall use the following result, announced in (**1**): there exists a function $L(\lambda)$ such that, if $\lambda^1(G) \geqslant \lambda$, and $L = L(\lambda)$, then there exist graphs $\tilde{G}$ and H such that

$$A(G) + A(\tilde{G}) = A(H), \tag{4.1}$$

$$\text{every vertex of } \tilde{G} \text{ has valence at most } L, \tag{4.2}$$

$$H \text{ has a distinguished family of cliques } K^1, K^2, \ldots, \tag{4.3}$$

satisfying:

if two vertices of H are adjacent, at least one distinguished clique contains both; (4.3.1)

the number of distinguished cliques containing a given vertex is at most L; (4.3.2)

the number of vertices common to two different distinguished cliques is at most L. (4.3.3)

(A converse is also true. There exists a function $\lambda(L)$ such that, if G satisfies (4.1)–(4.3.3), then $\lambda^1(G) \geqslant \lambda(L)$).

To prove Theorem 2, let i be any vertex not adjacent to 0 in H. We prove

$$|V(H^{\{0,i\}}| \leqslant (L(\lambda))^3. \tag{4.4}$$

If not, from (4.3.1) and (4.3.2), $V(H^{\{0,i\}})$ contains a subset S such that $|S| > (L(\lambda))^2$ and $\langle\{0\} \cup S\rangle \subset K^a$ for some a. Similarly, S contains a subset U such that $|U| > L(\lambda)$, and $\langle\{i\} \cup U\rangle \subset K^b$ for some b. If $a \neq b$, $U \subset V(K^a) \cap V(K^b)$ violates (4.3.3). Hence, $a = b$. But this violates the fact that 0 and i are not adjacent in H. Hence, (4.4) holds.

Since every edge of G is an edge of H, it follows that

$$|V(G^{\{0,i\}})| \leqslant (L(\lambda))^3. \tag{4.5}$$

Thus,

$$\left|\{i \mid i \text{ is not adjacent to 0 in } G, |VG^{\{0,i\}})| > (L(\lambda)^3)\}\right|$$

is at most the number of vertices which are not adjacent to 0 in G but are adjacent to 0 in H. By (4.1) and (4.2), this number is at most $L(\lambda)$. Thus $g(\lambda) = (L(\lambda))^3$ ($\geqslant L(\lambda)$) proves Theorem 2.

References

1. HOFFMAN, A. J. $-1-\sqrt{2}$? *Proceedings of the Calgary International Conference on Combinatorial Structures and their Applications; Calgary, Canada, June 1969* (Gordon and Breech, New York, 1970), 173–176.
2. HOFFMAN, A. J. On eigenvalues and colorings of graphs. *Proceedings of the Advanced Seminar on Graph Theory and its Applications* (Army Mathematical Center, Madison, Wisconsin, U.S.A; October 1969). To appear.
3. HOFFMAN, A. J. On eigenvalues and colorings of graphs, II. *Proceedings of the International Conference on Combinatorial Mathematics* (New York, U.S.A; April 1970). *Annals of New York Academy of Sciences.* To appear.

Connectivity in Infinite Graphs

H. A. Jung

1. Introduction

There are various investigations on the structure of infinite graphs to be found in the literature. Thus, to quote only a few examples, in (**5**), (**6**), and (**1**), R. Rado was concerned with different aspects of the theory of infinite graphs. The concepts introduced in this paper refer to the connectivity of infinite graphs.

This subject had already been studied in (**2**) and (**3**). As an attempt to isolate the specifically infinite part of connectivity, we define the concept of a reducing subgraph and the concept of the topology of ends. The ends of a graph are equivalence classes of one-way infinite paths. This equivalence relation was introduced by R. Halin in (**2**) (see section 2). A reducing factor of G has in a certain sense the same infinite structure as G with regard to connectivity. If there is a reducing factor in G which is a tree, we have a simple approach to the topology of ends (section 5).

2. Notation

Let $V(G)$ denote the set of vertices of the graph G. For a subgraph G' of G we write $G' \subseteq G$. If $G' \subseteq G$ and $V(G) = V(G')$, the graph G' is called a *factor* of G.

A set $V_0 \subseteq V(G)$ *separates* $V_1, V_2 \subseteq V(G)$ in G if every path in G connecting some $v_1 \in V_1$ to some $v_2 \in V_2$ contains at least one $v \in V_0$. A graph $G' \subseteq G$ is a *reducing subgraph of* G if any two sets $V_1, V_2 \subseteq V(G')$ can be separated in G by a finite set whenever V_1, V_2 can be separated in G' by a finite set.

For two (one-way) infinite paths P_1, P_2 in G we put $P_1 \sim_G P_2$ if there is no finite set separating $V(P_1), V(P_2)$ in G. It is easily seen that $\sim_G$ defines an equivalence relation on the set of all infinite paths of G. Every equivalence class of $\sim_G$ is an *end* of G.

We shall now define a topology on the set of ends of G. Let $F \subseteq V(G)$ be finite and let H be the union of some components of $G - F$, i.e. the restriction graph of G with $V(G - F) = V(G) - F$. Further let $\mathcal{O}_H$ denote the set of all ends which contain some $P \subseteq H$. If F, H and F', H' of the above kind are given, the graph $H \cap H'$ is the union of some components of $G - (F \cup F')$ and $\mathcal{O}_{H \cap H'} = \mathcal{O}_H \cap \mathcal{O}_{H'}$. Thus forming all unions of sets $\mathcal{O}_H$ we obtain a topology on the set of ends of G. Since every set $\mathcal{O}_H$ is open and closed, this topological space $\mathcal{T}(G)$ is totally disconnected.

3. Reducing subgraphs and the topology of ends

To make precise a remark in the introduction, it will appear by the following theorem that for a reducing factor G' of G the spaces $\mathcal{T}(G)$ and $\mathcal{T}(G')$ are homeomorphic.

THEOREM 1. *Let G' be a reducing subgraph of G and let, for the end $\mathcal{E}'$ of G', $\phi(\mathcal{E}')$ denote the end $\mathcal{E}$ of G with $\mathcal{E}' \subseteq \mathcal{E}$. Then ϕ defines a homeomorphism of $\mathcal{T}(G')$ into $\mathcal{T}(G)$. The end $\mathcal{E}$ of G is in the image of ϕ if and only if there is some $P \in \mathcal{E}$ with infinite set $V(P) \cap V(G')$.*

For the proof of Theorem 1 we need a result which might be of interest. An infinite set $V \subseteq V(G)$ is defined to be *tight* in G if for every finite $F \subseteq V(G)$ all but finitely many $v \in V$ are vertices of the same component of $G - F$. Clearly in a reducing subgraph G' of G the set $V \subseteq V(G')$ is tight if and only if V is tight in G.

For example, for the infinite path P in G the set $V(P)$ is tight in G. On the other hand we have

THEOREM 2. *For every tight set V in G there is an infinite path P in G such that $V \cup V(P)$ is also tight in G.*

Proof. We shall construct for every n a path P_n and pairwise disjoint paths $P'_{n,\nu}$ $(1 \leqslant \nu \leqslant n)$ each connecting P_n to V. Moreover the terminal vertex v_n of P_n will be a vertex of the component C_n of $G - F_n$ with infinite $V(C_n) \cap V$, where

$$F_n = \left(V(P_n) \cup \bigcup_{\nu=1}^{n} V(P'_{n,\nu}) \right) - \{v_n\}.$$

For $n = 1$ we first determine C_0 as the component of G with infinite $V(C_0) \cap V$. We then fix some $v_1 \in V(C_0) \cap V$ and denote by $P_1 = P'_{1,1}$ the path with vertex v_1 only. In the general case, we choose a path P' in C_n from v_n to some $v \in V$. Let C'_{n+1} be the component of $G - (F_n \cup V(P'))$ with infinite $V(C'_{n+1}) \cap V$. Since $C'_{n+1} \subseteq C_n$ there is an edge joining some $v_{n+1} \in C'_{n+1}$ to some $v'_{n+1} \in V(P')$. If we walk along P_n and proceed on P' until v'_{n+1} and then terminate at

v_{n+1} we get the path P_{n+1}. The subpath of P' between v'_{n+1} and v is $P'_{n+1,n+1}$ while $P'_{n+1,\nu} = P'_{n,\nu}$ for $1 \leqslant \nu \leqslant n$. Since $C'_{n+1} \subseteq C_{n+1}$ the above condition is satisfied.

Now let P be the union of all P_n. The paths $P_n' = P'_{n,n}$ $(n = 1, 2, \dots)$ are pairwise disjoint and connect $V(P)$ to V. Hence $V(P) \cup V$ is tight in G.

Proof of theorem 1. For infinite paths P_1', P_2' in G' we have $P_1' \sim_{G'} P_2'$ if and only if $P_1' \sim_G P_2'$ whence the mapping ϕ is defined and injective.

Let a finite $F \subseteq V(G)$ and the union H of some components of $G - F$ be given. The restriction graph H' of G' with $V(H') = V(H) \cap V(G')$ is the union of some components of $G' - F$. Clearly $\phi(\mathcal{O}_{H'}) \subseteq \mathcal{O}_H$. If $\mathscr{E} \in \mathcal{O}_H$ and $P \in \mathscr{E}$ with infinite $V(P) \cap V(G')$, the set $V(P) \cap V(G')$ is tight in G and hence also tight in G'. By Theorem 2 there is an infinite path P' in G' such that $V(P') \cup (V(P) \cap V(G'))$ is tight in G' and hence also tight in G. Thus $P' \in \mathscr{E}$, and some infinite subpath of P' is contained in H'. We conclude that ϕ is continuous. With regard to the case $F = \emptyset$ and $H = G$, the assertion about the image of ϕ is also p roved.

On the other hand, let a finite $F' \subseteq V(G')$ and the union H_1' of some components of $G' - F'$ be given. There is a finite set $F \subseteq V(G)$ separating $V(H_1')$ and $V(H_2')$ in G where $H_2' = G' - (F' \cup V(H_1'))$. We may assume $F \supseteq F'$. Let H' be the restriction graph of G' defined by $V(H') = V(H_1') - F$. Since $V(H')$ is not joined to $G' - (V(H') \cup F)$, the set $\mathcal{O}_{H'}$ is defined and

$$\phi(\mathcal{O}_{H_1'}) = \phi(\mathcal{O}_{H'}) \subseteq \mathcal{O}_H$$

where H is the union of all components C of $G - F$ with $V(C) \cap V(H') \neq \emptyset$. Suppose $P \in \mathscr{E} \in \mathcal{O}_H$, where $V(P) \cap V(G')$ is infinite. By the first part of the proof we may assume that P is also an infinite path in $G' - F$. We deduce that $V(P) \subseteq V(H')$. Otherwise $V(P) \subseteq V(H_2')$, yielding the existence of a path in $G - F$ connecting H_1' to H_2'. This completes the proof of Theorem 1.

Given a finite set $F \subseteq V(G)$ and an end $\mathscr{E}$ of G, the *component of* $\mathscr{E}$ in $G - F$ is the unique component of $G - F$ containing some $P \in \mathscr{E}$. The set F *separates the ends* $\mathscr{E}_1, \mathscr{E}_2$ *in* G if the components of $\mathscr{E}_1$ and $\mathscr{E}_2$ in $G - F$ are different.

By definition, the set $V \subseteq V(G)$ is *scattered in* G if for any end $\mathscr{E}$ in G there is some finite $F \subseteq V(G)$ such that the component of $\mathscr{E}$ in $G - F$ contains no $v \in V$.

4. Reducing subgraphs and scattered sets

In a certain sense the concept of scattered sets is complementary to the concept of tight sets.

THEOREM 3. *The set* $V(G)$ *is scattered in* G *if and only if there is no tight set* V' *in* G *with* $V' \subseteq V$.

Proof. Let V' be tight in G and $V' \subseteq V$. By Theorem 2 there is an infinite path P such that $V' \cup V(P)$ is tight in G. There is no finite set separating V' and $V(P)$ whence V is not scattered in G. On the other hand suppose that there is some end $\mathscr{E}$ in G such that for every finite $F \subseteq V(G)$ the component of $\mathscr{E}$ in $G - F$ contains infinitely many $v \in V$. Fix some $P \in \mathscr{E}$. It is easy to construct pairwise disjoint paths P_m connecting some $v_m \in V$ to some $v_m' \in V(P)$ $(m = 1, 2, \ldots)$. The set $\{v_1, v_2, \ldots\}$ is tight in G.

In the sequel it will appear that countable sets play an important role in our discussion.

THEOREM 4. *The subgraph G' of G is a reducing subgraph of G if and only if the following conditions* (i) *and* (ii) *are satisfied.*

(i) *Every countable set $V \subseteq V(G')$ tight in G is tight in G'.*

(ii) *In G', scattered countable sets $V, \bar{V} \subseteq V(G')$ can be separated in G by some finite set whenever they can be separated in G' by some finite set.*

Proof. Clearly conditions (i) and (ii) are satisfied if G' is a reducing subgraph of G. On the other hand, suppose that the finite set $F' \subseteq V(G')$ separates $V, \bar{V} \subseteq V(G')$ in G'. When there is no finite set which separates $V, \bar{V}$ in G', we can easily construct pairwise disjoint paths P_m connecting some $v_m \in V$ to some $\bar{v}_m \in \bar{V}$ $(m = 1, 2, \ldots)$. In view of (ii) we need only consider the case when $\{v_1, v_2, \ldots\}$ is not scattered in G'. But then, by Theorem 3, some set $V_1 = \{v_{m_1}, v_{m_2}, \ldots\}$ is tight in G'. Hence $V' = V_1 \cup \{\bar{v}_{m_1}, \bar{v}_{m_2}, \ldots\}$ is tight in G yielding, by (i), a contradiction.

In a graph G containing at least one infinite path there is no minimal reducing factor in G. For we may delete in such a reducing factor an arbitrary edge producing another reducing factor. Thus we ask whether there is a minimal reducing connected factor in G. As just remarked, the answer is Yes if and only if there is a reducing factor of G which is a tree.

THEOREM 5. *Let G be a connected graph. There is a reducing factor in G which is a tree if and only if there is a representation*

$$V(G) = \bigcup_{n=1}^{\infty} V_n,$$

where every V_n is scattered in G.

Proof. We fix some vertex $v_0 \in V(G)$. Let T be a reducing factor in G, where T is a tree. Denote by V_n the set of all $v \in V(G)$ for which there is a path in T, of exactly n vertices, connecting v_0 to v. Clearly V_n is scattered in T and hence also scattered in G.

Now suppose that a representation

$$V(G) = \bigcup_{n=1}^{\infty} V_n$$

with scattered sets V_n can be found. By Satz 6 in (**3**) there is a factor T in G such that T is a tree and every path in G connecting v to $\bar{v}$ contains some $v' \in V(G)$ located 'below' v and $\bar{v}$. By definition, v' is below v if the path in T connecting v_0 to v contains v'. Let F be a finite set separating $V, \bar{V}$ in T. For $v \in F$ let $\bar{F}(v)$ denote the set of all vertices below v. Then

$$\bar{F} = \bigcup_{v \in F} \bar{F}(v)$$

is finite. If P is a path in G connecting $v \in V$ to $\bar{v} \in \bar{V}$ we find some v' on P below v and $\bar{v}$. We may suppose that there is no v'' on P properly below v'. Since $V(P) \cap F \neq \emptyset$ there is a subpath P' of P connecting v' to some $w \in F$. Again there is some v'' on P' below v' and w. Hence $v'' = v'$ and $v' \in \bar{F}$. We infer that $\bar{F}$ separates $V, \bar{V}$ in G. This completes the proof of the theorem.

The reducing factor T of G in the preceding proof has an interesting property: the construction of $\bar{F}$ does not depend on $V, \bar{V}$. At first sight this property seems to be much stronger than the condition on reducing subgraphs.

THEOREM 6. *Let G' be a reducing subgraph of G. Then for every finite $F' \subseteq V(G')$ there is a finite $F \subseteq V(G)$ separating $V, \bar{V} \subseteq V(G')$ in G whenever F' separates $V, \bar{V}$ in G'.*

Proof. Suppose that for a given finite $F' \subseteq V(G')$ we cannot find a finite F satisfying the above condition. It is easy to construct pairwise disjoint paths P_m in $G - F'$ each connecting vertices v_m' and v_m'' of different components C_m', C_m'' resp. of $G' - F'$ ($m = 1, 2, \ldots$). Since there is no C' such that $C' = C_m'$ for infinitely many m we may assume $C_m' \neq C_n'$, and analogously $C_m'' \neq C_n''$, for arbitrary $m \neq n$. We may moreover assume that $C_m' \neq C_n''$ for arbitrary m, n. But then F' separates $\{v_1', v_2', \ldots\}$ and $\{v_1'', v_2'', \ldots\}$ in G' while there is no finite F separating these sets in G.

In the next section we study the topology of ends for graphs G which allow a representation

$$V(G) = \bigcup_{n=1}^{\infty} V_n$$

with scattered sets V_n. By definition a graph with this property is *of countable character*. Obviously every graph G with countable set $V(G)$ is of countable character.

5. The space $\mathscr{T}(G)$ for graphs of countable character

It is easy to construct graphs G for which no metrics exist inducing the topology of $\mathscr{T}(G)$. By means of Theorem 5, we can prove the following result.

THEOREM 7. *Let G be a graph of countable character. There are metrics d inducing the topology of ends and satisfying the inequality*

$$d(\mathscr{E}_1, \mathscr{E}_3) \leqslant \max\big(d(\mathscr{E}_1, \mathscr{E}_2), d(\mathscr{E}_2, \mathscr{E}_3)\big)$$

for arbitrary ends $\mathscr{E}_1, \mathscr{E}_2, \mathscr{E}_3$ of G.

Let $\mathscr{E}_1, \mathscr{E}_2$ be different ends of G. We put

$$p_G(\mathscr{E}_1, \mathscr{E}_2) = \min\,(|F| : F \text{ separates } \mathscr{E}_1, \mathscr{E}_2 \text{ in } G)$$

and

$$d_G(\mathscr{E}_1, \mathscr{E}_2) = (1 + p_G(\mathscr{E}_1, \mathscr{E}_2))^{-1}; \; d_G(\mathscr{E}, \mathscr{E}) = 0.$$

For given ends $\mathscr{E}_1, \mathscr{E}_2, \mathscr{E}_3$ of G we choose a finite set F with $|F| = p_G(\mathscr{E}_1, \mathscr{E}_3)$ separating $\mathscr{E}_1, \mathscr{E}_3$ in G. Since F separates $\mathscr{E}_1, \mathscr{E}_2$ in G or $\mathscr{E}_2, \mathscr{E}_3$ in G, we infer that $d_G(\mathscr{E}_1, \mathscr{E}_3) \leqslant \max\big(d_G(\mathscr{E}_1, \mathscr{E}_2), d_G(\mathscr{E}_2, \mathscr{E}_3)\big)$.

In many cases d_G does not induce the topology of ends.

It is convenient to formulate a lemma for the proof of Theorem 7. Let a tree T and a vertex $v_0 \in V(T)$ be given. We add edges between vertices $v, \bar{v}$ whenever v is below $\bar{v}$ (cf. proof of Theorem 5). The resulting graph is G'.

LEMMA. *The tree T is a reducing factor of G' and the topology of $\mathscr{T}(G')$ is induced by $d_{G'}$.*

Proof. Let the finite set F separate $V, \bar{V} \subseteq V(T)$ in T. Then the set $\bar{F}$ of all $v \in V(T)$ which are below v_1 for some $v_1 \in F$ is finite and separates $V, \bar{V}$ in G'. Hence T is a reducing factor of G'. Clearly there is a one-one correspondence between the set of ends of T and the set Π of infinite paths in T beginning at v_0. Let F be a finite set separating the ends $\mathscr{E}_1, \mathscr{E}_2$ of G'. By Theorem 1 there are infinite paths $P_\nu \in \mathscr{E}_\nu \cap \Pi$ $(\nu = 1, 2)$. Every $v \in V(P_1) \cap V(P_2)$ is joined in G' to every $\bar{v} \in V(P_1) \cup V(P_2)$, whence $V(P_1) \cap V(P_2) \subseteq F$. On the other hand $V(P_1) \cap V(P_2)$ separates $\mathscr{E}_1, \mathscr{E}_2$ in G'. Now fix some end $\mathscr{E}_0$ of G. Let F_n denote the set of the first n vertices of the infinite path $P_0 \in \mathscr{E}_0 \cap \Pi$. We have $p_{G'}(\mathscr{E}_0, \mathscr{E}) > n - 1$ if and only if $|V(P_0) \cap V(P)| \geqslant n$, where $P \in \mathscr{E} \cap \Pi$. Hence $d_{G'}(\mathscr{E}_0, \mathscr{E}) < 1/n$ if and only if $V(P_0) \cap V(P) \supseteq F_n$. Thus $d_{G'}(\mathscr{E}_0, \mathscr{E}) < 1/n$ if and only if the components of $\mathscr{E}_0$ and $\mathscr{E}$ in $G' - F_{n-1}$ are the same. This gives the second proposition of the lemma.

Now, for a connected graph G, Theorem 7 is proved by applications of Theorem 5, Theorem 1 and the lemma. The general case is readily derived from the special one.

THEOREM 8. *Let G be a graph of countable character. Then the space* $\mathscr{T}(G)$ *is complete, i.e. every Cauchy sequence in* $\mathscr{T}(G)$ *converges. And* $\mathscr{T}(G)$ *is a compact space if and only if for every finite* $F \subseteq V(G)$ *only finitely many components of* $G - F$ *contain infinite paths.*

Proof. Fix some $v_0 \in V(G)$. For a finite $F \subseteq V(G)$, the set of all $\mathcal{O}_H$ where H runs through all components of $G - F$ is an open covering of $\mathscr{T}(G)$. This yields one half of the compactness assertion. In the sequel we may assume that G is connected and, in view of Theorems 1, 5 and 6, that G is a tree T. Moreover we may assume $\deg_T(v) > 1$ for $v \in V(T)$, $v \neq v_0$, where $\deg_T(v)$ is the cardinal of the set of edges issuing from v in T. Let Π be defined as in the proof of the lemma.

Let $\mathscr{E}_1, \mathscr{E}_2, \ldots$ be a Cauchy sequence in $\mathscr{T}(T)$. Since $d_{G'}(\mathscr{E}_k, \mathscr{E}_{k'}) < 1/n$ implies $|V(P_k) \cap V(P_{k'})| \geqslant n$ ($P_k \in \mathscr{E}_k \cap \Pi$; cf. the proof of the lemma), there is some $P \in \Pi$ such that the sequence $|V(P_k) \cap V(P)|$ ($k = 1, 2, \ldots$) tends to infinity. Let $\mathscr{E}$ be the end of P. Obviously $\mathscr{E}_1, \mathscr{E}_2, \ldots$ converges to $\mathscr{E}$.

Finally assume that the compactness condition of the theorem is satisfied. Then T is locally finite. For $v \in V(T)$, let $H(v)$ denote the branch of v, i.e. the subtree of T consisting of all v' above v. Given an open covering Σ of $\mathscr{T}(T)$, a vertex v is a 'bad' vertex if there is no finite set $\{\mathcal{O}_1, \mathcal{O}_2, \ldots \mathcal{O}_n\} \subseteq \Sigma$ with $\mathcal{O}_1 \cup \mathcal{O}_2 \cup \ldots \cup \mathcal{O}_n \supseteq \mathcal{O}_{H(v)}$. If there is no finite covering $\Sigma' \subseteq \Sigma$, v_0 is a bad vertex. In this case we can construct some $P \in \Pi$, every vertex of P being a bad one. This contradicts the fact that $P \in \mathscr{E} \in \mathcal{O}$ for some $\mathcal{O} \in \Sigma$.

References

1. ERDÖS, P. and RADO, R. A partition calculus in set theory. *Bull. American Math. Soc.* **62** (1956), 427–489.
2. HALIN, R. Über unendliche Wege in Graphen. *Math. Ann.* **157** (1964), 125–137
3. JUNG, H. A. Wurzelbäume und unendliche Wege in Graphen. *Math. Nachr.* **41** (1969), 1–22.
4. KALUZA Jr., TH. Strucktur- und Mächtigkeitsuntersuchungen an gewissen unendlichen Graphen mit einigen Anwendungen auf lineare Punktmengen. *Math. Ann.* **122** (1950), 235–258.
5. RADO, R. Universal graphs and universal functions. *Acta Arith.* **9** (1964), 331–340.
6. RADO, R. Note on the transfinite case of Hall's theorem on representatives. *J. London Math. Soc.* **42** (1967), 321–324.

Intersection Numbers of t-Designs

N. S. MENDELSOHN

Abstract

Intersection numbers have been introduced by R. G. Stanton and D. A. Sprott in connection with Balanced Incomplete Block Designs. They have been used successfully by Stanton, Sprott, Mullin and their students in the construction of block designs.

A balanced incomplete block design is a particular case with $t = 2$ of a t-design. For t-designs we get an extended set of equations for the intersection numbers. We also define higher order intersection numbers and obtain equations which must be satisfied by these.

As an application of intersection numbers it is shown that, apart from two trivial types, there are no symmetric t-designs with $t > 2$.

Introduction

A balanced incomplete block design (B.I.B.D.) is a system consisting of v points and b blocks with each block containing k points, each point belonging to r blocks and every pair of points belongs to λ blocks. The numbers v, b, r, k, λ satisfy two equations, namely; $vr = bk$ and $\lambda(v - 1) = r(k - 1)$. For any B.I.B.D. it is known that $b \geqslant v$. If $b = v$ the design is called symmetric and in this case $r = k$. There are two types of symmetric designs which we denote as trivial. The first is the type in which every point is on each block i.e. $v = b = r = k = \lambda$. The second is the case where each block consists of all but one point and each point appears in all but one block. Here $v = b = k + 1 = r + 1 = \lambda + 2$.

We now define a t-design. A t-design is a system with v points and b blocks, each block containing k points and each point contained in r blocks. Also any t points are in λ_t blocks. Regarding t-designs the following is known.

$$\lambda_t \binom{v}{t} = b \binom{k}{t}. \tag{1}$$

For each $s \leqslant t$ every t-design is an s-design with

$$\lambda_s = \frac{\lambda_t \binom{v-s}{t-s}}{\binom{k-s}{t-s}}. \tag{2}$$

Here $\binom{n}{r}$ is the usual binomial coefficient.

For symmetry of notation it is convenient to put $r = \lambda_1$ and $b = \lambda_0$. Hence a t-design has parameters $v, k, \lambda_0, \lambda_1, \lambda_2, \ldots, \lambda_t$. A symmetric t-design has $v = \lambda_0$, $k = \lambda_1$.

The intersection numbers

Before these numbers are introduced, we first mention a method of combinatorial counting (see Dulmage and Mendelsohn, (**1**)). The following notation is used: A is a v by b matrix whose entries are 0 and 1 exclusively; r_i is the sum of the entries in the ith row of A, c_j is the sum of the entries in the jth column of A. $r_{i_1 i_2 \ldots i_s}$ is equal to the number of columns of A in each of which the rows labelled $i_1, i_2, \ldots, i_s$ have an entry 1. In particular r_{uv} is the scalar product of the uth and vth rows.

$c_{j_1 j_2 \ldots j_m}$ is equal to the number of rows of A in each of which the columns labelled $j_1, j_2, \ldots, j_m$ have an entry 1. In particular c_{uv} is the scalar product of the uth and vth columns. The fundamental equation is the following.

For any 0, 1 matrix A

$$\sum \binom{r_{\alpha_1 \alpha_2 \ldots \alpha_m}}{n} = \sum \binom{c_{\beta_1 \beta_2 \ldots \beta_n}}{m}. \tag{3}$$

Here $(\alpha_1, \alpha_2, \ldots, \alpha_m)$ ranges over all combinations of m integers taken from the set $1, 2, \ldots, v$ and $(\beta_1, \beta_2, \ldots, \beta_n)$ ranges over all combinations of n integers taken from the set $1, 2, \ldots, b$.

Suppose, now, that we have a t-design. With respect to a fixed block B we define intersection numbers $x_0, x_1, \ldots, x_k$ as follows: for $i = 0, 1, 2, \ldots, k$, x_i is the number of blocks, each of which has exactly i points in common with the block B. The block B is omitted in the count.

THEOREM 1. *For any t-design the intersection numbers $x_0, x_1, \ldots, x_k$ with respect to any block B satisfy the equations.*

$$(a_0) \quad \sum_{i=0}^{k} x_i = b - 1 = (\lambda_0 - 1)\binom{k}{0}$$

$$(a_1) \quad \sum_{i=1}^{k} i x_i = (r-1)k = (\lambda_1 - 1)\binom{k}{1}$$

$$(a_2) \quad \sum_{i=2}^{k} \binom{i}{2} x_i = (\lambda_2 - 1)\binom{k}{2}$$

$$\vdots$$

$$(a_t) \quad \sum_{i=t}^{k} \binom{i}{t} x_i = (\lambda_t - 1)\binom{k}{t}.$$

The equations (a_0), (a_1), (a_2) *are the Stanton–Sprott equations valid for any B.I.B.D.*

Proof: For the given design construct the v by b incidence matrix C whose entries are a_{ij} where $a_{ij} = 1$ if the ith point is in the jth block and $a_{ij} = 0$ otherwise. We suppose that the block B is the first block and the points are labelled so that B contains the first k points.

$$C = \left(\begin{array}{c|c} 1 & \\ 1 & \\ 1 & \\ 1 & A \\ 1 & \\ \vdots & \\ 1 & \\ \hline 0 & \\ 0 & \\ 0 & \\ 0 & \\ \vdots & \\ 0 & \end{array}\right)$$

Let A be the sub-matrix of C consisting of rows 1, 2, 3, …, k and columns 2, 3, …, b. A is a 0, 1 matrix with parameters $r_{\alpha_1 \alpha_2 \dots \alpha_s} = \lambda_s - 1$ for $s = 1, 2, \dots, t$.

By equation (3)

$$\sum \binom{c_r}{s} = \sum r_{\alpha_1 \alpha_2 \dots \alpha_s} = (\lambda_s - 1)\binom{k}{s}, \qquad s = 1, 2, \dots, t.$$

But

$$\sum \binom{c_r}{s} = \sum_{j=s}^{k} \binom{j}{s} x_j,$$

since on the left side if we group together the terms with $c_i = j$ there are x_j such terms. Also $\sum_{i=0}^{k} x_j = b - 1$ since this simply counts blocks except for the first. Hence the theorem is proved.

The intersection numbers of higher order

The intersection numbers defined in the previous section are now referred to as intersection numbers of the first order $x_i = x_i^{(1)}$. We now define intersection numbers of order s, $x_i^{(s)}$, $s = 1, 2, \ldots; i = 0, 1, 2, \ldots, k$. For any block B, define $x_i^{(2)}$ as the number of pairs of blocks which intersect B in i points. (Note a pair of blocks B_r, B_s intersects B in i points if $|B \cap B_r \cap B_s| = i$.) More generally, define intersection numbers $x_i^{(s)}$ of order s to be the number of s-tuples of blocks which intersect B in i places.

THEOREM 2. *For* $s = 1, 2, \ldots, i = 0, 1, 2, \ldots, k$ *the intersection numbers of order* s *satisfy the equations*

$$(b_0) \quad \sum_{i=0}^{k} x_i^{(s)} = \binom{b-1}{s} = \binom{\lambda_0 - 1}{s}\binom{k}{0}$$

$$(b_1) \quad \sum_{i=1}^{k} \binom{i}{1} x_i^{(s)} = \binom{r-1}{s}\binom{k}{1} = \binom{\lambda_1 - 1}{s}\binom{k}{1}$$

$$(b_2) \quad \sum_{i=2}^{k} \binom{i}{2} x_i^{(s)} = \binom{\lambda_2 - 1}{s}\binom{k}{2}$$

$$\vdots$$

$$(b_t) \quad \sum_{i=t}^{k} \binom{i}{t} x_i^{(s)} = \binom{\lambda_t - 1}{s}\binom{k}{t}.$$

Proof: As in Theorem 1, (b_0) follows from a count of the numbers of s-tuples of blocks exclusive of B. Using the same matrix A of Theorem 1, and equation (3) we obtain

$$\sum \binom{c_{j_1 j_2 \ldots j_s}}{u} = \sum \binom{r_{i_1 i_2 \ldots i_u}}{s}.$$

On the left members of this equation group together the terms for which $c_{j_1 j_2 \ldots j_s} = i$; in the right hand member there are $\binom{k}{u}$ terms each equal $\binom{\lambda_u - 1}{s}$.

Hence $\sum_{i=0}^{k} \binom{i}{u} x_i^{(s)} = \binom{\lambda_u - 1}{s} \binom{k}{u}$, which proves the theorem.

The author believes that the higher intersection numbers can be used to aid in the construction of t-designs and in particular ordinary 2-designs.

An application

As an application of the first order intersection numbers we prove the following theorem.

THEOREM 3. *There are no non-trivial symmetric t-designs for $t \geqslant 3$.*

Proof: Since a t-design for $t \geqslant 3$ is a 3-design it is sufficient to show the non-existence of symmetric 3-designs. Let the parameters be, $v, k, \lambda_2, \lambda_3$ where

$$\lambda_2(v-1) = k(k-1), \quad \text{and from (2),} \quad \lambda_3 = \lambda_2 \frac{(k-2)}{(v-2)}.$$

Furthermore, from the intersection equation (a_3) we obtain $(\lambda_2 - 1)(\lambda_2 - 2) = (\lambda_3 - 1)(k-2)$. The latter equation has made use of the fact that for a symmetric B.I.B.D. $x_0 = 0$, $x_1 = 0$, $x_2 = 0$, ... $x_{\lambda_2} = v - 1$, $x_{\lambda_2+1} = 0$, ..., $x_k = 0$. Eliminating v and λ_3 from these equations we obtain

$$\lambda_2^3 - (3k-1)\lambda_2^2 + (3k^2 - 2k)\lambda_2 - (k^3 - k^2) = 0$$

or $(\lambda_2 - k)^2(\lambda_2 - (k-1)) = 0$. Hence $\lambda_2 = k$ or $\lambda_2 = k - 1$.

These correspond to the trivial symmetric designs.

Further intersection numbers

Since symmetric t-designs of a non-trivial character do not exist with $t \geqslant 3$ we will now confine our considerations to symmetric 2-designs. These are the standard (v, k, λ) designs with $\lambda(v-1) = k(k-1)$. Such designs all have the property that every pair of blocks intersect in the same number λ of points. Suppose we now fix a pair B_1, B_2 of blocks and consider the submatrix A of the incidence matrix whose rows are the λ rows corresponding to the λ points common to B_1 and B_2 and whose columns are those corresponding to the $v - 2$ blocks other than B_1 and B_2. A is a λ by $v - 2$ matrix with $r_i = k - 2$ and $r_{ij} = \lambda - 2$.

We now define intersection numbers corresponding to the block pair B_1, B_2. If we let $y_i = y_i^{(1)}$ be the number of blocks intersecting the block pair in i

points then exactly as in the previous sections, using the matrix A just described, we obtain the equations

$$\sum_{i=0}^{\lambda} y_i = v - 2$$

$$\sum_{i=1}^{\lambda} i y_i = (k - 2)\lambda$$

$$\sum_{i=2}^{\lambda} \binom{i}{2} y_i = \frac{(\lambda - 2)\lambda(\lambda - 1)}{2}.$$

Analogously, if $y_i^{(s)}$ is the number of s-tuples of blocks which intersect the given block pair in i points then, as before, the following equations are obtained

$$\sum_{i=0}^{\lambda} y_i^{(s)} = \binom{v-2}{s}$$

$$\sum_{i=1}^{\lambda} i y_i^{(s)} = \binom{k-2}{s}\lambda$$

$$\sum_{i=2}^{\lambda} \binom{i}{2} y_i^{(s)} = \binom{\lambda-2}{s}\binom{\lambda}{2}.$$

It is expected that these intersection equations should be helpful in the construction of (v, k, λ) designs.

References

1. Dulmage, A. L. and Mendelsohn, N. S. A systematic method for combinatorial counts. *Proceedings of a S.I.A.M. Symposium on Combinatorial Mathematics held in Santa Barbara, California* 1967. To appear.
2. Hughes, D. R. *Proc. Symposia in Pure Mathematics, Vol.* 6. (Amer. Math. Soc. Providence, 1962), 39–42.
3. Stanton, R. J. and Sprott, D. Block intersections in balanced incomplete block designs. *Canad. Math. Bull.* 7 (1964), 539–548.

A Proof of Rado's Theorem on Independent Transversals

L. MIRSKY

1. Introduction

P. Hall's classical theorem on systems of distinct representatives (**6**) was generalized by R. Rado (**15**), who replaced the notion of 'distinctness' by an axiomatically formulated notion of 'independence'. Rado's work was published almost thirty years ago, but its pivotal position in transversal theory has emerged only very recently, largely as the result of investigations of Edmonds and Fulkerson (**3**, §1), Hazel Perfect (**12**; see also **11**), Welsh (**18**, **20**), and Brualdi (**2**). An expository account dealing with some applications of Rado's theorem will be found in (**9**). Here it suffices to note that this theorem provides a firm link between the initially separate disciplines of transversal theory and the theory of abstract independence.

In the present note, we offer a proof of Rado's theorem different from that given in the original treatment. This proof was found early in 1967, and the techniques it employs are now in all likelihood thoroughly familiar to mathematicians working in transversal theory. It seems, nevertheless, useful to have a record of the method.

2. Definitions and notation

The cardinal of a set X will be denoted by $|X|$.

Let $\mathscr{E}$ be a non-empty collection of subsets of a non-empty set E. We shall say that $\mathscr{E}$ is an *independence structure* on E if it satisfies the following axioms.

I(1) If $X \in \mathscr{E}$ and $Y \subseteq X$, then $Y \in \mathscr{E}$.

I(2) If X, Y are finite members of $\mathscr{E}$ such that $|Y| = |X| + 1$, then there exists an element $y \in Y \backslash X$ which satisfies the relation $X \cup \{y\} \in \mathscr{E}$.

I(3) $\mathscr{E}$ has finite character.

A collection $\mathscr{E}$ which satisfies I(1) and I(2) will be called a *pre-independence structure* on E. (If E is finite, the distinction between independence and pre-independence naturally disappears.) If $\mathscr{E}$ is an independence or a pre-independence structure on E, then its members are called *independent sets* (or independent subsets of E). The idea of an independence structure derives from the work of Whitney (**21**).

Let $\mathscr{E}$ be a pre-independence structure on E, and let $X \subseteq E$. If n is a natural number and X possesses an independent subset of cardinal n but no independent subset of cardinal $n + 1$, we shall say that the *rank* of X is n. If X possesses an independent subset of cardinal n for every natural number n, we shall say that the rank of X is ∞ (with the symbol ∞ satisfying the usual conventions). The rank of X will be denoted by $\rho(X)$, and ρ will be called the *rank function* of $\mathscr{E}$.

Let $\mathfrak{A} = (A_i: i \in I)$ be a family of (not necessarily different) subsets of a set E. If $J \subseteq I$, then the family $(A_i: i \in J)$ will be said to be a *subfamily* of $\mathfrak{A}$. We shall say that a subset T of E is a *transversal* of $\mathfrak{A}$ if there exists a bijection $\phi : T \to I$ such that $x \in A_{\phi(x)}$ for all $x \in T$. A transversal of a subfamily of $\mathfrak{A}$ is called a *partial transversal* of $\mathfrak{A}$. In particular, then, a partial transversal of cardinal n of the family $(A_i : 1 \leqslant i \leqslant n)$ is simply a transversal.

If $\mathfrak{A} = (A_i: i \in I)$ is a family of sets and $J \subseteq I$, we shall write

$$A(J) = \bigcup_{i \in J} A_i,$$

and similarly for families denoted by other letters.

3. Rado's theorem

Rado's theorem (**15**) which we propose to prove may be stated in the following terms.

THEOREM. *Let $\mathscr{E}$ be a pre-independence structure, with rank function ρ, on a set* E. *The family $\mathfrak{A} = (A_1, \ldots, A_n)$ of subsets of* E *then possesses an independent transversal* (*i.e. a transversal* T *with* $T \in \mathscr{E}$) *if and only if, for all* $I \subseteq \{1, \ldots, n\}$,

$$\rho(A(I)) \geqslant |I|. \tag{1}$$

In the case when $\mathscr{E}$ is the collection of *all* subsets of E, Rado's theorem reduces to Hall's (**6**). An extremely simple and transparent proof of this special case was given by Halmos and Vaughan (**7**). Here we adapt their idea to frame a proof of Rado's theorem.

We shall, in the first place, suppose that E is finite. If $F \subseteq E$ and $F \in \mathscr{E}$, we shall denote by $\mathscr{E}_F$ the collection of all subsets X of $E \backslash F$ such that $X \cup F \in \mathscr{E}$. It is then a matter of immediate verification that $\mathscr{E}_F$ is a (pre)-independence structure on $E \backslash F$. Its rank function will be denoted by ρ_F.

We begin by observing that, if $F \subseteq G \subseteq H \subseteq E$ and $F \in \mathscr{E}$, then

$$\rho_F(H \backslash G) \geqslant \rho(H) - \rho(G). \tag{2}$$

For, by axiom I (2), we infer at once the existence of a set H* such that

$$H^* \in \mathscr{E}, \qquad F \subseteq H^* \subseteq H, \qquad \rho(H) = |H^*|.$$

Write $H^* \cap G = G^*$, $H^* \cap (H \backslash G) = X^*$ (so that $G^* \cup X^* = H^*$ and $G^* \cap X^* = \emptyset$). Then

$$G^* \cup X^* \in \mathscr{E}, \qquad F \subseteq G^* \subseteq G, \qquad X^* \subseteq H \backslash G, \qquad \rho(H) = |G^*| + |X^*|.$$

Since $G^* \in \mathscr{E}$, we have $\rho(G) \geqslant |G^*|$. Further, since $G^* \cup X^* \in \mathscr{E}$, we have $F \cup X^* \in \mathscr{E}$ i.e. $X^* \in \mathscr{E}_F$. But $X^* \subseteq H \backslash G$ and so $\rho_F(H \backslash G) \geqslant |X^*|$. Thus

$$\rho_F(H \backslash G) + \rho(G) \geqslant |X^*| + |G^*| = \rho(H),$$

and (2) is proved. An alternative procedure would be to obtain first the easy identity $\rho_F(X) = \rho(X \cup F) - |F|$ for $X \subseteq E \backslash F$ and then make use of the 'modular inequality' for the rank function.

In proving the theorem, we need only establish the sufficiency of condition (1), since its necessity is obvious. The assertion is certainly valid for families consisting of a single set. Let $n \geqslant 2$ and assume that the assertion is valid for families consisting of at most $n - 1$ sets. We shall write $I_0 = \{1, \ldots, n\}$.

Suppose, in the first place, that

$$\rho(A(I)) > |I|$$

whenever $\emptyset \subset I \subset I_0$. Since, by (1), $\rho(A_1) \geqslant 1$ there exists an element $x_1 \in A_1$ with $\{x_1\} \in \mathscr{E}$. Put $B_i = A_i \backslash \{x_1\}$ $(2 \leqslant i \leqslant n)$ and let $\emptyset \subset I \subseteq \{2, \ldots, n\}$. Taking $F = G = \{x_1\}$, $H = B(I) \cup \{x_1\}$, we have, by (2),

$$\begin{aligned} \rho_F(B(I)) &\geqslant \rho(B(I) \cup \{x_1\}) - \rho(\{x_1\}) \\ &= \rho(A(I)) - 1 \geqslant |I|. \end{aligned}$$

The family $(B_2, \ldots, B_n)$ therefore has a transversal $T \in \mathscr{E}_F$ by the induction hypothesis; and hence $\mathfrak{A}$ has a transversal $\{x_1\} \cup T \in \mathscr{E}$.

Next, suppose that, for some I^* with $\emptyset \subset I^* \subset I_0$,

$$\rho(A(I^*)) = |I^*|.$$

Applying the induction hypothesis to the family $(A_i\colon i \in I^*)$, we infer the existence of a transversal $F \in \mathscr{E}$. Write $B_i = A_i \backslash F$ $(i \in I_0 \backslash I^*)$, and let $I \subseteq I_0 \backslash I^*$. Taking

$$G = A(I^*), \qquad H = B(I) \cup A(I^*)$$

in (2), we obtain

$$\begin{aligned} \rho_F(B(I)) &\geqslant \rho_F(B(I) \backslash A(I^*)) \\ &\geqslant \rho(B(I) \cup A(I^*)) - \rho(A(I^*)) \\ &= \rho(A(I) \cup A(I^*)) - |I^*| \\ &= \rho(A(I \cup I^*)) - |I^*| \\ &\geqslant |I \cup I^*| - |I^*| = |I|. \end{aligned}$$

Hence, by the induction hypothesis, the family $(B_i: i \in I_0 \backslash I^*)$ possesses a transversal $F' \in \mathscr{E}_F$; and it follows that $\mathfrak{A}$ possesses a transversal $F \cup F' \in \mathscr{E}$.

The case of a finite E has therefore been dealt with. Now let E be arbitrary. By (1), A(I) contains an independent subset, say C(I), of cardinal |I|. Write

$$C = \bigcup_{I \subseteq I_0} C(I), \qquad A_i^* = A_i \cap C \qquad (1 \leqslant i \leqslant n).$$

Then, for each $I \subseteq I_0$,

$$\rho\left(\bigcup_{i \in I} A_i^*\right) = \rho(A(I) \cap C) \geqslant \rho(C(I)) = |I|.$$

Now the A_i^* are subsets of a finite set C, and the members of $\mathscr{E}$ which are subsets of C clearly constitute a (pre)-independence structure. Hence, by the result already established, we infer the existence of an independent transversal of $(A_1^*, \ldots, A_n^*)$ which is, a fortiori, also an independent transversal of $\mathfrak{A}$.

It should be noted that a different proof of the above theorem, based on a 'reduction' process devised by Rado (**17**) for dealing with Hall's original criterion, is to be found in a recent paper by J. S. Pym and Hazel Perfect (**14**, §2).

4. Some extensions

We shall conclude by mentioning briefly a few generalizations of Rado's theorem. Let $\mathscr{E}$, ρ, and $\mathfrak{A}$ be as previously defined and let $1 \leqslant k \leqslant n$. Then (as was pointed out to me by Professor Helge Tverberg), $\mathfrak{A}$ possesses an independent partial transversal of cardinal k if and only if, for all $I \subseteq \{1, \ldots, n\}$,

$$\rho(A(I)) \geqslant |I| + k - n.$$

To prove this, let D be any set such that $E \cap D = \varnothing$, $|D| = n - k$, and consider the collection $\mathscr{E}^*$ of all subsets of $E \cup D$ of the form $X \cup Y$, where $X \in \mathscr{E}$ and $Y \subseteq D$. Plainly $\mathscr{E}^*$ is again a pre-independence structure, and its rank function ρ^* is given by the equation

$$\rho^*(X \cup Y) = \rho(X) + |Y| \qquad (X \subseteq E, \quad Y \subseteq D).$$

Applying Rado's theorem to the family $(A_1 \cup D, \ldots, A_n \cup D)$ and the pre-independence structure $\mathscr{E}^*$, we derive the required result.

A generalization in a different direction is obtained by considering families with infinite index sets, though in this case certain additional restrictions have to be imposed. Let, then, $\mathscr{E}$ be an *independence* structure on an arbitrary set E and let $\mathfrak{A} = (A_i: i \in J)$ be a family of *finite* subsets of E, indexed by an infinite set J. Then $\mathfrak{A}$ possesses an independent transversal if and only if (1) holds for every finite subset I of J. This conclusion had been noticed by Rado (**16**,

Lemma 2) who used a general selection principle (**16**, Lemma 1; cf. also **4** and **10**, §4.4) to derive it from the finite case discussed above. When $\mathscr{E}$ is the collection of all subsets of E, this result had been originally proved by M. Hall Jr. (**5**). Quite recently, J. H. Mason (**8**) observed that we do not need to insist on the finiteness of the A_i: it suffices to assume that they are rank- finite.

Again, it is possible to combine the problem of partial transversals with that of infinite families. In this context, the following result was proved by Hazel Perfect (**13**). Let $\mathscr{E}$ be a pre-independence structure, with rank function ρ, on a set E; let $\mathfrak{A} = (A_i : i \in J)$ be an arbitrary family of subsets of E; and let k be a natural number. Then $\mathfrak{A}$ possesses an independent partial transversal of cardinal k if and only if, for every (cofinite) subset I of J,

$$\rho(A(I)) + |J \backslash I| \geqslant k.$$

Yet other generalizations of Rado's theorem were discovered by R. A. Brualdi (**1**) and by D. J. A. Welsh (**19**). In Brualdi's treatment *two* independence structures are considered; one on the ground set E, and the other on the index set of the family. Indeed, there is no shortage either of applications or of refinements of Rado's theorem. Surveying the field of transversal theory, one is drawn to the conclusion that the momentum generated by this result is as yet far from spent.

References

1. BRUALDI, R. A. Symmetrized form of R. Rado's theorem on independent transversals. Not published, 1967.
2. BRUALDI, R. A. A general theorem concerning common transversals. *Proceedings of the Oxford Conference on Combinatorial Mathematics and its Applications, 1969*. To appear.
3. EDMONDS, J. and FULKERSON, D. R. Transversals and matroid partition. *J. Res. Nat. Bur. Standards* **69B** (1965), 147–153.
4. GOTTSCHALK, W. H. Choice functions and Tychonoff's theorem. *Proc. Amer. Math. Soc.* **2** (1951), 172.
5. HALL, M. Jr. Distinct representatives of subsets. *Bull. Amer. Math. Soc.* **54** (1948), 922–928.
6. HALL, P. On representatives of subsets. *J. London Math. Soc.* **10** (1935), 26–30.
7. HALMOS, P. R. and VAUGHAN, H. E. The marriage problem. *Amer. J. Math.* **72** (1950), 214–215.
8. MASON, J. H. Representations of independence spaces. PhD Dissertation, University of Wisconsin, 1969.
9. MIRSKY, L. Transversal theory and the study of abstract independence. *J. Math. Analysis Appl.* **25** (1969), 209–217.
10. MIRSKY, L. and PERFECT, HAZEL. Systems of representatives. *J. Math. Analysis Appl.* **15** (1966), 520–568.
11. MIRSKY, L. and PERFECT, HAZEL. Applications of the notion of independence to problems of combinatorial analysis. *J. Combinatorial Theory* **2** (1967), 327–357.

12. PERFECT, HAZEL. Independence spaces and combinatorial problems. *Proc. London Math. Soc.* (3), **19** (1969), 17–30.
13. PERFECT, HAZEL. A generalization of Rado's theorem on independent transversals. *Proc. Cambridge Phil. Soc.* **66** (1969), 513–515.
14. PYM, J. S. and PERFECT, HAZEL. Submodular functions and independence structures. *J. Math. Analysis Appl.* **30** (1970), 1–31.
15. RADO, R. A theorem on independence relations. *Quart. J. Math.* (Oxford) **13** (1942), 83–89.
16. RADO, R. Axiomatic treatment of rank in infinite sets. *Canad. J. Math.* **1** (1949), 337–343.
17. RADO, R. Note on the transfinite case of Hall's theorem on representatives. *J. London Math. Soc.* **42** (1967), 321–324.
18. WELSH, D. J. A. Some applications of a theorem of Rado. *Mathematika* **15** (1968), 199–203.
19. WELSH, D. J. A. Transversal theory and matroids. *Canad. J. Math.* **21** (1969), 1323–1330.
20. WELSH, D. J. A. On matroid theorems of Edmonds and Rado. *J. London Math. Soc.* (2), **2** (1970), 251–256.
21. WHITNEY, H. On the abstract properties of linear dependence. *Amer. J. Math.* **57** (1935), 509–533.

Edge-Disjoint Hamiltonian Circuits in Graphs with Vertices of Large Valency

C. St.J. A. Nash-Williams*

1. Introduction

In this paper, a *graph* G consists of two disjoint finite sets $V(G)$, $E(G)$ and a one-to-one function I_G from $E(G)$ into the set of all subsets of $V(G)$ whose cardinal number is 2. Elements of $V(G)$ and $E(G)$ are called respectively *vertices* and *edges* of G. A vertex ξ and edge λ are *incident* with each other if $\xi \in I_G(\lambda)$. An edge λ *joins* the two vertices in $I_G(\lambda)$. Note that according to these definitions an edge cannot join a vertex to itself and two vertices cannot be joined by more than one edge. Throughout this paper, G will denote a graph and n will be considered as a symbol for $|V(G)|$. The *valency* $v(\xi)$ of a vertex ξ is the number of edges incident with it. A sequence

$$\xi_0, \lambda_1, \xi_1, \lambda_2, \xi_2, \lambda_3, \ldots, \lambda_m, \xi_m \tag{1}$$

(where $m \geqslant 0$) is a *track* in G if the ξ_i are vertices of G and the λ_i are edges of G and λ_i joins ξ_{i-1} to ξ_i for $i = 1, \ldots, m$. When $m = 0$, the track has just one term ξ_0. The track (1) is an *arc* if all its terms are distinct. It is a *circuit* if $m \geqslant 3$ and $\lambda_1, \ldots, \lambda_m$ are distinct and $\xi_1, \ldots, \xi_m$ are distinct and $\xi_0 = \xi_m$. A number of tracks in a graph are *disjoint* if no vertex appears in more than one of them, and are *edge-disjoint* if no edge appears in more than one of them. An arc or circuit in G which includes all the vertices of G is *Hamiltonian*. Dirac proved the following well known theorem (**4**, Theorem 3; **9**, page 56).

Theorem 1. *If $n \geqslant 3$ and $v(\xi) \geqslant \frac{1}{2}n$ for every $\xi \in V(G)$, then G has a Hamiltonian circuit.*

This theorem has been sharpened in at least two interesting directions: Ghouila-Houri (**5**) generalized it by extension to directed graphs and the following theorem of Pósa (**10**) does so by relaxing the hypothesis concerning the valencies.

* Research supported by the National Research Council of Canada.

THEOREM 2. *Let the vertices of G be $\xi_1, \ldots, \xi_n$. Suppose that $n \geqslant 3$ and $v(\xi_i) \geqslant i+1$ for every positive integer i less than $\frac{1}{2}(n-1)$ and $v(\xi_i) \geqslant \frac{1}{2}n$ for every integer i such that $\frac{1}{2}n \leqslant i \leqslant n$, and if n is odd suppose that $v(\xi_{(n-1)/2}) \geqslant \frac{1}{2}(n-1)$. Then G has a Hamiltonian circuit.*

(An alternative proof of Theorem 2 is given in (**8**), and Bondy (**2**) has shown that a slight further relaxation of the hypothesis concerning the valencies is possible.)

The purpose of the present paper is to prove the following theorem, which, for large graphs, sharpens Theorem 1 in a new direction. In this theorem and subsequently, $[x]$ denotes the greatest integer less than or equal to x, and ε_t is defined to be 1 for any odd integer t and 0 for any even integer t.

THEOREM 3. *If $v(\xi) \geqslant \frac{1}{2}n$ for every $\xi \in V(G)$, then there exists a set of $[5(n+\varepsilon_n+10)/224]$ edge-disjoint Hamiltonian circuits in G.*

This theorem is perhaps somewhat striking in view of the fact that a graph G can fail to have a Hamiltonian circuit at all if it satisfies the apparently only slightly weaker condition that $v(\xi) \geqslant [\frac{1}{2}(n-1)]$ for every $\xi \in V(G)$: this is illustrated for $n = 11$ by the two graphs in Figure 1. Perhaps the 'explanation' lies in Theorem 2, which indicates that, if a graph G has no vertex of valency less than $[\frac{1}{2}(n-1)]$ and no Hamiltonian circuit, it must have a considerable number of vertices of valency $[\frac{1}{2}(n-1)]$ and must in that sense be relatively

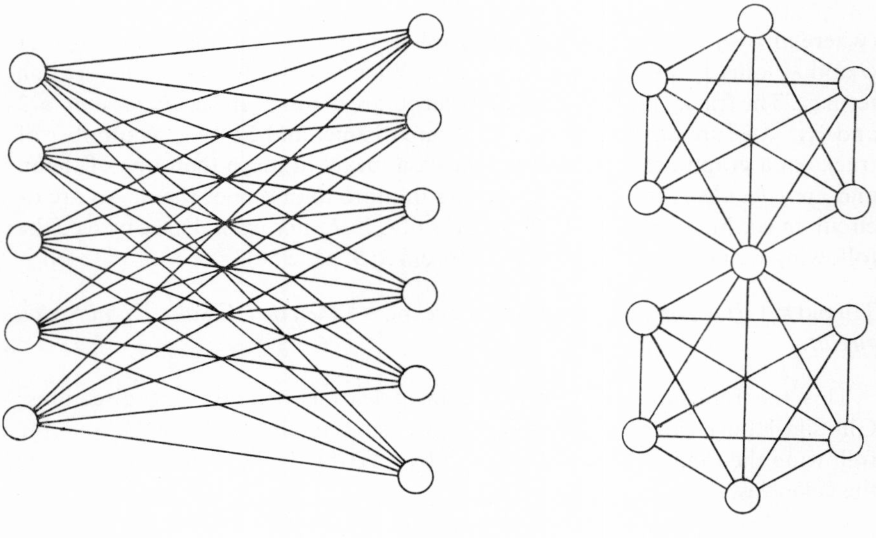

FIGURE 1

far from satisfying the hypothesis of Theorem 3. In fact, the key to our proof of Theorem 3 will be a lemma (Lemma 4) which, roughly speaking, indicates that a graph G which has no Hamiltonian circuit but in which no valencies are too far below $\frac{1}{2}n$ must be somewhat like one of the two graphs in Figure 1 (with the left hand graph possibly augmented by the addition of some edges joining vertices on the left hand side of the graph, which clearly cannot introduce a Hamiltonian circuit). This lemma ensures that, if removal of the edges of less than $[5(n + \varepsilon_n + 10)/224]$ edge-disjoint Hamiltonian circuits from a graph G satisfying the hypothesis of Theorem 3 leaves no Hamiltonian circuit remaining, then we know enough about the structure of the remaining graph to infer that a larger number of edge-disjoint Hamiltonian circuits could have been found in G by choosing them better. I am indebted to Dr. J. A. Bondy for a suggestion that Theorem 4 of (**4**) can be used in the proof of Lemma 4: this suggestion enabled me to establish Lemma 4 with a weaker hypothesis concerning valencies than I had previously found necessary.

To avoid making a complicated discussion even more so, I have not striven for the utmost possible sharpness in Theorem 3, and have tried to keep numerical work in this paper fairly simple. Hence a mere adjustment of the numbers throughout certain parts of the proof, without any change in the structure of the argument, would achieve a very slight improvement in the expression $[5(n + \varepsilon_n + 10)/224]$, although I think it unlikely that this type of adjustment alone would improve it even as far as $[n/44]$. On the other hand, given sufficient time and patience, I suspect that it would be tolerably easy to improve the actual structure of the argument so as to obtain a substantially better expression than, say, $[n/44]$. It might, however, be much harder to improve $[5(n + \varepsilon_n + 10)/224]$ to the extent of achieving anything near a best possible result: I do not even know whether there exists a graph G satisfying the hypothesis of Theorem 3 in which there are not $[\frac{1}{4}(n + 1)]$ edge-disjoint Hamiltonian circuits.†

For additional background to this work, the reader may be referred to (**7**).

2. Graphs G with valencies greater than $\frac{1}{3}(n + 1)$ and no Hamiltonian Circuit

The reader is reminded that G always denotes a graph and n always denotes the number of vertices of G. We shall say that G is a *Dirac graph* if $v(\xi) \geqslant \frac{1}{2}n$ for every $\xi \in V(G)$. Since valencies are integers, G is a Dirac graph if and only if $v(\xi) \geqslant \frac{1}{2}(n + \varepsilon_n)$ for every $\xi \in V(G)$. Two vertices of G are *adjacent* if they are joined by an edge. If $\xi \in V(G)$, the vertices adjacent to ξ will be called

† *Note.* A very simple construction for such a graph has now been found by Mr. L. Babai: details will appear in a paper by the present author in the Proceedings of the Combinatorics Conference held at Balatonfüred, Hungary in August 1969.

neighbours of ξ, and the set of neighbours of ξ will be denoted by $N(\xi)$. If $X \subseteq V(G)$ and no two elements of X are adjacent, we shall say that X is an *independent* set of vertices and that the elements of X are *independent* vertices. A *$\xi\eta$-edge* is an edge which joins the vertices ξ and η. A *subgraph* of G is a graph H such that $V(H) \subseteq V(G)$, $E(H) \subseteq E(G)$ and each edge of H joins in H the same vertices as it joins in G. If $L \subseteq E(G)$, $G - L$ will denote the subgraph H of G such that $V(H) = V(G)$ and $E(H) = E(G)\backslash L$. The *union* $H_1 \cup \ldots \cup H_r$ of the subgraphs $H_1, \ldots, H_r$ of G is the subgraph S of G such that $V(S) = V(H_1) \cup \ldots \cup V(H_r)$, $E(S) = E(H_1) \cup \ldots \cup E(H_r)$. G is *empty* if $V(G) = \varnothing$. Any specified subgraphs of G are *disjoint* if no two of them have a common vertex, and *edge-disjoint* if no two of them have a common edge. G is *disconnected* if it is the union of two non-empty disjoint subgraphs. G is *separable* if it has two subgraphs H, K such that

$$|V(H)| \geqslant 2, \quad |V(K)| \geqslant 2, \quad |V(H) \cap V(K)| = 1 \text{ and } H \cup K = G.$$

Note that a disconnected graph with three or more vertices is separable in the sense of this definition. G is *connected* if it is not disconnected. Any graph G determines a unique set of non-empty disjoint connected subgraphs of G whose union is G: these subgraphs are the *components* of G. The first and last terms of a finite sequence s will be denoted by $\mathbf{F}(s)$, $\mathbf{L}(s)$ respectively. If s denotes a track $\xi_0, \lambda_1, \xi_1, \lambda_2, \ldots, \lambda_m, \xi_m$ in G then $V(s)$ will denote the subset $\{\xi_0, \xi_1, \ldots, \xi_m\}$ of $V(G)$ and $E(s)$ will denote the subset $\{\lambda_1, \lambda_2, \ldots, \lambda_m\}$ of $E(G)$. Elements of $V(s)$ and $E(s)$ will be called *vertices* and *edges* respectively of s, and the subgraph $\|s\|$ of G *derived* from s is the subgraph H of G such that $V(H) = V(s)$, $E(H) = E(s)$. A subgraph H of G will be called an *arcoid* if $H = \|s\|$ for some arc s in G, and will be called a *circuitoid* if $H = \|s\|$ for some circuit s in G. If s denotes the track (1) then the *length* $l(s)$ of s is m. A *$\xi\eta$-track* (*$\xi\eta$-arc*) is a track (arc) s such that $\mathbf{F}(s) = \xi$, $\mathbf{L}(s) = \eta$. If ξ, η are vertices of the same component of G then $\rho(\xi, \eta)$, the *distance* from ξ to η, is defined to be the minimum of the lengths of all $\xi\eta$-tracks in G: since it is easily seen that a $\xi\eta$-track of length $\rho(\xi, \eta)$ must be an arc, $\rho(\xi, \eta)$ may equivalently be defined as the minimum of the lengths of all $\xi\eta$-arcs in G. A circuit c in G will be said to be *extreme* if $l(c) \geqslant l(d)$ for every circuit d in G. Let c be a circuit in G: then an arc a in G will be said to be *c-extreme* if a, c are disjoint and $l(a) \geqslant l(b)$ for every arc b in G such that b, c are disjoint. Let c be a circuit in G and a be an arc in G such that a, c are disjoint. Then a is *strongly joined* to c if there exist distinct elements ξ, η of $V(c)$ such that ξ is adjacent to $\mathbf{F}(a)$ and η is adjacent to $\mathbf{L}(a)$; and a is *weakly joined* to c if it is not strongly joined to c, i.e., if either $N(\mathbf{F}(a)) \cap V(c) = \varnothing$ or $N(\mathbf{L}(a)) \cap V(c) = \varnothing$ or

$$N(\mathbf{F}(a)) \cap V(c) = N(\mathbf{L}(a)) \cap V(c) = \{\omega\} \text{ for some vertex } \omega.$$

When the context does not clearly identify the graph in which a graph-theoretic word (such as 'valency') or symbol (such as v) is defined, this will be indicated by attaching the letter denoting the graph to the word by means of a hyphen or to the symbol as a suffix: for example, a common vertex ξ of two graphs H, K will have an 'H-valency' $v_H(\xi)$ and a 'K-valency' $v_K(\xi)$. When, however, two or more graphs are under discussion and one of them is denoted by the letter G, all graph-theoretic words and symbols will be understood to relate to G unless the contrary is indicated: for example, if ξ is a common vertex of two graphs G and H then the expressions 'valency of ξ' and '$v(\xi)$' will automatically mean $v_G(\xi)$ and not $v_H(\xi)$.

If C is a circuitoid and r is a positive integer, a (C, r)-*scheme* is an ordered pair (X, Y) of subsets of $V(C)$ such that X is C-independent and Y is C-independent and $\rho_C(\xi, \eta) \geqslant r$ for every pair ξ, η of vertices such that $\xi \in X$, $\eta \in Y$ and $\xi \neq \eta$. A (C, r)-scheme (X, Y) is *non-trivial* if there exists at least one pair of vertices ξ, η such that $\xi \in X, \eta \in Y$ and $\xi \neq \eta$.

LEMMA 1. *Let C be a circuitoid with k vertices, r be an integer greater than or equal to 2 and (X, Y) be a non-trivial (C, r)-scheme. Then $r \leqslant \frac{1}{2}k$ and*

$$|X| + |Y| \leqslant \max\left(\tfrac{1}{2}k - r + 3, 2k/r\right). \tag{2}$$

Proof. Since (X, Y) is non-trivial, we can select $\xi \in X$, $\eta \in Y$ so that $\xi \neq \eta$. Then $r \leqslant \rho_C(\xi, \eta)$ since (X, Y) is a (C, r)-scheme and $\rho_C(\xi, \eta) \leqslant \frac{1}{2}k$ since C is a circuitoid with k vertices: therefore $r \leqslant \frac{1}{2}k$.

Since C is a circuitoid, we can select a cyclic permutation s of $V(C)$ such that each vertex ξ of C is C-adjacent to ξs and ξs^{-1}. For each $\xi \in X \cup Y$, let $f(\xi)$ be the smallest positive integer i for which $\xi s^i \in X \cup Y$. Then

$$k = \Sigma_{\xi \in X \cup Y} f(\xi). \tag{3}$$

Let t be the permutation of $X \cup Y$ such that $\xi t = \xi s^{f(\xi)}$ for every $\xi \in X \cup Y$. Let $g(\xi)$ denote 1 if $\xi \in (X \backslash Y) \cup (Y \backslash X)$ and 2 if $\xi \in X \cap Y$. Then

$$|X| + |Y| = \Sigma_{\xi \in X \cup Y}\, g(\xi). \tag{4}$$

If $X = Y$ then $f(\xi) \geqslant r$ for every $\xi \in X$ because (X, Y) is a non-trivial (C, r)-scheme and hence by (3) $k \geqslant r|X| = \frac{1}{2}r(|X| + |Y|)$, which implies (2). In any case, since (X, Y) is a non-trivial (C, r)-scheme and $r \geqslant 2$, we have $f(\xi) \geqslant r$ for $\xi \in X \cap Y$ and $f(\xi) \geqslant 2$ for $\xi \in (X \backslash Y) \cup (Y \backslash X)$, which if $r \leqslant 4$ implies that $f(\xi) \geqslant \frac{1}{2}rg(\xi)$ for all $\xi \in X \cup Y$, which by (3) and (4) implies that $k \geqslant \frac{1}{2}r(|X| + |Y|)$, which again yields (2). We may therefore now assume that $X \neq Y$ and $r \geqslant 5$. Then $X \backslash Y$ or $Y \backslash X$ is non-empty: suppose without loss of generality that $X \backslash Y$ is non-empty and select $\alpha \in X \backslash Y$. Let p be the smallest positive integer such that $\alpha t^p \in Y$ and q be the smallest positive integer such that $\alpha t^{-q} \in Y$. Then αt^{-q+1} and αt^{p-1} belong to $X \backslash Y$ so that since (X, Y) is a (C, r)-scheme we have

$$f(\alpha t^{-q}) \geqslant r \geqslant 2g(\alpha t^{-q}) + r - 4, \quad f(\alpha t^{p-1}) \geqslant r = 2g(\alpha t^{p-1}) + r - 2$$

and for all $\xi \in (X \cup Y) \backslash \{\alpha t^{-q}, \alpha t^{p-1}\}$ we have either $\xi \in X \cap Y$ and $f(\xi) \geqslant r \geqslant 5 > 2g(\xi)$ or $\xi \in (X \backslash Y) \cup (Y \backslash X)$ and $f(\xi) \geqslant 2 = 2g(\xi)$, so that from (3) and (4) we obtain $k \geqslant 2(|X| + |Y|) + 2r - 6$, which implies (2).

LEMMA 2. *Let c be an extreme circuit in G and a be an arc in G which is disjoint from c and strongly joined to c. Let $|V(c)| = k$, $|V(a)| = q$, $\mathbf{F}(a) = \theta$, $\mathbf{L}(a) = \phi$. Then $q \leqslant \frac{1}{2}k - 1$. Furthermore, if a is c-extreme, then*

$$v(\theta) + v(\phi) \leqslant \max\left(\tfrac{1}{2}k + q,\ 2k(q+1)^{-1} + 2q - 2\right).$$

Proof. Let $X = N(\theta) \cap V(c)$, $Y = N(\phi) \cap V(c)$. If two elements of X were adjacent in $\|c\|$, then $V(c) \cup \{\theta\}$ would be the set of vertices of a circuit, which is impossible since c is extreme. Therefore X is $\|c\|$-independent. Similarly Y is $\|c\|$-independent. If $\xi \in X, \eta \in Y$ and $\xi \neq \eta$ then there is a $\xi\eta$-arc b in c with $k - \rho_{\|c\|}(\xi, \eta) + 1$ vertices and $V(a) \cup V(b)$ is the set of vertices of a circuit in G so that, since c is extreme,

$$k = |V(c)| \geqslant |V(a) \cup V(b)| = q + k - \rho_{\|c\|}(\xi, \eta) + 1,$$

i.e., $\rho_{\|c\|}(\xi, \eta) \geqslant q + 1$. These remarks show that (X, Y) is a $(\|c\|, q+1)$-scheme, which is non-trivial since a is strongly joined to c. Therefore, by Lemma 1, $q + 1 \leqslant \frac{1}{2}k$ (which proves the first part of Lemma 2) and

$$|X| + |Y| \leqslant \max\left(\tfrac{1}{2}k - q + 2,\ 2k/(q+1)\right). \tag{5}$$

Furthermore, since a is c-extreme, $N(\theta)$ can only include vertices which belong to $V(c)$ or to $V(a) \backslash \{\theta\}$ and hence $v(\theta) \leqslant |X| + q - 1$. Similarly $v(\phi) \leqslant |Y| + q - 1$. From these inequalities and (5) the second part of Lemma 2 follows.

LEMMA 3. *Suppose that $v(\xi) > \frac{1}{3}(n+1)$ for every $\xi \in V(G)$. Let c be an extreme circuit in G and a be a c-extreme arc in G. Then $|V(a)| = 1$ or a is weakly joined to c.*

Proof. Let $|V(c)| = k$, $|V(a)| = q$, $\mathbf{F}(a) = \theta$, $\mathbf{L}(a) = \phi$. Then

$$q + k \leqslant n \tag{6}$$

since a, c are disjoint. Suppose that a is strongly joined to c. Then by Lemma 2,

$$q \leqslant \tfrac{1}{2}k - 1, \tag{7}$$

$$\max\left(\tfrac{1}{2}k + q,\ \frac{2k}{q+1} + 2q - 2\right) \geqslant v(\theta) + v(\phi) > \tfrac{2}{3}(n+1). \tag{8}$$

Since $\frac{1}{2}k + q \leqslant \frac{1}{3}(2n - 1)$ by (6) and (7), it follows from (8) and (6) that

$$\tfrac{2}{3}(n+1) < \frac{2k}{q+1} + 2q - 2 \leqslant \frac{2(n-q)}{q+1} + 2q - 2,$$

i.e., $(q - 2)\big(q - \frac{1}{3}(n - 2)\big) > 0$. But $q \leqslant \frac{1}{3}(n - 2)$ by (6) and (7). Therefore $q < 2$. We have thus shown that, if a is strongly joined to c, then $|V(a)| < 2$, which proves Lemma 3.

The following result is Theorem 4 of (**4**) (and some further details concerning a lemma used in its proof may be found in (**1**, pp. 198–199)).

THEOREM 4. *If k is an integer greater than or equal to 2 and $v(\xi) \geqslant k$ for every $\xi \in V(G)$ and $n \geqslant 2k$, then either G is separable or there is a circuit of length $\geqslant 2k$ in G.*

LEMMA 4. *Suppose that $n \geqslant 3$ and k is an integer greater than or equal to $\frac{1}{3}(n + 2)$ and $v(\xi) \geqslant k$ for every $\xi \in V(G)$. Then G either has a Hamiltonian circuit or is separable or has $k + 1$ independent vertices.*

Proof. If G has a Hamiltonian circuit there is nothing further to prove. We may therefore suppose that G has no Hamiltonian circuit. Then $n > 2k$ by Theorem 1. Let c be an extreme circuit in G. Since c is not Hamiltonian, we can select a c-extreme arc a in G. Suppose first that $|V(a)| \geqslant 2$. Then, by Lemma 3, a is weakly joined to c. Therefore either

$$|N(\mathbf{F}(a)) \cap V(c)| \leqslant 1 \quad \text{or} \quad |N(\mathbf{L}(a)) \cap V(c)| \leqslant 1:$$

without loss of generality suppose that the first of these inequalities is true. Since a is c-extreme, $N(\mathbf{F}(a)) \subseteq V(a) \cup V(c)$, and furthermore $|N(\mathbf{F}(a))| \geqslant k$: hence $V(a)$ includes at least $k - 1$ elements of $N(\mathbf{F}(a))$ as well as $\mathbf{F}(a)$ and consequently $|V(a)| \geqslant k$. Therefore $|V(c)| \leqslant n - k < 2k$, and since we have seen that $n > 2k$ it follows by Theorem 4 that G is separable. Now suppose that $|V(a)| = 1$. Let $V(a) = \{\omega\}$. Let s be a cyclic permutation of $V(c)$ such that each element ξ of $V(c)$ is adjacent in $||c||$ to ξs and ξs^{-1}. We observe that $N(\omega) \subseteq V(c)$ since a is c-extreme and that $|N(\omega)| \geqslant k$: hence it will suffice to prove that $N(\omega)\, s \cup \{\omega\}$ is independent. But if ω were adjacent to ξs for some $\xi \in N(\omega)$ then the vertices and edges of c other than the $\xi(\xi s)$-edge together with ω and the edges joining ω to ξ, ξs would yield a circuit longer than c; and if ξs were adjacent to ηs for some $\xi, \eta \in N(\omega)$ then the vertices and edges of c other than the edges joining ξ, η to ξs, ηs respectively together with ω, the $\omega\xi$-edge, the $\omega\eta$-edge and the $(\xi s)\,(\eta s)$-edge would yield a circuit longer than c. Hence $N(\omega)\, s \cup \{\omega\}$ is independent and Lemma 4 is proved.

LEMMA 5. *Suppose that G is a Dirac graph and h is a positive integer less than or equal to $(n + 3\varepsilon_n - 4)/12$ and $c_1, \ldots, c_h$ are edge-disjoint Hamiltonian circuits of G and $H = G - (E(c_1) \cup \ldots \cup E(c_h))$ and H has no Hamiltonian circuit. Then either H is separable or there exist $\frac{1}{2}(n + \varepsilon_n) - 2h + 1$ H-independent vertices.*

Proof. Since $1 \leqslant h \leqslant (n + 3\varepsilon_n - 4)/12$, it follows that $n \geqslant 13$. Since G is a Dirac graph, it follows that $v(\xi) \geqslant \frac{1}{2}(n + \varepsilon_n)$ and hence $v_H(\xi) \geqslant \frac{1}{2}(n + \varepsilon_n) - 2h$ for every $\xi \in V(G) = V(H)$. Furthermore, $\frac{1}{2}(n + \varepsilon_n) - 2h \geqslant \frac{1}{3}(n + 2)$ since $h \leqslant (n + 3\varepsilon_n - 4)/12$. The required conclusion now follows from Lemma 4.

Our procedure for completing the proof of Theorem 3 will now involve showing that if G is a Dirac graph and h is a positive integer less than $[5(n + \varepsilon_n + 10)/224]$ and G has h edge-disjoint Hamiltonian circuits $c_1, \ldots, c_h$ such that $H = G - (E(c_1) \cup \ldots \cup E(c_h))$ has no Hamiltonian circuit, then G has $h + 1$ edge-disjoint Hamiltonian circuits: this will show that no number less than $[5(n + \varepsilon_n + 10)/224]$ can be the *maximum* number of edge-disjoint Hamiltonian circuits in G. The proof that G has $h + 1$ edge-disjoint Hamiltonian circuits will use the fact that, by Lemma 5, H is separable or has $\frac{1}{2}(n + \varepsilon_n) - 2h + 1$ independent vertices.

3. The case in which H is separable

G is *complete* if every two distinct vertices of G are adjacent. If $\xi \in V(G)$, $G - \xi$ denotes the subgraph obtained from G by removing ξ and its incident edges. Let X, Y denote subsets of $V(G)$. Then $\overline{X}$ or (if notationally more convenient) $\mathbf{C}X$ denotes $V(G) \backslash X$, $X \nabla Y$ denotes the set of all edges of G which join elements of X to elements of Y, and $X\delta$ denotes $X \nabla \overline{X}$. An *X-pair* in G is a subset P of $X\delta$ such that $|P| = 2$ and no vertex is incident with both elements of P. Two or more subsets of $E(G)$ will be said to be *edge-disjoint* if no edge belongs to more than one of them: although the word 'disjoint', in its set-theoretic sense, could be used for this purpose, 'edge-disjoint' seems clearer.

LEMMA 6. *If G is a Dirac graph and $X \subseteq V(G)$ and $2 \leqslant |X| \leqslant n - 2$, then there exist $[\frac{1}{4}(n + 1)]$ edge-disjoint X-pairs in G.*

Proof. Let $P_1, \ldots, P_t$ be edge-disjoint X-pairs in G such that t is as large as possible, and let $P = P_1 \cup \ldots \cup P_t$. Then $X\delta \backslash P$ contains no X-pair, from which it is easily inferred that some vertex ξ is incident with all elements of $X\delta \backslash P$. Therefore all elements of $X\delta$ not incident with ξ belong to P. Therefore $Y \nabla Z \subseteq P$, where Y, Z are $X \backslash \{\xi\}$, $\overline{X} \backslash \{\xi\}$ in some order and $|Y| \leqslant |Z|$. Since G is a Dirac graph, each element of Y is adjacent to at least $\frac{1}{2}(n + \varepsilon_n) - |Y|$ elements of Z, from which it follows that $|Y \nabla Z| \geqslant |Y| \left(\frac{1}{2}(n + \varepsilon_n) - |Y|\right)$, which is greater than or equal to $\frac{1}{2}(n + \varepsilon_n) - 1$ since $1 \leqslant |Y| \leqslant \frac{1}{2}(n + \varepsilon_n) - 1$. Hence $t = \frac{1}{2}|P| \geqslant \frac{1}{2}|Y \nabla Z| \geqslant \frac{1}{2}(\frac{1}{2}(n + \varepsilon_n) - 1)$, which, since t is an integer, implies that $t \geqslant [\frac{1}{4}(n + 1)]$.

LEMMA 7. *Let ω, α, β be vertices of G such that $\alpha \neq \beta$. If $v(\omega) \geqslant 3$ and $v(\xi) \geqslant \frac{1}{2}(n + 1)$ for every $\xi \in V(G)\backslash\{\omega\}$ then G has a Hamiltonian $\alpha\beta$-arc.*

Proof. Form a new graph by adjoining to G a new vertex γ and a $\gamma\alpha$-edge and a $\gamma\beta$-edge. This graph has a Hamiltonian circuit by Theorem 2, and so G has a Hamiltonian $\alpha\beta$-arc.

COROLLARY 7A. *Let ω, $\alpha_1, \ldots, \alpha_t$, $\beta_1, \ldots, \beta_t$ be vertices of G such that $\alpha_i \neq \beta_i$ $(i = 1, \ldots, t)$. Suppose that $v(\omega) \geqslant 2t + 1$ and $v(\xi) \geqslant \frac{1}{2}(n - 3) + 2t$ for every $\xi \in V(G)\backslash\{\omega\}$. Then G has edge-disjoint Hamiltonian arcs $a_1, \ldots, a_t$ such that $\mathbf{F}(a_i) = \alpha_i$ and $\mathbf{L}(a_i) = \beta_i$ for $i = 1, \ldots, t$.*

Proof. If we have found edge-disjoint Hamiltonian arcs $a_1, \ldots, a_s$ of G such that $\mathbf{F}(a_i) = \alpha_i$ and $\mathbf{L}(a_i) = \beta_i$ for $i = 1, \ldots, s$ and if $s \leqslant t - 1$, then by Lemma 7 there exists a Hamiltonian $\alpha_{s+1}\beta_{s+1}$-arc of $G - (E(a_1) \cup \ldots \cup E(a_s))$.

COROLLARY 7B. *Let $\alpha_1, \ldots, \alpha_t$, $\beta_1, \ldots, \beta_t$ be vertices of G such that $\alpha_i \neq \beta_i$ $(i = 1, \ldots, t)$, and suppose that $v(\xi) \geqslant \frac{1}{2}(n - 3) + 2t$ for every $\xi \in V(G)$. Then G has edge-disjoint Hamiltonian arcs $a_1, \ldots, a_t$ such that $\mathbf{F}(a_i) = \alpha_i$ and $\mathbf{L}(a_i) = \beta_i$ for $i = 1, \ldots, t$.*

Proof. Taking any vertex of G as ω, Corollary 7A implies the required conclusion if $n \geqslant 5$. If $n \leqslant 4$ the hypothesis concerning valencies can only be satisfied when either $t = 1$, $3 \leqslant n \leqslant 4$ and G is complete or $t = 0$, and the required proof is trivial in these cases.

LEMMA 8. *Suppose that G is a Dirac graph and $c_1, \ldots, c_h$ are edge-disjoint Hamiltonian circuits of G and $G - (E(c_1) \cup \ldots \cup E(c_h))$ is separable and*

$$1 \leqslant h \leqslant (n - 4)/20. \tag{9}$$

Then G has $h + 1$ edge-disjoint Hamiltonian circuits.

Proof. Let $H = G - (E(c_1) \cup \ldots \cup E(c_h))$. Since H is separable we can write $H = M \cup N$ where M, N are subgraphs of H such that $|V(M)| \geqslant 2$, $|V(N)| \geqslant 2$ and $V(M) \cap V(N) = \{\omega\}$ for some vertex ω, and we can assign the notation so that $v_M(\omega) \geqslant v_N(\omega)$. Then

$$v_M(\omega) \geqslant \tfrac{1}{2}v_H(\omega) = \tfrac{1}{2}(v(\omega) - 2h) \geqslant \tfrac{1}{4}n - h. \tag{10}$$

For any $\xi \in V(M)\backslash\{\omega\}$,

$$v_M(\xi) = v_H(\xi) = v(\xi) - 2h \geqslant \tfrac{1}{2}n - 2h, \tag{11}$$

which implies that $|V(M)| \geqslant \frac{1}{2}n - 2h + 1$. Similarly $|V(N)| \geqslant \frac{1}{2}n - 2h + 1$, and since $|V(M)| + |V(N)| = n + 1$ we conclude that

$$\tfrac{1}{2}n - 2h + 1 \leqslant |V(Q)| \leqslant \tfrac{1}{2}n + 2h \text{ for } Q = M, N. \tag{12}$$

By (9), $n \geqslant 24$, and hence it is easy to see from (9) and (12) that $h + 1 < [\frac{1}{4}(n + 1)]$ and $2 < |V(M)| < n - 2$. Therefore, by Lemma 6, we can select $h + 1$ edge-disjoint $V(M)$-pairs $\{\lambda_1, \mu_1\}, \{\lambda_2, \mu_2\}, \ldots, \{\lambda_{h+1}, \mu_{h+1}\}$ in G. Let λ_i join $\alpha_i \in V(M)$ to $\alpha_1' \in \mathbf{C}V(M)$ and μ_i join $\beta_i \in V(M)$ to $\beta_i' \in \mathbf{C}V(M)$. By (10) and (9), $v_M(\omega) \geqslant 4h + 1 \geqslant 2h + 3$, and by (9), (11) and (12), $v_M(\xi) > \frac{1}{2}(|V(M)| + 1) + 2h$ for every $\xi \in V(M)\backslash\{\omega\}$: therefore, by Corollary 7A, M has edge-disjoint Hamiltonian arcs $a_1, \ldots, a_{h+1}$ such that $\mathbf{F}(a_i) = \alpha_i$, $\mathbf{L}(a_i) = \beta_i$ for $i = 1, \ldots, h + 1$. For every $\xi \in V(N - \omega)$ we have $v_N(\xi) \geqslant \frac{1}{2}n - 2h$ by an argument similar to (11) and therefore $v_{N-\omega}(\xi) \geqslant \frac{1}{2}n - 2h - 1$ and therefore, by (9) and (12), $v_{N-\omega}(\xi) \geqslant \frac{1}{2}(|V(N - \omega)| + 1) + 2h$. Therefore, by Corollary 7B, $N - \omega$ has edge-disjoint Hamiltonian arcs $b_1, b_2, \ldots, b_{h+1}$ such that $\mathbf{F}(b_i) = \alpha_i'$, $\mathbf{L}(b_i) = \beta_i'$ for $i = 1, \ldots, h + 1$. If d_i is a Hamiltonian circuit of G such that $E(d_i) = E(a_i) \cup E(b_i) \cup \{\lambda_i, \mu_i\}$ then $d_1, \ldots, d_{h+1}$ are edge-disjoint and Lemma 8 is proved.

4. The case in which H has $\frac{1}{2}(n + \varepsilon_n) - 2h + 1$ independent vertices

An *ordering* of a finite set A is a sequence $a_1, \ldots, a_{|A|}$ such that $A = \{a_1, \ldots, a_{|A|}\}$.

Let X, Y denote subsets of $V(G)$. Then X^*, $X\natural$ denote the subgraphs of G defined by $V(X^*) = V(X\natural) = X$, $E(X^*) = X \triangledown X$, $E(X\natural) = \emptyset$. For any vertex ξ, $v(\xi, X)$ denotes $|\{\xi\} \triangledown X|$; and $\Lambda_r(X)$ denotes $\{\xi \in X : v(\xi, \overline{X}) \leqslant r\}$. For any integers b, c, d with $d \geqslant 0$, we shall say that X is $[b, c, d; Y]$-*attached* if for $i = 0, 1, \ldots, d$ the number of elements ξ of X such that $v(\xi, Y) \leqslant b + i$ is less than or equal to $c + i$; and we shall say that X is $[b, c, d]$-*attached* if it is $[b, c, d; \overline{X}]$-attached, i.e., if $|\Lambda_{b+i}(X)| \leqslant c + i$ for $i = 0, 1, \ldots, d$. We shall call X r-*allowable* if there exists an ordering $\xi_1, \ldots, \xi_{|X|}$ of X such that $v(\xi_i) \geqslant 2i + |X| + r - 1$ for $i = 1, \ldots, |X|$. A *spanning subgraph* of G is a subgraph S of G such that $V(S) = V(G)$. If S is a spanning subgraph of G, we call G a *spanned supergraph* of S. The number of components of G is denoted by $c(G)$. An *arc-forest* is a graph each of whose components is an arcoid with at least one edge. (The empty graph is vacuously an arc-forest since it has no components.) For any arc-forest F, $I(F)$ denotes $\{\xi \in V(F) : v_F(\xi) = 2\}$. An *arc-subforest* of G is a subgraph of G which is an arc-forest. If z is a non-negative integer, a z-*arc-subforest* of G is an arc-subforest F of G such that $|E(F)| = z$. If

$X \subseteq V(G)$, an *X-arc-subforest* of G is an arc-subforest F of G such that $I(F) = X$ and each component of F has exactly two edges. An *extension* of an arc-forest F is an arc-forest F' such that F is a subgraph of F' and no two components of F are contained in the same component of F'.

Throughout Sections 4 and 5, ε (without suffix) denotes $\varepsilon_n = \varepsilon_{|V(G)|}$.

Our next lemma is a generalization of the theorem of (**6**). Both of these results are somewhat similar in kind to Theorem 2, and our proof of Lemma 9 is based on the argument of (**6**) which was in turn based on the method used by Pósa (**10**) for proving Theorem 2. The alternative method of proving Theorem 2 described in (**8**) does not, so far as I can see, yield alternative proofs of Lemma 9 or the theorem of (**6**).

LEMMA 9. *Let X be a subset of $V(G)$ and k be a positive integer and z, p, q be non-negative integers and F be a z-arc-subforest of X^*. Suppose that $|X| = k+z$, $|\overline{X}| = k$, $p+q \geqslant k-3$, $X \backslash I(F)$ is $[1, 0, p; \overline{X}]$-attached and $\overline{X}$ is $[z+1, 0, q]$-attached. Then G has a Hamiltonian circuit c such that $E(F) \subseteq E(c) \subseteq X\delta \cup E(F)$.*

Proof. Let $\overline{X} = \{\eta_1, \ldots, \eta_k\}$. Let a Hamiltonian arc or circuit s of a spanned supergraph K of G be called *admissible* if $E(F) \subseteq E(s) \subseteq X\delta_K \cup E(F)$. Suppose that G has no admissible Hamiltonian circuit. Then we can select a spanned supergraph Γ of G such that Γ has no admissible Hamiltonian circuit and $|E(\Gamma)|$ is as large as possible subject to this requirement. Since $|V(F)| = z + c(F)$ it follows that $|X \backslash V(F)| = k - c(F)$ and so there are disjoint arcs $a_1, \ldots, a_k$ in X^* such that $\|a_1\|, \ldots, \|a_k\|$ are the components of $(X \backslash V(F))\natural \cup F$. If all elements of X were Γ-adjacent to all elements of $\overline{X}$ then Γ would have an admissible Hamiltonian circuit whose edges were the edges in $a_1, \ldots, a_k$ together with the edges joining η_i to $\mathbf{L}(a_i)$ and $\mathbf{F}(a_{i+1})$ ($i = 1, \ldots, k$), $\mathbf{F}(a_{k+1})$ being interpreted as $\mathbf{F}(a_1)$. This would contradict the definition of Γ. Therefore we can select $\theta \in X$, $\phi \in \overline{X}$ so that θ, ϕ are not adjacent in Γ and subject to this requirement $v_\Gamma(\theta, \overline{X}) + v_\Gamma(\phi, X)$ is as large as possible. The maximality of $|E(\Gamma)|$ ensures that the addition of a $\theta\phi$-edge to Γ would introduce an admissible Hamiltonian circuit, which implies that Γ has an admissible Hamiltonian $\theta\phi$-arc b, say. Let μ_i be the edge immediately preceding η_i in b and let ξ_i be the vertex joined to η_i by μ_i: then $\xi_i \in X$ since b is admissible. If θ, ϕ were joined to η_i, ξ_i respectively by edges ν, ρ respectively of Γ then $(E(b)\backslash\{\mu_i\}) \cup \{\nu, \rho\}$ would be the set of edges of an admissible Hamiltonian circuit of Γ. Therefore there is no $i \in \{1, \ldots, k\}$ for which θ is Γ-adjacent to η_i and ϕ is Γ-adjacent to ξ_i, and hence

$$v_\Gamma(\theta, \overline{X}) + v_\Gamma(\phi, X) \leqslant |\overline{X}| + |X| - k = k + z \leqslant p + q + z + 3. \qquad (13)$$

We have just seen that if θ is Γ-adjacent to η_i then ξ_i is not Γ-adjacent to ϕ, which by the definition of θ and ϕ implies that $v_\Gamma(\theta, \overline{X}) \geqslant v_\Gamma(\xi_i, \overline{X})$. Therefore there are at least $v_\Gamma(\theta, \overline{X})$ values of i for which $v_\Gamma(\theta, \overline{X}) \geqslant v_\Gamma(\xi_i, \overline{X}) \geqslant v(\xi_i, \overline{X})$. Furthermore $\xi_1, \ldots, \xi_k \in X\backslash I(F)$ since b is admissible. From these remarks and the hypothesis that $X\backslash I(F)$ is $[1, 0, p; \overline{X}]$-attached (in G) we conclude that $v_\Gamma(\theta, \overline{X}) - 1 \notin \{0, 1, \ldots, p\}$. But the admissibility of b implies that $\theta \in X\backslash I(F)$, which, since $X\backslash I(F)$ is $[1, 0, p; \overline{X}]$-attached, implies that $2 \leqslant v(\theta, \overline{X}) \leqslant v_\Gamma(\theta, \overline{X})$. Hence

$$v_\Gamma(\theta, \overline{X}) \geqslant p + 2. \tag{14}$$

Since $|X| = k + z$, it follows that ϕ cannot be Γ-adjacent to less than $v_\Gamma(\phi, X) - z$ of the elements $\xi_1, \ldots, \xi_k$ of X. Moreover, if ϕ is Γ-adjacent to ξ_i, then the remarks preceding (13) show that θ is not Γ-adjacent to η_i, so that $v_\Gamma(\phi, X) \geqslant v_\Gamma(\eta_i, X)$ by the definition of θ and ϕ. Therefore there are at least $v_\Gamma(\phi, X) - z$ values of i for which $v_\Gamma(\phi, X) \geqslant v_\Gamma(\eta_i, X) \geqslant v(\eta_i, X)$. From this and the fact that $\overline{X}$ is $[z + 1, 0, q]$-attached (in G) it follows that $v_\Gamma(\phi, X) - z - 1 \notin \{0, 1, \ldots, q\}$. But $v_\Gamma(\phi, X) \geqslant v(\phi, X) \geqslant z + 2$ since $\phi \in \overline{X}$ and $\overline{X}$ is $[z + 1, 0, q]$-attached. Hence $v_\Gamma(\phi, X) \geqslant z + q + 2$. Since this is incompatible with (13) and (14), the supposition that G has no admissible Hamiltonian circuit leads to a contradiction, and Lemma 9 is proved.

COROLLARY 9A. *Let X be a subset of $V(G)$ and k, t be positive integers and z, p, q be non-negative integers. Suppose that $|X| = k + z$, $|\overline{X}| = k, p + q \geqslant k-3$ and $\overline{X}$ is $[2t + z - 1, 0, q]$-attached and that X^* has edge-disjoint z-arc-subforests $F_1, \ldots, F_t$ such that $X\backslash M$ is $[2t - 1, 0, p; \overline{X}]$-attached for some subset M of $I(F_1) \cap \ldots \cap I(F_t)$. Then G has t edge-disjoint Hamiltonian circuits.*

Proof. Suppose that $s \leqslant t - 1$ and that we have found edge-disjoint Hamiltonian circuits $c_1, \ldots, c_s$ of G such that

$$E(F_i) \subseteq E(c_i) \subseteq X\delta \cup E(F_i) \text{ for } i = 1, \ldots, s.$$

Let $J = G - (E(c_1) \cup \ldots \cup E(c_s))$. Then

$$v_J(\xi) = v(\xi) - 2s \geqslant v(\xi) - 2t + 2 \text{ for every } \xi \in V(G).$$

Therefore, since $\overline{X}$ is $[2t + z - 1, 0, q]$-attached and $X\backslash M$ is $[2t-1, 0, p; \overline{X}]$-attached in G, it follows that $\overline{X}$ is $[z + 1, 0, q]$-attached and $X\backslash M$ is $[1, 0, p; \overline{X}]$-attached in J, and since $M \subseteq I(F_{s+1})$ it follows that $X\backslash I(F_{s+1})$ is also $[1, 0, p; \overline{X}]$-attached in J. Therefore, by Lemma 9, J has a Hamiltonian circuit c_{s+1} such that $E(F_{s+1}) \subseteq E(c_{s+1}) \subseteq X\delta_J \cup E(F_{s+1})$, and so G has edge-disjoint Hamiltonian circuits $c_1, \ldots, c_{s+1}$ such that $E(F_i) \subseteq E(c\ ) \subseteq X\delta \cup E(F_i)$ for $i = 1, \ldots, s + 1$. Clearly this proves Corollary 9A.

LEMMA 10. *If* $X \subseteq Y \subseteq Z \subseteq V(G)$, *then*

$$\sum_{\xi \in \bar{Z}} v(\xi, \bar{X}) \leqslant 2|\bar{Z} \nabla \bar{Y}| + \sum_{\xi \in Y \setminus X} v(\xi, \bar{Z}).$$

Proof. Since $\bar{Z} \subseteq \bar{X}$, it follows that $\sum_{\xi \in \bar{Z}} v(\xi, \bar{X})$ counts elements of $\bar{Z} \nabla \bar{Z}$ twice and elements of $\bar{Z} \nabla (Z \setminus X)$ once and hence equals

$$\begin{aligned} 2|\bar{Z} \nabla \bar{Z}| + |\bar{Z} \nabla (Z\setminus X)| &= 2|\bar{Z} \nabla \bar{Z}| + |\bar{Z} \nabla (Z\setminus Y)| + |\bar{Z} \nabla (Y \setminus X)| \\ &\leqslant 2(|\bar{Z} \nabla \bar{Z}| + |\bar{Z} \nabla (Z\setminus Y)|) + |\bar{Z} \nabla (Y\setminus X)| \\ &= 2|\bar{Z} \nabla \bar{Y}| + \sum_{\xi \in Y\setminus X} v(\xi, \bar{Z}). \end{aligned}$$

LEMMA 11. $|I(F)| = |E(F)| - c(F)$ *for any arc-forest* F.

Proof. Sum the relation $|I(A)| = |E(A)| - 1$ over the components A of F.

LEMMA 12. *If* $X \subseteq V(G)$ *and* F *is an arc-subforest of* G *which is an extension of an* X*-arc-subforest of* G, *then*

$$|I(F)\setminus X| \leqslant |E(F)| - 2|X|, \tag{15}$$

$$|V(F)| \leqslant 2|E(F)| - |X|. \tag{16}$$

Proof. $|X| \leqslant c(F)$ because each element of X belongs to a different component of F, and $|I(F)\setminus X| = |I(F)| - |X|$ because $X \subseteq I(F)$: these observations and Lemma 11 imply (15). Furthermore,

$$2|E(F)| = \sum_{\xi \in V(F)} v_F(\xi) \geqslant |X| + |V(F)|$$

because $v_F(\xi) = 2$ for all $\xi \in X$ and $v_F(\xi) \geqslant 1$ for all $\xi \in V(F)$.

LEMMA 13. *If* X *is a* 0*-allowable subset of* $V(G)$, *then* G *has an* X*-arc-subforest.*

Proof. Let $\xi_1, \ldots, \xi_x$ be an ordering of X such that $v(\xi_i) \geqslant 2i + x - 1$ for $i = 1, \ldots, x$. Then $v(\xi_i, \bar{X}\setminus S_i) \geqslant 2$ for any subset S_i of $\bar{X}$ such that $|S_i| = 2i-2$. Therefore we can select in succession vertices $\eta_1, \ldots, \eta_{2x}$ such that η_{2i-1} and η_{2i} are distinct elements of $N(\xi_i) \cap (\bar{X}\setminus\{\eta_1, \ldots, \eta_{2i-2}\})$ for $i = 1, \ldots, x$. If A_i is the arcoid whose edges are those which join ξ_i to η_{2i-1} and η_{2i} then $A_1 \cup \ldots \cup A_x$ is an X-arc-subforest of G.

COROLLARY 13A. *If* t *is a positive integer and* X *is a* $(2t-2)$*-allowable subset of* $V(G)$, *then* G *has* t *edge-disjoint* X*-arc-subforests.*

Proof. If we have found edge-disjoint X-arc-subforests $F_1, \ldots, F_s$ of G and

$s \leqslant t-1$ then X is $(2t-2-2s)$-allowable, and therefore 0-allowable, in $G - E(F_1 \cup \ldots \cup F_s)$, which consequently has an X-arc-subforest by Lemma 13.

LEMMA 14. *Let A, B, C, k, w, x be real numbers such that $A > 0, 0 \leqslant w \leqslant x < k$. Let $f(s)$ denote $(As^2 + Bs + C)/(k - s)$. Then $f(w) \leqslant f(0)$ or $f(w) \leqslant f(x)$.*

Proof. $(k-s)^2 f'(s) = -As^2 + 2Aks + Bk + C$, which increases as s increases when $s < k$. Therefore either $f'(s) \leqslant 0$ for all s in the closed interval $[0, x]$ or $f'(s) \geqslant 0$ for all such s or there is a p between 0 and x such that $f'(s) < 0$ for $0 \leqslant s < p$ and $f'(s) > 0$ for $p < s \leqslant x$. Hence the largest value attained by $f(s)$ as s ranges over $[0, x]$ is either $f(0)$ or $f(x)$, which proves Lemma 14.

LEMMA 15. *Let t, z be integers such that*

$$t \geqslant 2, \tag{17}$$

$$z \geqslant 1. \tag{18}$$

Let

$$y = \tfrac{1}{2}(z + \varepsilon_z) \tag{19}$$

and let M be a subset of $V(G)$ such that

$$|M| \leqslant \tfrac{1}{2}z, \tag{20}$$

$$v(\xi) \geqslant 2t + 3y - 3 \qquad (\xi \in M). \tag{21}$$

Suppose further that

$$v(\xi) \geqslant \tfrac{1}{2}z \qquad (\xi \in V(G)), \tag{22}$$

$$|V(G)| \geqslant 8t + \tfrac{1}{2}(5z + \varepsilon_z) - 13, \tag{23}$$

$$|V(G)| > 8t + 2z - 12 - \frac{4t-6}{z} + \frac{(5z - 12t + 8)^2}{24z} \quad \text{if } z > \frac{12t-8}{5}. \tag{24}$$

Then G has t edge-disjoint z-arc-subforests $F_1, \ldots, F_t$ such that

$$M \subseteq I(F_1) \cap \ldots \cap I(F_t).$$

Proof. Let $\xi_1, \ldots, \xi_n$ be an ordering of $V(G)$ such that

$$v(\xi_1) \geqslant v(\xi_2) \geqslant \ldots \geqslant v(\xi_n). \tag{25}$$

Let x be the largest integer in $\{0, 1, \ldots, n\}$ for which it is true that

$$v(\xi_i) \geqslant 2t + 3x - 2i - 1 \qquad (i = 1, 2, \ldots, x). \tag{26}$$

Let X denote $\{\xi_1, \ldots, \xi_x\}$ and m denote $|M|$.

Case I: *Suppose that* $x \geqslant y$. Since $m = |M| \leqslant y \leqslant x$ by (20), (19) and the hypothesis of Case I, we can select a subsequence $\zeta_1, \zeta_2, \ldots, \zeta_{y-m}$ of the sequence $\xi_x, \xi_{x-1}, \ldots, \xi_1$ whose terms belong to $\overline{M}$, and then (26) implies that

$$v(\zeta_j) \geqslant 2t + x + 2j - 3 \geqslant 2t + y + 2j - 3 \qquad (j = 1, 2, \ldots, y - m).$$

Let $\zeta_{y-m+1}, \zeta_{y-m+2}, \ldots, \zeta_y$ denote the elements of M. Then by (21),

$$v(\zeta_j) \geqslant 2t + 3y - 3 \geqslant 2t + y + 2j - 3 \qquad (j = y - m + 1, \ldots, y).$$

Hence $\{\zeta_1, \ldots, \zeta_y\}$ is $(2t - 2)$-allowable and so G has by Corollary 13A t edge-disjoint $\{\zeta_1, \ldots, \zeta_y\}$-arc-subforests $F_1', \ldots, F_t'$. Since $M \subseteq \{\zeta_1, \ldots, \zeta_y\}$ and $|M| \leqslant \frac{1}{2}z$, each F_i' has a z-arc-subforest F_i such that $M \subseteq I(F_i)$, and thus we obtain the desired z-arc-subforests $F_1, \ldots, F_t$ of G.

Case II: *Suppose that*

$$x \leqslant y - 1. \tag{27}$$

Then by (27), (19), (23), (17) and (18), $x < \frac{1}{2}z < |V(G)| = n$, so that $x + 1 \in \{0, 1, \ldots, n\}$ and therefore, by the definition of x, replacement of each x in (26) by $x + 1$ yields a false statement, i.e., there is a $w \in \{0, 1, \ldots, x\}$ such that

$$v(\xi_{w+1}) \leqslant 2t + 3x - 2w - 1. \tag{28}$$

Let $W = \{\xi_1, \ldots, \xi_w\}$: then

$$W \subseteq X \tag{29}$$

because $w \leqslant x$, and $v(\xi_i) > v(\xi_{w+1})$ for every $\xi_i \in M$ by (21), (27) and (28), so that in view of (25) we have

$$M \subseteq W. \tag{30}$$

Since $v(\xi_{x+1-j}) \geqslant 2t + x + 2j - 3$ for $j = 1, \ldots, x$ by (26), X is $(2t - 2)$-allowable and so by Corollary 13A G has t edge-disjoint X-arc-subforests $\Phi_1, \ldots, \Phi_t$. Since $|E(\Phi_i)| = 2x < z$ by (27) and (19) for $i = 1, \ldots, t$ we can select edge-disjoint arc-subforests $F_1, \ldots, F_t$ of G such that $|E(F_i)| \leqslant z$ and F_i is an extension of Φ_i for $i = 1, \ldots, t$ and such that subject to these requirements $|E(F_1 \cup \ldots \cup F_t)|$ is as large as possible.

Suppose that $r \in \{1, \ldots, t\}$ and

$$|E(F_r)| \leqslant z - 1. \tag{31}$$

Then the maximality of $|E(F_1 \cup \ldots \cup F_t)|$ implies that F_r has no extension in $G - \bigcup \{E(F_i): i \neq r\}$, which implies that

$$\mathbf{C}V(F_r) \mathbin{\nabla} \mathbf{C}I(F_r) \subseteq \bigcup \{E(F_i): i \neq r\}.$$

Moreover

$$\mathbf{C}V(F_r) \mathbin{\nabla} \mathbf{C}I(F_r) \subseteq \overline{X} \mathbin{\nabla} \overline{X}$$

because

$$X = I(\Phi_r) \subseteq I(F_r) \subseteq V(F_r). \tag{32}$$

Hence

$$|\mathbf{C}V(F_r) \nabla \mathbf{C}I(F_r)| \leqslant \sum_{i \neq r} |E(F_i) \cap (\overline{X} \nabla \overline{X})| = \sum_{i \neq r} |E(F_i) \backslash E(\Phi_i)| \leqslant (t-1)(z-2x). \qquad (33)$$

We note that, by (16) and (31),

$$|V(F_r)| \leqslant 2(z-1) - x, \qquad (34)$$

so that, by (23) and (34), $|\mathbf{C}V(F_r)| \geqslant 8t + \frac{1}{2}(z + \varepsilon_z) + x - 11$ and therefore, by (19) and (27),

$$|\mathbf{C}V(F_r)| \geqslant 8t + 2x - 10. \qquad (35)$$

By (29) and (32), $W \subseteq I(F_r) \subseteq V(F_r)$ and therefore, by Lemma 10,

$$\sum_{\xi \in \mathbf{C}V(F_r)} v(\xi, \overline{W}) \leqslant 2|\mathbf{C}V(F_r) \nabla \mathbf{C}I(F_r)| + \sum_{\xi \in I(F_r) \backslash W} v(\xi, \mathbf{C}V(F_r)). \qquad (36)$$

But $v(\xi, \overline{W}) \geqslant v(\xi) - |W| \geqslant \frac{1}{2}z - w$ by (22) for every $\xi \in V(G)$. Therefore

$$\sum_{\xi \in \mathbf{C}V(F_r)} v(\xi, \overline{W}) \geqslant (\tfrac{1}{2}z - w)\,|\mathbf{C}V(F_r)|. \qquad (37)$$

By (25) and (28), $v(\xi_i) \leqslant 2t + 3x - 2w - 1$ for every $\xi_i \in \overline{W}$, and clearly $v(\xi, \mathbf{C}V(F_r)) \leqslant v(\xi) - 2$ for every $\xi \in I(F_r)$. Therefore

$$v(\xi, \mathbf{C}V(F_r)) \leqslant 2t + 3x - 2w - 3 \text{ for every } \xi \in I(F_r) \backslash W.$$

Moreover

$$|I(F_r) \backslash X| \leqslant z - 1 - 2x$$

by (15) and (31), and $|X \backslash W| = x - w$, whence

$$|I(F_r) \backslash W| \leqslant z - 1 - x - w.$$

Hence

$$\sum_{\xi \in I(F_r) \backslash W} v(\xi, \mathbf{C}V(F_r)) \leqslant (z - 1 - x - w)(2t + 3x - 2w - 3). \qquad (38)$$

Substituting from (37), (33) and (38) into (36) gives

$$(\tfrac{1}{2}z - w)\,|\mathbf{C}V(F_r)| \leqslant 2(t-1)(z-2x) + (z - 1 - x - w)(2t + 3x - 2w - 3). \qquad (39)$$

By (19) and (27), $\frac{1}{2}z > x \geqslant w \geqslant 0$: hence by (39) and Lemma 14 either

$$|\mathbf{C}V(F_r)| \leqslant \big(2(t-1)(z-2x) + (z-1-x)(2t+3x-3)\big)/\tfrac{1}{2}z \qquad (40)$$

or

$$\begin{aligned} |\mathbf{C}V(F_r)| &\leqslant \big(2(t-1)(z-2x) + (z-1-2x)(2t+x-3)\big)/(\tfrac{1}{2}z - x) \\ &< \big(2(t-1)(z-2x) + (z-2x)(2t+x-3)\big)/(\tfrac{1}{2}z - x) \\ &= 8t + 2x - 10, \end{aligned}$$

and since the latter alternative is incompatible with (35), we must have (40), which together with (34) implies that

$$z|V(G)| \leqslant -6x^2 + x(5z - 12t + 8) + 8tz + 2z^2 - 4t - 12z + 6. \quad (41)$$

If x were to range over all real values (with t, z fixed), the maximum value attained by the right hand side of (41) would be

$$\frac{(5z - 12t + 8)^2}{24} + 8tz + 2z^2 - 4t - 12z + 6$$

and hence (41) contradicts (24) if $z > (12t - 8)/5$. If $z \leqslant (12t - 8)/5$ then, since $x \geqslant 0$, the right hand side of (41) does not exceed $8tz + 2z^2 - 4t - 12z + 6$, which by (17) is less than $z(8t + 2z - 12)$, which by (18) cannot exceed $z(8t + \frac{1}{2}(5z + \varepsilon_z) - 13)$, so that (41) contradicts (23) if $z \leqslant (12t - 8)/5$. Thus our supposition that (31) holds for some r leads to a contradiction. We conclude that $F_1, \ldots, F_t$ are z-arc-subforests of G, and since by (30) and (29) $M \subseteq X = I(\Phi_i) \subseteq I(F_i)$ for $i = 1, \ldots, t$ the lemma is proved.

COROLLARY 15A. *Let t, z be integers such that $t \geqslant 2, z \geqslant 1$ and*

$$z \leqslant 36t/5. \quad (42)$$

Suppose that

$$|V(G)| \geqslant 8t + \tfrac{1}{2}(5z - \varepsilon_z) - 8 \quad (43)$$

and $v(\xi) \geqslant \frac{1}{2}z$ for every $\xi \in V(G)$. Let M be a subset of $V(G)$ such that $|M| \leqslant \frac{1}{2}z$ and $v(\xi) \geqslant 2t + (3/2)(z + \varepsilon_z) - 3$ for every $\xi \in M$. Then G has t edge-disjoint z-arc-subforests $F_1, \ldots, F_t$ such that $M \subseteq I(F_1) \cap \ldots \cap I(F_t)$.

Proof. By Lemma 15, it will suffice to prove (24). Assume therefore that $z > (12t - 8)/5$. Then $5z - 12t + 8$ is positive, and is by (42) less than or equal to $(10z/3) + 8$. Hence

$$8t + 2z - 12 - \frac{4t - 6}{z} + \frac{(5z - 12t + 8)^2}{24z}$$

$$\leqslant 8t + 2z - 12 - \frac{4t - 6}{z} + \frac{((10z/3) + 8)^2}{24z}$$

$$= 8t + \frac{133}{54}z - \frac{88}{9} + \frac{26 - 12t}{3z} \leqslant 8t + \frac{133}{54}z - \frac{82}{9},$$

which by (43) is less than $|V(G)|$; and (24) is proved.

LEMMA 16. *Suppose that G is a Dirac graph. Let t, u be integers such that* $t \geqslant 2$,

$$0 \leqslant u \leqslant \tfrac{18}{5}t - \tfrac{1}{2}\varepsilon, \tag{44}$$

$$u + 2t \leqslant (n - 3\varepsilon + 10)/8. \tag{45}$$

Let $z = 2u + \varepsilon$. *Let X be a subset of* $V(G)$ *such that* $|X| = \frac{1}{2}(n + \varepsilon) + u$ *and M be a subset of X such that* $|M| \leqslant u$ *and* $v(\xi, \bar{X}) \leqslant \frac{1}{2}(n - 5\varepsilon) - 2t - 3u + 3$ *for every* $\xi \in M$. *Then* X^* *has t edge-disjoint z-arc-subforests* $F_1, \ldots, F_t$ *such that* $M \subseteq I(F_1) \cap \ldots \cap I(F_t)$.

Proof. If $z = 0$ then $M = \emptyset$ because $|M| \leqslant u \leqslant \frac{1}{2}z$, so that in this case the required conclusion can be reached by taking each of $F_1, \ldots, F_t$ to be the empty graph. We may therefore henceforward assume that $z \geqslant 1$. Using (45) and the fact that $\varepsilon_z = \varepsilon$ we see that

$$\begin{aligned} |V(X^*)| &= |X| = \tfrac{1}{2}(n + \varepsilon) + 5u - 4u \\ &\geqslant \tfrac{1}{2}(n + \varepsilon) + 5u - 4\big(\tfrac{1}{8}(n - 3\varepsilon + 10) - 2t\big) = 8t + 2\varepsilon + 5u - 5 \\ &= 8t + \tfrac{1}{2}(5z - \varepsilon_z) - 5. \end{aligned}$$

Since G is a Dirac graph, we have $v(\xi) \geqslant \frac{1}{2}(n + \varepsilon)$ for every vertex ξ and therefore for every $\xi \in X$,

$$v_{X^*}(\xi) \geqslant \tfrac{1}{2}(n + \varepsilon) - |\bar{X}| = |X| + \tfrac{1}{2}\varepsilon - \tfrac{1}{2}n = u + \varepsilon \geqslant \tfrac{1}{2}z$$

and for every $\xi \in M$,

$$v_{X^*}(\xi) \geqslant \tfrac{1}{2}(n + \varepsilon) - v(\xi, \bar{X}) \geqslant 2t + 3u + 3\varepsilon - 3 = 2t + \tfrac{3}{2}(z + \varepsilon_z) - 3.$$

Moreover $z \leqslant 36t/5$ by (44) and $|M| \leqslant u \leqslant \frac{1}{2}z$. Hence, by Corollary 15A, X^* has t edge-disjoint z-arc-subforests $F_1, \ldots, F_t$ such that $M \subseteq I(F_1) \cap \ldots \cap I(F_t)$.

LEMMA 17. *Suppose that G is a Dirac graph and t is an integer greater than or equal to 2 and u, p, q, m are non-negative integers such that* $m \leqslant u \leqslant (18t/5) - \frac{1}{2}\varepsilon$, $u + 2t \leqslant (n - 3\varepsilon + 10)/8$ *and* $p + q \geqslant \frac{1}{2}(n - \varepsilon) - u - 3$. *Suppose that* $V(G)$ *has a subset X such that* $|X| = \frac{1}{2}(n + \varepsilon) + u$ *and X is* $[2t - 1, m, p]$*-attached and* $\bar{X}$ *is* $[2t + 2u + \varepsilon - 1, 0, q]$*-attached and* $|\Lambda_{((n-5\varepsilon)/2)-2t-3u+3}(X)| \geqslant m$ *Then G has t edge-disjoint Hamiltonian circuits.*

Proof. Write $k = \frac{1}{2}(n - \varepsilon) - u$, $z = 2u + \varepsilon$. Since

$$|\Lambda_{((n-5\varepsilon)/2)-2t-3u+3}(X)| \geqslant m,$$

we can select a subset M of $\Lambda_{((n-5\varepsilon)/2)-2t-3u+3}(X)$ such that $|M| = m$ and $v(\xi, \bar{X}) \leqslant v(\xi', \bar{X})$ whenever $\xi \in M, \xi' \in X \backslash M$. Since $|M| = m \leqslant u$, X^* has by Lemma 16 t edge-disjoint z-arc-subforests $F_1, \ldots, F_t$ such that $M \subseteq I(F_1) \cap \ldots \cap I(F_t)$. Since X is $[2t - 1, m, p]$-attached, it follows from the definition of M

that $X \backslash M$ is $[2t-1, 0, p; \bar{X}]$-attached. Furthermore, the hypotheses of Lemma 17 imply that $p+q \geqslant k-3$, $|X| = k+z$, $\bar{X}$ is $[2t+z-1, 0, q]$-attached and $|\bar{X}| = n - |X| = \frac{1}{2}(n-\varepsilon) - u = k$. Since $u \leqslant u + 2t - 4 \leqslant \frac{1}{8}(n - 3\varepsilon + 10) - 4 < \frac{1}{2}(n-\varepsilon)$ it follows that k is positive. Hence, by Corollary 9A, G has t edge-disjoint Hamiltonian circuits.

LEMMA 18. *Suppose that G is a Dirac graph and X is a subset of $V(G)$ and t is an integer greater than or equal to 2 and u, p, q are non-negative integers and*

$$u \leqslant (18t/5) - \tfrac{1}{2}\varepsilon, \qquad u + 2t \leqslant (n - 3\varepsilon + 10)/8,$$
$$p + q \geqslant \tfrac{1}{2}(n-\varepsilon) - u - 3, \qquad |X| = \tfrac{1}{2}(n+\varepsilon) + u$$

and X is $[2t-1, u, p]$-attached and $\bar{X}$ is $[2t+2u+\varepsilon-1, 0, q]$-attached. Suppose in addition that either (i) $4t + 3u + p \leqslant \frac{1}{2}(n-5\varepsilon) + 4$ *or* (ii) $|\Lambda_{2t-1+p}(X)| \leqslant \frac{1}{2}(n-5\varepsilon) - 4t - 3u + 5$. *Then G has t edge-disjoint Hamiltonian circuits.*

Proof. If $|\Lambda_{((n-5\varepsilon)/2)-2t-3u+3}(X)| \geqslant u$ then the desired conclusion follows by taking $m = u$ in Lemma 17. We will therefore assume that

$$|\Lambda_{((n-5\varepsilon)/2)-2t-3u+3}(X)| < u$$

and we will let m denote $|\Lambda_{((n-5\varepsilon)/2)-2t-3u+3}(X)|$: then by Lemma 17 it will suffice to prove that X is $[2t-1, m, p]$-attached. Consider any $i \in \{0, 1, \ldots, p\}$. If $i \leqslant \frac{1}{2}(n-5\varepsilon) - 4t - 3u + 4$, then

$$2t - 1 + i \leqslant \tfrac{1}{2}(n-5\varepsilon) - 2t - 3u + 3$$

and hence

$$|\Lambda_{2t-1+i}(X)| \leqslant |\Lambda_{((n-5\varepsilon)/2)-2t-3u+3}(X)| = m \leqslant m + i.$$

If $i > \frac{1}{2}(n-5\varepsilon) - 4t - 3u + 4$ then (i) must be false because $i \leqslant p$ and so (ii) must be true, and we then have

$$|\Lambda_{2t-1+i}(X)| \leqslant |\Lambda_{2t-1+p}(X)| \leqslant \tfrac{1}{2}(n-5\varepsilon) - 4t - 3u + 5 \leqslant i \leqslant m + i.$$

This shows that X is $[2t-1, m, p]$-attached, and Lemma 18 is proved.

LEMMA 19. *Let A, B, R be subsets of $V(G)$ such that $B \subseteq A \subseteq \bar{R}$. Let e, u, p be non-negative integers. Suppose that*

(i) $v(\xi, \mathbf{C}(R \cup A)) \geqslant |A| - |B| + e - u$ *for every* $\xi \in A$;

(ii) $v(\xi, \mathbf{C}(R \cup A)) \geqslant |A| + e - u$ *for every* $\xi \in B$;

(iii) $v(\xi, \mathbf{C}(R \cup A)) \geqslant e + p + 1$ *for every* $\xi \in R$.

Then $R \cup A$ is $[e, u, p]$-attached.

Proof. Let $i \in \{0, 1, ..., p\}$. Then by (iii) no element of $\Lambda_{e+i}(R \cup A)$ belongs to R: hence

$$\Lambda_{e+i}(R \cup A) \subseteq A. \tag{46}$$

If $i < |A| - |B| - u$, then, by (i), no element of A can belong to $\Lambda_{e+i}(R \cup A)$ and hence, by (46), $\Lambda_{e+i}(R \cup A) = \emptyset$ and so trivially $|\Lambda_{e+i}(R \cup A)| \leqslant u + i$. If $|A| - |B| - u \leqslant i < |A| - u$ then, by (ii), no element of B belongs to $\Lambda_{e+i}(R \cup A)$ and so, by (46), $\Lambda_{e+i}(R \cup A) \subseteq A \backslash B$ and therefore

$$|\Lambda_{e+i}(R \cup A)| \leqslant |A| - |B| \leqslant u + i.$$

If $i \geqslant |A| - u$, then by (46) $|\Lambda_{e+i}(R \cup A)| \leqslant |A| \leqslant u + i$.

LEMMA 20. *Let X be a subset of $V(G)$ and $\xi_1, ..., \xi_m$ be an ordering of X such that $v(\xi_1, \bar{X}) \leqslant v(\xi_2, \bar{X}) \leqslant ... \leqslant v(\xi_m, \bar{X})$. Let b, c, d be non-negative integers, and suppose that $c + d + 1 \leqslant m$. Then X is $[b, c, d]$-attached if and only if $v(\xi_{c+i}, \bar{X}) \geqslant b + i$ for $i = 1, 2, ..., d + 1$.*

The proof may be left to the reader.

LEMMA 21. *Suppose that G is a Dirac graph, R is a subset of $V(G)$, t is an integer,*

$$t \geqslant 2, \tag{47}$$

$$t \leqslant 5(n + \varepsilon + 10)/224, \tag{48}$$

$$|R| = \tfrac{1}{2}(n + \varepsilon) - 2t + 3 \tag{49}$$

and

$$v(\xi, \bar{R}) \geqslant \tfrac{1}{2}(n + \varepsilon) - 2t + 2 \text{ for every } \xi \in R. \tag{50}$$

Suppose also that there is a non-negative integer x such that

$$x \leqslant \tfrac{18}{5}t - \tfrac{1}{2}\varepsilon \tag{51}$$

and

$$\bar{R} \text{ is } [2t + 2x + \varepsilon - 1,\ 2t + x - 3,\ 6t - 8 - \varepsilon]\text{-attached.} \tag{52}$$

Then G has t edge-disjoint Hamiltonian circuits.

Proof. Suppose first that $\bar{R}$ is $[2t - 1, 2t - 3 - \varepsilon, 6t - 8 - \varepsilon]$-attached. Let $u = 2t - 3 - \varepsilon$, $p = 6t - 8 - \varepsilon$, $q = \tfrac{1}{2}(n + 3\varepsilon) - 8t + 8$. Then $\bar{R}$ is $[2t - 1, u, p]$-attached, and $p + q = \tfrac{1}{2}(n - \varepsilon) - u - 3$ and $u < (18t/5) - \tfrac{1}{2}\varepsilon$. From (47) and the fact that $\varepsilon \in \{0, 1\}$ we see that $u \geqslant 0$ and $p > 0$. By (48),

$$q \geqslant (9n + 37\varepsilon + 174)/28 > 0,$$

$$u + 2t \leqslant (5n - 51\varepsilon - 118)/56 < (n - 3\varepsilon + 10)/8,$$

$$4t + 3u + p \leqslant (5n - 51\varepsilon - 188)/14 < \tfrac{1}{2}(n - 5\varepsilon) + 4.$$

By (50), $v(\xi, \bar{R}) > 2t + 2u + \varepsilon - 1 + q$ for every $\xi \in R$ and therefore R is $[2t + 2u + \varepsilon - 1, 0, q]$-attached. By (49), $|\bar{R}| = n - |R| = \frac{1}{2}(n + \varepsilon) + u$. Hence, by Lemma 18, G has t edge-disjoint Hamiltonian circuits.

Now suppose that

$$\bar{R} \text{ is not } [2t - 1,\ 2t - 3 - \varepsilon,\ 6t - 8 - \varepsilon]\text{-attached.} \tag{53}$$

Let $\xi_1, \ldots, \xi_m$ be an ordering of $\bar{R}$ such that

$$v(\xi_1, R) \leqslant v(\xi_2, R) \leqslant \ldots \leqslant v(\xi_m, R). \tag{54}$$

Then by (49),

$$m = \tfrac{1}{2}(n - \varepsilon) + 2t - 3 \tag{55}$$

and, since $(48t/5) - 7 - \varepsilon \leqslant (3/14)(n + \varepsilon + 10) - 7 - \varepsilon < \frac{1}{2}(n - \varepsilon)$ by (48), it follows from (55) that

$$(2t - 3) + \tfrac{18}{5}t + (6t - 8 - \varepsilon) + 1 < m. \tag{56}$$

This implies that $(2t - 3 - \varepsilon) + (6t - 8 - \varepsilon) + 1 < m$, so that by (53) and Lemma 20 there is an I such that

$$I \in \{1, 2, \ldots, 6t - 7 - \varepsilon\}, \tag{57}$$

$$v(\xi_{2t-3-\varepsilon+I}, R) \leqslant 2t - 2 + I. \tag{58}$$

Abandoning the previous meaning of the symbol u, let us re-define it as the smallest non-negative integral value of x for which (52) is true: then

$$\bar{R} \text{ is } [2t + 2u + \varepsilon - 1,\ 2t + u - 3,\ 6t - 8 - \varepsilon]\text{-attached.} \tag{59}$$

By (51),

$$u \leqslant \tfrac{18}{5}t - \tfrac{1}{2}\varepsilon. \tag{60}$$

By (60) and (48),

$$u + 2t \leqslant (n - 3\varepsilon + 10)/8. \tag{61}$$

By (56) and (60), $(2t + u - 3) + (6t - 8 - \varepsilon) + 1 < m$, and therefore, by (59) and Lemma 20,

$$v(\xi_{2t+u-3+i}, R) \geqslant 2t + 2u + \varepsilon - 1 + i \quad (i = 1, 2, \ldots, 6t - 7 - \varepsilon). \tag{62}$$

If $I \geqslant u + \varepsilon + 1$, then, by (57), we would be able to take $i = I - u - \varepsilon$ in (62), which would contradict (58). Therefore

$$I \leqslant u + \varepsilon. \tag{63}$$

Suppose, first, that $u \geqslant 1$. Then the definition of u implies that $\bar{R}$ is not

$$[2t + 2u + \varepsilon - 3,\ 2t + u - 4,\ 6t - 8 - \varepsilon]\text{-attached,}$$

and since $(2t + u - 4) + (6t - 8 - \varepsilon) + 1 < m$ by (56) and (60), it follows by Lemma 20 that there is a $J \in \{1, 2, \ldots, 6t - 7 - \varepsilon\}$ such that

$$v(\xi_{2t+u-4+J}, R) \leqslant 2t + 2u + \varepsilon - 4 + J. \tag{64}$$

If $J \geqslant 2$, then taking $i = J - 1$ in (62) contradicts (64). Hence $J = 1$ and (64) gives $v(\xi_{2t+u-3}, R) \leqslant 2t + 2u + \varepsilon - 3$, when $u \geqslant 1$. Moreover, when $u = 0$, (57) and (63) imply that $I = \varepsilon = 1$ and hence (58) implies that $v(\xi_{2t-3}, R) \leqslant 2t - 1 = 2t + \varepsilon - 2$. Hence the inequality

$$v(\xi_{2t+u-3}, R) \leqslant 2t + 2u + \varepsilon - 2 \tag{65}$$

holds regardless of the value of u.

By (47), (60), and (56), $1 \leqslant 2t + u - 3 < m$ and so we may define A to be the subset $\{\xi_1, \xi_2, \ldots, \xi_{2t+u-3}\}$ of $\bar{R}$. Then, by (49),

$$|R \cup A| = \tfrac{1}{2}(n + \varepsilon) + u. \tag{66}$$

Re-define p and q by letting $p = \frac{1}{2}(n + \varepsilon) + 5 - 6t - u, q = 6t - 8 - \varepsilon$. Then

$$p + q = \tfrac{1}{2}(n - \varepsilon) - u - 3 \tag{67}$$

and, by (47),

$$q > 0 \tag{68}$$

and, by (48) and (60),

$$p \geqslant \tfrac{112}{5}t - 6t - (\tfrac{18}{5}t - \tfrac{1}{2}\varepsilon) = \tfrac{64}{5}t + \tfrac{1}{2}\varepsilon > 0. \tag{69}$$

By (59) and (54), $\bar{R}\backslash A$ is $[2t + 2u + \varepsilon - 1, 0, q; R]$-attached and hence *a fortiori* $[2t + 2u + \varepsilon - 1, 0, q; R \cup A]$-attached, i.e.,

$$\mathbf{C}(R \cup A) \text{ is } [2t + 2u + \varepsilon - 1, 0, q]\text{-attached.} \tag{70}$$

By (63), $B = \{\xi_1, \xi_2, \ldots, \xi_{2t-3-\varepsilon+I}\}$ is a subset of A. By (54), (58) and (65), $v(\xi, R) \leqslant 2t - 2 + I$ for all $\xi \in B$ and $v(\xi, R) \leqslant 2t + 2u + \varepsilon - 2$ for all $\xi \in A$; and moreover $v(\xi, A) \leqslant |A| - 1 \leqslant 2t - 4 + u$ for all $\xi \in A$ and $v(\xi) \geqslant \frac{1}{2}(n + \varepsilon)$ for all $\xi \in V(G)$ because G is a Dirac graph; from all these observations it follows that

$$v(\xi, \mathbf{C}(R \cup A)) \geqslant \tfrac{1}{2}(n + \varepsilon) - 4t - u - I + 6 \qquad (\xi \in B), \tag{71}$$

$$v(\xi, \mathbf{C}(R \cup A)) \geqslant \tfrac{1}{2}(n + \varepsilon) - 4t - 3u - \varepsilon + 6 \qquad (\xi \in A). \tag{72}$$

We observe that, by (48), (57), and (60),

$$\begin{aligned} &\tfrac{1}{2}(n + \varepsilon) - 4t - u - I + 6 \\ &\quad \geqslant \tfrac{112}{5}t - 5 - 4t - (\tfrac{18}{5}t - \tfrac{1}{2}\varepsilon) - (6t - 7 - \varepsilon) + 6 \\ &\quad = \tfrac{44}{5}t + \tfrac{3}{2}\varepsilon + 8 > 4t - 4 = |A| + 2t - 1 - u, \end{aligned}$$

$$\begin{aligned} \tfrac{1}{2}(n + \varepsilon) - 4t - 3u - \varepsilon + 6 &\geqslant \tfrac{112}{5}t - 5 - 4t - 3(\tfrac{18}{5}t - \tfrac{1}{2}\varepsilon) - \varepsilon + 6 \\ &= \tfrac{38}{5}t + \tfrac{1}{2}\varepsilon + 1 > 2t + \varepsilon - 1 - I = |A| - |B| + 2t - 1 - u, \end{aligned}$$

and combining these computations with (71) and (72) gives

$$v(\xi, \mathbf{C}(R \cup A)) > |A| + 2t - 1 - u \qquad (\xi \in B), \tag{73}$$

$$v(\xi, \mathbf{C}(R \cup A)) > |A| - |B| + 2t - 1 - u \qquad (\xi \in A). \tag{74}$$

Moreover $v(\xi, \mathbf{C}(R \cup A)) \geqslant v(\xi, \bar{R}) - |A| = v(\xi, \bar{R}) - 2t - u + 3$ for all $\xi \in R$, so that in view of (50) and the definition of p,

$$v(\xi, \mathbf{C}(R \cup A)) \geqslant p + 2t \qquad (\xi \in R). \tag{75}$$

By (73), (74), (75), (47), (69), and Lemma 19,

$$R \cup A \text{ is } [2t - 1, u, p]\text{-attached.} \tag{76}$$

By (60) and (48),

$$6t + 4u \leqslant \tfrac{102}{5} t - 2\varepsilon \leqslant \tfrac{51}{112} (n + \varepsilon + 10) - 2\varepsilon < \tfrac{1}{2} (n - 5\varepsilon) + 8$$

and hence $|A| = 2t + u - 3 < \frac{1}{2}(n - 5\varepsilon) - 4t - 3u + 5$, so that, since

$$\Lambda_{2t-1+p}(R \cup A) \subseteq A$$

by (75), we have

$$|\Lambda_{2t-1+p}(R \cup A)| < \tfrac{1}{2}(n - 5\varepsilon) - 4t - 3u + 5. \tag{77}$$

By (47), (69), (68), (60), (61), (67), (66), (76), (70), (77), and Lemma 18, G has t edge-disjoint Hamiltonian circuits.

LEMMA 22. *Let a, b, c, d, p, q be integers such that $a \geqslant 0$, $c \geqslant 0$, $d \geqslant 0$,*

$$b \geqslant 1, \tag{78}$$

$$p \geqslant a + b + 2c + d, \tag{79}$$

$$q \geqslant b + c + d. \tag{80}$$

Let $v_1, \ldots, v_q$ be integers such that

$$v_1 \leqslant v_2 \leqslant \ldots \leqslant v_q \leqslant p \tag{81}$$

and suppose that, for each $x \in \{0, 1, \ldots, c\}$, there exists an integer y such that

$$b + x \leqslant y \leqslant b + c + d \quad \text{and} \quad v_y \leqslant a - b + x + y. \tag{82}$$

Then $v_1 + \ldots + v_q \leqslant (a + c)(b + c) + (q - b - c)p$.

Proof. For each $x \in \{0, 1, \dots, c\}$, let $y(x)$ be the largest integer y for which (82) is true. Then

$$b + x \leqslant y(x) \leqslant b + c + d \qquad (x = 0, 1, \dots, c), \tag{83}$$

$$v_{y(x)} \leqslant a - b + x + y(x) \qquad (x = 0, 1, \dots, c). \tag{84}$$

Suppose that $I \in \{0, 1, \dots, c-1\}$ and

$$y(I) > y(I+1). \tag{85}$$

Then from (85) and the truth of (83) for $x = I, I+1$ it follows that $b + I + 1 < y(I) \leqslant b + c + d$, and from the truth of (84) for $x = I$ it follows that $v_{y(I)} < a - b + I + 1 + y(I)$, so that (82) is true for $x = I+1$, $y = y(I)$, which together with (85) contradicts the definition of $y(I+1)$. We conclude that (85) must be false for $I = 0, 1, \dots, c-1$. From this observation and (78), (83) and (80) it follows that $1 \leqslant y(0) \leqslant y(1) \leqslant \dots \leqslant y(c) \leqslant q$, and therefore it follows from (81) that

$$v_1 + \dots + v_q \leqslant y(0)\, v_{y(0)} + \sum_{x=1}^{c} (y(x) - y(x-1))\, v_{y(x)} + (q - y(c))\, p,$$

which by (84) is less than or equal to

$$y(0)\,(a - b + y(0)) + \sum_{x=1}^{c} (y(x) - y(x-1))\,(a - b + x + y(x)) + (q - y(c))\, p. \tag{86}$$

Furthermore, $y(x-1) - x \geqslant 0$ for $x = 1, \dots, c$ by (83) and (78), and $y(c) - b - c \geqslant 0$ by (83), and $p - a - c - y(c) \geqslant 0$ by (79) and (83), and we have seen that $y(0) \leqslant y(1) \leqslant \dots \leqslant y(c)$. Therefore

$$\sum_{x=1}^{c} (y(x) - y(x-1))\,(y(x-1) - x) + (y(c) - b - c)\,(p - a - c - y(c)) \tag{87}$$

is non-negative, and since we have shown that $v_1 + \dots + v_q$ does not exceed (86), it follows that it does not exceed the sum of (86) and (87), which is $(b + c)(a + c) + (q - b - c)\, p$.

LEMMA 23. *Suppose that G is a Dirac graph and t is an integer such that* $2 \leqslant t \leqslant 5(n + \varepsilon + 10)/224$ *and* $V(G)$ *has a subset R such that* $|R| = \frac{1}{2}(n + \varepsilon) - 2t + 3$ *and* $v(\xi, \bar{R}) \geqslant \frac{1}{2}(n + \varepsilon) - 2t + 2$ *for every* $\xi \in R$. *Then G has t edge-disjoint Hamiltonian circuits.*

Proof. Let $a = 2t - 1 + \varepsilon$, $b = 2t - 2$, $c = [(18/5)t - \frac{1}{2}\varepsilon]$, $d = 6t - 8 - \varepsilon$, $p = \frac{1}{2}(n + \varepsilon) - 2t + 3$, $q = \frac{1}{2}(n - \varepsilon) + 2t - 3$. Then $|R| = p$ and hence

$|\bar{R}| = n - p = q$. Let $\xi_1, \ldots, \xi_q$ be an ordering of $\bar{R}$ such that $v_1 \leqslant v_2 \leqslant \ldots \leqslant v_q$, where v_i denotes $v(\xi_i, R)$. Then $v_1 \leqslant v_2 \leqslant \ldots \leqslant v_q \leqslant p$ because $v(\xi_q, R) \leqslant |R|$. Since $t \geqslant 2$, it follows that $a > 0, b > 1, c > 0, d > 0$. Since $c \leqslant (18/5)\,t - \frac{1}{2}\varepsilon$, it follows that

$$q - b - c - d \geqslant \tfrac{1}{2}n + \varepsilon + 7 - \tfrac{48}{5}t \geqslant \tfrac{1}{2}n + \varepsilon + 7 - \tfrac{3}{14}(n + \varepsilon + 10) > 0,$$

$$\begin{aligned} p - a - b - 2c - d &\geqslant \tfrac{1}{2}(n + 3\varepsilon) + 14 - \tfrac{96}{5}t \\ &\geqslant \tfrac{1}{2}(n + 3\varepsilon) + 14 - \tfrac{3}{7}(n + \varepsilon + 10) > 0, \end{aligned}$$

i.e., $q > b + c + d$, $p > a + b + 2c + d$. From $q > b + c + d$ it follows that

$$(b - 1 + x) + d + 1 < q \qquad (x = 0, 1, \ldots, c). \tag{88}$$

Suppose that G does not possess t edge-disjoint Hamiltonian circuits. Then by Lemma 21 there is no $x \in \{0, 1, \ldots, c\}$ for which $\bar{R}$ is $[a + 2x, b - 1 + x, d]$-attached. This is by (88) and Lemma 20 equivalent to saying that for each $x \in \{0, 1, \ldots, c\}$ there is an $i \in \{1, 2, \ldots, d + 1\}$ such that $v_{b-1+x+i} \leqslant a + 2x + i - 1$, i.e., for each $x \in \{0, 1, \ldots, c\}$ there is an integer y such that $b + x \leqslant y \leqslant b + x + d$ and $v_y \leqslant a - b + x + y$. If we observe that $y \leqslant b + x + d$ implies $y \leqslant b + c + d$ when $x \in \{0, 1, \ldots, c\}$, we see that all the hypotheses of Lemma 22 have now been established. Therefore

$$\begin{aligned} (a + c)(b + c) + (q - b - c)p &\geqslant v_1 + \ldots + v_q = \sum_{\xi \in \bar{R}} v(\xi, R) = |R \nabla \bar{R}| \\ &= \sum_{\xi \in R} v(\xi, \bar{R}) \geqslant |R|\,(\tfrac{1}{2}(n + \varepsilon) - 2t + 2) = p(q - b - 2t + \varepsilon + 3), \end{aligned}$$

whence

$$p(c - 2t + \varepsilon + 3) \leqslant (a + c)(b + c). \tag{89}$$

From the definitions of a, b, c and the inequality $t \geqslant 2$ it is clear that

$$0 < a + c < 28t/5, \quad 0 < b + c \leqslant (28t/5) - 2, \quad c - 2t + \varepsilon + 3 > 8t/5:$$

therefore (89) implies that

$$\frac{98}{5}t - 7 > p = \frac{112}{5} \cdot \frac{5(n + \varepsilon + 10)}{224} - 2t - 2 \geqslant \frac{112}{5}t - 2t - 2,$$

which contradicts the hypothesis that $t \geqslant 2$. This contradiction shows that G must have t edge-disjoint Hamiltonian circuits.

LEMMA 24. *Suppose that G is a Dirac graph and $c_1, \ldots, c_h$ are edge-disjoint Hamiltonian circuits of G and some set of $\frac{1}{2}(n + \varepsilon) - 2h + 1$ vertices is independent in $G - (E(c_1) \cup \ldots \cup E(c_h))$ and $1 \leqslant h < [5(n + \varepsilon + 10)/224]$. Then G has $h + 1$ edge-disjoint Hamiltonian circuits.*

Proof. Let $H = G - (E(c_1) \cup \ldots \cup E(c_h))$ and let R be a set of $\frac{1}{2}(n + \varepsilon) - 2h + 1$ H-independent vertices. Let $t = h + 1$. Then $|R| = \frac{1}{2}(n + \varepsilon) - 2t + 3$. Furthermore $t \geqslant 2$ because $h \geqslant 1$, and since $h < [5(n + \varepsilon + 10)/224]$ and both sides of this inequality are integers it follows that $t \leqslant 5(n + \varepsilon + 10)/224$. Since G is a Dirac graph, $\frac{1}{2}(n + \varepsilon) \leqslant v(\xi) = v_H(\xi) + 2h$ for every $\xi \in V(G)$, and since R is H-independent $v_H(\xi) = v_H(\xi, \bar{R}) \leqslant v(\xi, \bar{R})$ for every $\xi \in R$: therefore $v(\xi, \bar{R}) \geqslant \frac{1}{2}(n + \varepsilon) - 2h = \frac{1}{2}(n + \varepsilon) - 2t + 2$ for every $\xi \in R$. Hence, by Lemma 23, G has $t = h + 1$ edge-disjoint Hamiltonian circuits.

5. Proof of Theorem 3

Suppose that $v(\xi) \geqslant \frac{1}{2}n$ for every $\xi \in V(G)$. We wish to prove that G has a set of $[5(n + \varepsilon + 10)/224]$ edge-disjoint Hamiltonian circuits. Since this is vacuously true if $n \leqslant 34$, we may assume that $n \geqslant 35$. Let h be the maximum number of edge-disjoint Hamiltonian circuits which can be found in G: then $h \geqslant 1$ by Theorem 1. Let $c_1, \ldots, c_h$ be edge-disjoint Hamiltonian circuits of G and let $H = G - (E(c_1) \cup \ldots \cup E(c_h))$. Suppose that $h < [5(n + \varepsilon + 10)/224]$: then since both sides of this inequality are integers

$$h \leqslant \frac{5(n + \varepsilon + 10)}{224} - 1 = \frac{5n + 5\varepsilon - 174}{224}. \tag{90}$$

Therefore $h < (n + 3\varepsilon - 4)/12$. Also, the definition of h implies that H has no Hamiltonian circuit. Hence by Lemma 5 either H is separable or $\frac{1}{2}(n + \varepsilon) - 2h + 1$ vertices are independent in H. If H is separable, then since $h \leqslant (n - 4)/20$ by (90) it follows from Lemma 8 that G has $h + 1$ edge-disjoint Hamiltonian circuits, and if $\frac{1}{2}(n + \varepsilon) - 2h + 1$ vertices are H-independent it follows from Lemma 24 that G has $h + 1$ edge-disjoint Hamiltonian circuits: in both cases the definition of h is contradicted. This contradiction shows that

$$h \geqslant [5(n + \varepsilon + 10)/224],$$

and Theorem 3 is proved.

References

1. BERGE, C. *The Theory of Graphs and its Applications* (1958), English translation by A. Doig, Methuen, London and Wiley, New York, 1962.
2. BONDY, J. A. Properties of graphs with constraints on degrees. To appear in *Studia Scientiarum Mathematicarum Hungarica.*
3. CHARTRAND, G. and KAPOOR, S. F. (editors), *The Many Facets of Graph Theory* (Proceedings of a Conference at Western Michigan University in November 1968), Springer–Verlag, Berlin, Heidelberg and New York, 1969.
4. DIRAC, G. A. Some theorems on abstract graphs. *Proc. London Math. Soc.* (3) **2** (1952), 69–81.

5. Ghouila-Houri, A. Une condition suffisante d'existence d'un circuit Hamiltonien, *C.R. Acad. Sci. Paris* **251** (1960), 495–497.
6. Moon, J. and Moser, L. On Hamiltonian bipartite graphs. *Israel J. Math.* **1** (1963), 163–165.
7. Nash-Williams, C. St.J. A. Hamiltonian circuits in graphs and digraphs. To appear in **(3)**.
8. Nash-Williams, C. St.J. A. On Hamiltonian circuits in finite graphs. *Proc. Amer. Math. Soc.* **17** (1966), 466–467.
9. Ore, O. *Theory of Graphs* (American Mathematical Society, Providence, R.I., 1962).
10. Pósa, L. A theorem concerning Hamiltonian lines. *Magyar Tud. Akad. Mat. Kutató Int. Közl.* **7** (1962), 225–226.

Algebraically Closed Semigroups

B. H. Neumann

1. Introduction

Many questions that one may ask about groups make sense also when asked about semigroups; but even if the answers turn out to be the same, the methods of proof are often quite different. We shall illustrate this by extending to semigroups some notions and results about algebraically closed groups (see Scott (**6**), Neumann (**5**)).

Given a semigroup A, we consider systems of conditions of the form

$$f_i(x_1, x_2, \ldots) = f_i'(x_1, x_2, \ldots), \tag{1.1}$$

$$g_j(x_1, x_2, \ldots) \neq g_j'(x_1, x_2, \ldots); \tag{1.2}$$

here the f_i, f_i', g_j, g_j' are semigroup words in the *variables*† $x_1, x_2, \ldots$ and *constants*, that is elements of A; the suffixes i, j range over suitable index sets I, J, respectively. If $I \cup J$ is infinite, then the total number of variables in (1.1) and (1.2) may also be infinite. We shall, however, restrict our attention to the case that $I \cup J$ is finite‡, and then the number of variables in (1.1) and (1.2) is also finite. The system of conditions (1.1), (1.2) is called *compatible* over A if it can be solved in some semigroup containing A. The semigroup A is *algebraically closed* if every finite compatible system of conditions (1.1), (1.2) can be solved in A itself. The semigroup A is *weakly algebraically closed* if every finite compatible system of equations (1.1) only can be solved in A.

These notions belong to universal algebra rather than semigroup theory; and a standard argument, relying on well-order and also appropriate to universal algebra, shows that *every semigroup S can be embedded in an algebraically closed semigroup A*; and if S is finite then A can be made countable§, and if S is infinite then A can be made to have the same order§ as S.

† If there are only three or fewer variables, we use x, y, z instead.

‡ More generally we may replace 'finite' consistently by 'of cardinal less than some fixed infinite cardinal'; see Erdélyi (**3**).

§ *Mutatis mutandis* if infinite systems of conditions (1.1), (1.2) are admitted; see Scott (**6**), Erdélyi(**3**).

Clearly every algebraically closed semigroup is also weakly algebraically closed; and the trivial semigroup, which has only a single element, is weakly algebraically closed, but not algebraically closed. As in the case of groups this is, however, the only exception:

THEOREM 1. *If the weakly algebraically closed semigroup A has more than one element, then it is algebraically closed.*

The proof relies on a useful lemma, which is stated and proved in §2. The proof in the analogous case of groups (**5**) is rather shorter, because it uses generalized free product techniques, which are not available here.

Algebraically closed groups are simple (**5**, Corollary); in semigroups more than one notion of simplicity is of use and interest; the strongest notion is that of a *congruence simple* semigroup, that is a semigroup with only the obvious two congruences: the identity, modulo which it remains unchanged, and the universal congruence, modulo which it becomes trivial. Congruence simplicity in semigroups is analogous to simplicity in groups, and a simple group, considered as a semigroup, is congruence simple. We shall prove the analogue of the result on groups quoted above:

THEOREM 2. *Every algebraically closed semigroup is congruence simple.*

The notion of algebraic closure can be refined, following Levin (**4**), by imposing bounds on the number $|I|$ of equations (1.1), the number $|J|$ of inequalities (1.2), and the number n of variables in them. We shall obtain some correspondingly refined results, but do not here aim at the full analogues of Levin's best possible results.

2. The principal lemma

In this section we state and prove our main auxiliary result.

LEMMA 1. *Let A be a semigroup, and $\phi : A \to A$ a mapping of A into A (strictly speaking: a mapping of the set of elements, or carrier, of A into itself). Then there is a monomorphism (alias embedding) μ of A into a semigroup B containing two elements σ, τ with the property that for all elements a of A*

$$\tau(a\mu)\,\sigma = a\phi\mu. \tag{2.1}$$

Before we embark on the proof of the lemma, we make some remarks. Firstly, if A has a unit element, its image under μ will not in general be the unit element of B—in fact B need not have a unit element even if A does; and the same goes for a zero. Secondly, we shall arrange our proof so that σ and τ

commute; this is unnecessary for the applications of the lemma, but slightly simplifies the proof. Lastly, the lemma (with this second remark) can be paraphrased to say that *the system of equations*

$$yax = a\phi, \tag{2.2}$$

$$xy = yx, \tag{2.3}$$

where a ranges over an arbitrary semigroup A and ϕ is an arbitrary mapping of A into A, is compatible over A.

Proof of Lemma 1. We form the free product U, say, of A and a free monogenic semigroup generated by an element s; see, for example, Clifford and Preston (**2**, p. 140). The elements of U are of the form

$$u = a_0\, s^{p_1}\, a_1 \ldots a_{m-1}\, s^{p_m}\, a_m, \tag{2.4}$$

with $m \geqslant 0, p_1, \ldots, p_m \geqslant 1, a_0, \ldots, a_m$ elements of A, and if $m \geqslant 1$ then a_0 or a_m or both may be absent.

We also form the free product of A with another free monogenic semigroup generated by an element t; and we denote by V the set of those elements of this free product that start with a power of t; if the free product is V^+, then $V = tV^+$. Thus the elements of V are of the form

$$v = t^{q_1}\, b_1 \ldots b_{n-1}\, t^{q_n}\, b_n, \tag{2.5}$$

with $n \geqslant 1, q_1, \ldots, q_n \geqslant 1, b_1, \ldots, b_n$ elements of A, and b_n possibly absent.

Next we take a symbol 1 which we assume distinct from the elements of A, and we form

$$W = \{1\} \cup U \cup V \cup U \times V.$$

Thus the elements of W are of the form $w = 1$ or $w = u$ or $w = v$ or $w = (u, v)$, with u and v given by (2.4) and (2.5).

Certain mappings of W into W will now be defined; first to each element a of A a mapping $\rho(a)$, by

$$1\rho(a) = a \in U;$$

$$u\rho(a) = ua \in U;$$

$$v\rho(a) = va \in V;$$

$$(u, v)\, \rho(a) = (u, va) \in U \times V.$$

Thus $\rho(a)$ acts like right multiplication by a, interpreting $U \times V$ as UV in some semigroup containing both, for example their free product.

Next we define a mapping $\sigma : W \to W$; on V and correspondingly on $U \times V$ the definition splits into several cases:

$$1\sigma = s \in U;$$

$$u\sigma = us \in U;$$

if $v = t^{q_1}$, then $v\sigma = (s, t^{q_1}) \in U \times V$;

if $v = tb_1$, then $v\sigma = b_1 \phi \in U$;

if $v = t^{q_1}b_1$ with $q_1 \geqslant 2$, then $v\sigma = t^{q_1-1}(b_1 \phi) \in V$;

if $v = tb_1 t^{q_2}$, then $v\sigma = (b_1 \phi, t^{q_2}) \in U \times V$;

if $v = v_1 t^{q_n}$ with $v_1 = t^{q_1} b_1 \dots b_{n-1}$ and $q_1 \geqslant 2$ or $n \geqslant 3$, then $v\sigma = v_1 \sigma t^{q_n} \in V$;

if $v = t^{q_1} b_1 \dots b_{n-1} tb_n$ with $n \geqslant 2$, then $v\sigma = t^{q_1} b_1 \dots (b_{n-1} (b_n \phi)) \in V$;

if $v = t^{q_1} b_1 \dots b_{n-1} t^{q_n} b_n$ with $n \geqslant 2$ and $q_n \geqslant 2$, then $v\sigma = t^{q_1} b_1 \dots b_{n-1} t^{q_n-1} (b_n \phi) \in V$;

if $v = t^{q_1}$, then $(u, v)\sigma = (us, t^{q_1}) \in U \times V$;

if $v = tb_1$, then $(u, v)\sigma = u(b_1 \phi) \in U$;

if $v = tb_1 t^{q_2}$, then $(u, v)\sigma = (u(b_1 \phi), t^{q_2}) \in U \times V$;

if $v \in V$ is not of the form t^{q_1} or tb_1 or $tb_1 t^{q_2}$, then $(u, v)\sigma = (u, v\sigma) \in U \times V$.

Finally we define a mapping $\tau : W \to W$ by

$$1\tau = t \in V;$$

$$u\tau = (u, t) \in U \times V;$$

$$v\tau = vt \in V;$$

$$(u, v)\tau = (u, vt) \in U \times V.$$

Denote by B the semigroup of mappings $W \to W$ generated by all $\rho(a)$, σ, τ. Then one sees at once that for all $a, b \in A$

$$\rho(a)\,\rho(b) = \rho(ab);$$

hence the mapping $\mu : A \to B$ defined by

$$a\mu = \rho(a),$$

for all $a \in A$, is a homomorphism. It is in fact a monomorphism, because if $a\mu = b\mu$, that is if $\rho(a) = \rho(b)$, then

$$a = 1\rho(a) = 1\rho(b) = b.$$

Next we verify (2.1) in the form

$$\tau\rho(a)\,\sigma = \rho(a\phi):$$

$$1\tau\rho(a)\,\sigma = t\,\rho(a)\,\sigma = ta\sigma = a\phi = 1\rho(a\phi);$$

$$u\tau\rho(a)\,\sigma = (u, t)\,\rho(a)\,\sigma = (u, ta)\,\sigma = u(a\phi) = u\rho(a\phi);$$

$$v\tau\rho(a)\,\sigma = vt\,\rho(a)\,\sigma = vta\sigma = v(a\phi) = v\rho(a\phi);$$

$$(u, v)\,\tau\rho(a)\,\sigma = (u, vt)\,\rho(a)\,\sigma = (u, vta)\,\sigma = \big(u, v(a\phi)\big) = (u, v)\,\rho(a\phi).$$

This completes the proof of the lemma. The verification of the commutativity of σ and τ is straightforward and omitted, as it is in any case not required for our purposes. It is also clear that the elements of W can be thought of as providing a normal form for the elements of B with a unit element adjoined.

3. Proof of Theorems 1 and 2

To prove Theorem 1 we need another lemma.

LEMMA 2. *Every weakly algebraically closed semigroup with more than one element is infinite.*

Proof. Assume that A is weakly algebraically closed and finite. The system of equations

$$az = za = z^2 = z \tag{3.1}$$

for all $a \in A$ is finite and compatible over A, as a zero can be adjoined to any semigroup. Thus A contains a solution of (3.1), which we denote by 0. Next, if $\phi : A \to A$ is an arbitrary mapping, then the system of equations (2.2)

$$yax = a\phi,$$

with a ranging over A, is compatible over A and finite. Thus A contains elements s, t such that

$$tas = a\phi$$

for all $a \in A$. But

$$t0s = 0,$$

and thus $0\phi = 0$, whatever the mapping ϕ. It follows that 0 is the only element of A, and the lemma is proved.

Proof of Theorem 1. We now assume that A is weakly algebraically closed and non-trivial, hence, by Lemma 2, infinite. If (1.1), (1.2) is a finite compatible system of conditions, then there is a semigroup A^* containing A with elements $a_1^*, a_2^*, \ldots$ corresponding to the variables $x_1, x_2, \ldots$ such that, for all $i \in I$ and $j \in J$,

$$f_i(a_1^*, a_2^*, \ldots) = f_i'(a_1^*, a_2^*, \ldots),$$
$$g_j(a_1^*, a_2^*, \ldots) \neq g_j'(a_1^*, a_2^*, \ldots).$$

Choose elements $c_j, c_j' \in A$ for all $j \in J$ such that

$$\begin{aligned} c_j &= c_k \text{ if, and only if, } g_j(a_1^*, a_2^*, \ldots) = g_k(a_1^*, a_2^*, \ldots), \\ c_j &= c_k' \text{ if, and only if, } g_j(a_1^*, a_2^*, \ldots) = g_k'(a_1^*, a_2^*, \ldots), \\ c_j' &= c_k' \text{ if, and only if, } g_j'(a_1^*, a_2^*, \ldots) = g_k'(a_1^*, a_2^*, \ldots). \end{aligned}$$

This is possible because J is finite and A is infinite. Then

$$c_j \neq c_j' \text{ for all } j \in J. \tag{3.2}$$

Let $\phi : A^* \to A^*$ be a mapping that maps each $g_j(a_1^*, a_2^*, \ldots)$ on c_j and each $g_j'(a_1^*, a_2^*, \ldots)$ on c_j', and that is otherwise arbitrary: the c_j and c_j' have been so chosen that such a mapping exists. By Lemma 1 then there is an embedding μ of A^* in a semigroup B containing two elements σ, τ such that

$$\tau(a^*\mu)\,\sigma = a^*\phi\mu$$

for all $a^* \in A^*$. If we identify A^* with its image embedded in B, then A also becomes a subsemigroup of B, and it follows at once that the equations

$$f_i(x_1, x_2, \ldots) = f_i'(x_1, x_2, \ldots),$$
$$yg_j(x_1, x_2, \ldots)\,x = c_j,$$
$$yg_j'(x_1, x_2, \ldots)\,x = c_j',$$

which are solved in B by $a_1^*, a_2^*, \ldots, \sigma, \tau$ in place of $x_1, x_2, \ldots, x, y$, are compatible over A. As they are finite in number and A is weakly algebraically closed, they have solutions in A, say $a_1, a_2, \ldots, s, t$ in place of $x_1, x_2, \ldots, x, y$. These then satisfy, for all $i \in I, j \in J$,

$$f_i(a_1, a_2, \ldots) = f_i'(a_1, a_2, \ldots),$$
$$tg_j(a_1, a_2, \ldots)\,s = c_j,$$
$$tg_j'(a_1, a_2, \ldots)\,s = c_j'.$$

By (3.2) then also

$$g_j(a_1, a_2, \ldots) \neq g_j'(a_1, a_2, \ldots)$$

for all $j \in J$, which shows that $a_1, a_2, \ldots$ in place of $x_1, x_2, \ldots$ solve the system (1.1), (1.2) in A. Hence A is algebraically closed, and the theorem follows.

Proof of Theorem 2. Let A be an algebriacally closed semigroup, and let θ be a congruence, not the identity, on A. Let $(a, b) \in \theta$, where $a \neq b$, and let c, d be arbitrary elements of A, not necessarily distinct from a or b. It follows from Lemma 1 that the system of equations

$$yax = c, \qquad ybx = d$$

is compatible over A. Hence A contains elements s, t such that

$$tas = c, \qquad tbs = d.$$

But as θ is a congruence, then also $(c, d) \in \theta$, and as c, d were arbitrary, θ is the universal congruence on A. The theorem thus follows.

4. Extension of the results

The proofs of our theorems can be made to yield more, if we observe the number of equations and variables. We paraphrase Levin (**4**) and call the semigroup A *weakly* (m, n)*-algebraically closed* if every compatible system of at most m equations in at most n variables over A has a solution in A; and we call A (m, m', n)*-algebraically closed* if every compatible system of at most m equations and at most m' inequalities in (together) at most n variables over A has a solution in A. Then Theorem 1 can be refined to the following theorem, without change of proof.

THEOREM 3. *The semigroup A is (m, m', n)-algebraically closed if it is non-trivial and is weakly $(m + 2m', n + 2)$-algebraically closed.*

Similarly Theorem 2 can be refined, without change of proof:

THEOREM 4. *Every weakly* $(2, 2)$*-algebraically closed semigroup is congruence simple.*

It is highly plausible that $(2, 2)$ can here be improved to $(2, 1)$; and it is at least possible that it can be improved to $(1, 1)$.

Levin (**4**, Corollary) shows that a group that is $(m, 1)$-algebraically closed is also (m, n)-algebraically closed for all $n \leqslant \aleph_0$. The corresponding proposition for semigroups is likely to be true, too, and could probably be obtained by an adaptation of Levin's method. Here we content ourselves with a weaker theorem that can be obtained more cheaply.†

THEOREM 5. *If the semigroup A is weakly* $(m, 2)$*-algebraically closed, then it is weakly* (m, n)*-algebraically closed for all finite n.*

COROLLARY. *If all 2-variable equations that are compatible over the semigroup A of order* $|A| > 1$ *can be solved in A, then A is algebraically closed.*

Proof of the theorem. Let A satisfy the hypothesis of the theorem, and let

$$f_i(x_1, \ldots, x_n) = f_i'(x_1, \ldots, x_n), \qquad i = 1, \ldots, m,$$

be a compatible system of equations over A. Let $a_1^*, \ldots, a_n^*$ be elements of a semigroup A^* containing A such that

$$f_i(a_1^*, \ldots, a_n^*) = f_i'(a_1^*, \ldots, a_n^*), \qquad i = 1, \ldots, m.$$

Let $a_0 \in A$. Choose a mapping $\phi : A^* \to A^*$ such that

$$a_0 \phi = a_1^*, \quad a_1^* \phi = a_2^*, \ldots, a_{n-1}^* \phi = a_n^*.$$

By Lemma 1 we can adjoin elements s, t to A^* such that

$$t a_0 s = a_1^*, \quad t a_1^* s = a_2^*, \ldots, t a_{n-1}^* s = a_n^*.$$

Hence we have:

$$f_i(t a_0 s, \ldots, t^n a_0 s^n) = f_i'(t a_0 s, \ldots, t^n a_0 s^n), \qquad i = 1, \ldots, m,$$

are compatible over A. These are m equations in 2 variables, hence have a solution in A; and this solution clearly also solves the original equations. Thus the theorem follows.

5. Concluding remarks

The compatibility of the system (3.1) of equations shows that every finite set of elements of an algebraically closed semigroup has a 'local' zero. It follows at once that an algebraically closed semigroup can never be a group, or be embeddable in a group. Similarly the system of equations

$$xa = ax = a, \qquad x^2 = x \tag{5.1}$$

is compatible over every semigroup, with a ranging over all its elements. Hence every finite set of elements of an algebraically closed semigroup has a 'local' (two-sided) neutral element.

† See Note Added in Proof (1).

On the other hand, as the system of conditions

$$ax = x, \qquad x \neq a,$$

$$by = b, \qquad y \neq b,$$

is clearly compatible over any semigroup containing a and b, there can be no 'global' zero or neutral element in any algebraically closed semigroup.

It follows from the results stated in the introduction that every semigroup can be embedded in a congruence simple semigroup. I have it on very good authority that this fact has been known for some time, though a precise reference eludes me.†

One naturally asks whether every finite semigroup can be embedded in a finite congruence simple semigroup. This is, however, not the case. A finite congruence simple semigroup is (i) of order 2, or (ii) a simple group, or (iii) a Rees matrix semigroup (see Clifford and Preston (**1**, §§ 3.1, 3.2, 3.4)) with trivial structure group and certain restrictions on its sandwich matrix; these facts are probably known, and I omit the proof. It follows in particular that in a finite congruence simple semigroup with 0 every element satisfies $a^2 = 0$ or $a^2 = a$ (see Clifford and Preston (**1**, Theorem 2.52 (i))), and therefore the semigroup $(C_2)^0$ obtained by adjoining a zero to the cyclic group of order 2 cannot be embedded in any finite congruence simple semigroup.

By contrast it is well known that every finite group can be embedded in a finite simple group.

Finally we prove, again in analogy with a known fact about groups, that *there are $2^{\aleph_0}$ mutually non-isomorphic algebraically closed semigroups of countable order*: for every countable semigroup contains only countably many 2-generator subsemigroups; but there are $2^{\aleph_0}$ mutually non-isomorphic 2-generator semigroups (and even groups), and each of them can be embedded in a countable algebraically closed semigroup. It would be interesting, but may be difficult, to construct two countable algebraically closed semigroups that can be proved to be non-isomorphic: the argument above is far from constructive.‡

Note Added in Proof

(1) Professor Frank Levin has now proved the conjecture in the paragraph preceding Theorem 5; this result, and much more, can be found in: Frank Levin, One variable equations over semigroups, *Bull. Austral. Math. Soc.* **2** (1970), 247-252.

(2) Professor W. D. Munn has kindly supplied me with the elusive reference

† See Note Added in Proof (2), (3).
‡ See Note Added in Proof (4).

to the embedding of a semigroup in a congruence simple one, namely: Šutov, È. G., Embeddings of semigroups into simple and complete semigroups, *Mat. Sbornik* (*N.S.*) **62** (**104**) (1963), 496-511 (Russian); quoted from *Math. Reviews* **30** (1965), # 2100.

(3) I am indebted to Professor G. B. Preston for the remark that algebraically closed semigroups are also *$\mathscr{D}$-simple*, that is to say to every pair of elements a, b there is an element c such that a and c generate the same left ideal and c and b the same right ideal; thus in particular *every semigroup can be embedded in a $\mathscr{D}$-simple semigroup*, a fact that Professor Preston had recently proved independently.

(4) For a further discussion of the problem of deciding when two algebraically closed groups or semigroups are isomorphic, see B. H. Neumann, The isomorphism problem for algebraically closed groups, *Proc. Conf. Decision Problems in Group Theory, Irvine, California, September 1969*, North Holland Publishing Co., Amsterdam 1971 For a discussion of related results and problems in cancellative semigroups, see B. H. Neumann, Some remarks on cancellative semigroups, *Math. Z.* **117** (1970), 97–111.

References

1. Clifford, A. H. and Preston, G. B. *The Algebraic Theory of Semigroups, Vol. I.* (Amer. Math. Soc., Providence, R.I., 1961).
2. Clifford, A. H. and Preston, G. B. *The Algebraic Theory of Semigroups, Vol. II.* (Amer. Math. Soc., Providence, R.I., 1967).
3. Erdélyi, Mária. On π-algebraically closed groups. *Publ. Math. Debrecen* **7** (1960), 310–315.
4. Levin, Frank. One variable equations over groups. *Arch. Math.* **15** (1964), 179–188.
5. Neumann, B. H. A note on algebraically closed groups. *J. London Math. Soc.* **27** (1952), 247–249.
6. Scott, W. R. Algebraically closed groups. *Proc. Amer. Math. Soc.* **2** (1951), 118–121.

The Irrationality or Rationality of Certain Infinite Series

A. Oppenheim

1. Introduction

Erdös and Straus **(1)** showed that if the sequence of increasing positive integers $\{n_i\}$ satisfies the two conditions

$$\text{(i)}\ \limsup n_i^2/n_{i+1} \leqslant 1,$$

$$\text{(ii) the sequence } \{N_i/N_{i+1}\} \text{ is bounded,}$$

where N_i is the least common multiple of the integers $n_1, n_2, \ldots, n_i$, then the Ahmes series $\Sigma 1/n_i$ is rational if and only if eventually

$$\text{(iii)}\ n_{i+1} = n_i^2 - n_i + 1.$$

This theorem admits of considerable extension. Thus if the integers e_i satisfy the condition $1 \leqslant e_i \leqslant E$($E$ fixed) and if the n_i satisfy (i) and (ii), then the series $\Sigma e_i/n_i$ is rational if and only if both (iii) and

$$\text{(iv)}\ e_{i+1} = e_i \quad \text{eventually.}$$

In particular suppose the integers m_i satisfy the conditions $m_i > 1$, $m_{i+1} = m_i^2 - m_i + 1$ $(i \geqslant 1)$ and let $e_i = 1$ or 2. Then $\Sigma e_i/m_i$ is rational if and only if from some point on all $e_i = 1$ or all $e_i = 2$.

It is possible also to consider terms of either sign. Thus if $\varepsilon_i = \pm 1$ and if the n_i satisfy conditions (i) and (ii), then the series $\Sigma \varepsilon_i/n_i$ is rational if and only if eventually

$$n_{i+1} - \varepsilon_{i+1}\varepsilon_{i+2} = n_i(n_i - \varepsilon_i \varepsilon_{i+1}).$$

More generally results are obtained for series of the type

$$\sum \frac{a_1 a_2 \ldots a_i}{n_1 n_2 \ldots n_i} \varepsilon_i e_i$$

whence also can be deduced statements for infinite products which were otherwise deduced in (**2**).

To obtain these results suitable modifications of the method of Erdös and Straus prove to be adequate.

2. Statement and proof of results

THEOREM 1. *Suppose that $\{a_i\}$, $\{n_i\}$, $\{e_i\}$ are sequences of positive integers such that*

$$\limsup a_{i+1} n_i^2/n_{i+1} \leqslant 1, \tag{2.1}$$

$$a_1 a_2 \dots a_{i+1} N_i/N_{i+1} \tag{2.2}$$

is bounded (*where N_i is the least common multiple of $n_1, n_2, \dots, n_i$*),

$$1 \leqslant e_i \leqslant E \qquad (\text{all } i). \tag{2.3}$$

Then the sum of the series

$$x = \sum \frac{a_1 a_2 \dots a_i}{n_i} e_i = \Sigma u_i$$

is rational if and only if for all $i \geqslant i_0$

$$n_{i+1} - 1 = a_{i+1} n_i(n_i - 1), \qquad e_i = e. \tag{2.4}$$

Proof. Suppose that x is rational, $x = a/b$ for positive integers a, b. Multiply by bN_i to get

$$bN_i u_{i+1} + bN_i u_{i+2} + \sum_{j \geqslant 3} bN_i u_{i+j} \equiv 0 \pmod 1. \tag{2.5}$$

Note that the convergence of the series implies that $n_i \to \infty$ as $i \to \infty$ and that the hypotheses imply

$$\sum_{j \geqslant 3} bN_i u_{i+j} = O\left(\frac{1}{n_{i+1} n_{i+2}}\right).$$

Define now (after Erdös and Straus) unique integers c_i, d_i by the conditions

$$bN_i e_{i+1} a_1 \dots a_{i+1} = c_i n_{i+1} - d_i, \tag{2.51}$$

$$0 \leqslant d_i < n_{i+1}, \qquad 1 \leqslant c_i.$$

Then on multiplication by n_{i+1} (2.5) yields

$$d_i = b_i N_i u_{i+2} n_{i+1} + O(1/n_{i+2}) + M_i n_{i+1} \tag{2.52}$$

for some integer M_i.

We prove now that, for large i, $M_i = 0$. The first term on the right of (2.52) is equal to

$$\frac{a_1 \dots a_{i+1} b N_i}{n_{i+1}} \frac{a_{i+2} n_{i+1}^2}{n_{i+2}} e_{i+2}$$

and is therefore bounded by (2.1), (2.2), (2.3). Thus

$$d_i = O(1) + M_i n_{i+1}, \qquad 0 \leqslant d_i < n_{i+1}$$

whence $M_i = 0$ for all large i and so

$$d_i = b N_i u_{i+2} n_{i+1} + o(1); \tag{2.53}$$

and therefore d_i is bounded.

Write now

$$n_{i+1} N_i = g_i N_{i+1}, \qquad g_i = (N_i, n_{i+1}) \geqslant 1. \tag{2.54}$$

Then (2.53) and (2.51) (with $i + 1$ in place of i) give

$$d_i = g_i \left(c_{i+1} - \frac{d_{i+1}}{n_{i+2}} \right) + o(1)$$

from which we deduce that $d_i = g_i c_{i+1}$ eventually. For

$$g_i d_{i+1} = O(n_{i+1}) = o(n_{i+2}), d_i = g_i c_{i+1} + o(1),$$

$$d_i = g_i c_{i+1} \qquad (\text{all } i > i_0) \tag{2.55}$$

since d_i, $g_i c_{i+1}$ are integers.

From (2.51), (2.54) and (2.55) we obtain

$$g_i e_{i+1} (c_{i+1} n_{i+2} - g_{i+1} c_{i+2}) = e_{i+2} a_{i+2} n_{i+1} (c_i n_{i+1} - g_i c_{i+1}) \qquad (i \geqslant i_0) \tag{2.6}$$

and this has been proved on the basis of (2.1), (2.2), (2.3) and the rationality of x.

We now show that $g_i = 1$ and then that $e_{i+1} = e_i$ for all large enough i. To show that $g_i = 1$, use (2.6), (2.1) and the boundedness of g_i, c_i, e_i to get

$$g_i e_{i+1} c_{i+1} = \frac{a_{i+2} n_{i+1}^2}{n_{i+2}} e_{i+2} c_i + o(1),$$

$$g_i e_{i+1} c_{i+1} \leqslant e_{i+2} c_i + o(1),$$

$$g_i e_{i+1} c_{i+1} \leqslant e_{i+2} c_i \qquad (i \geqslant j). \tag{2.61}$$

But from (2.61)

$$g_j g_{j+1} \cdots g_i e_{i+1} c_{i+1} \leqslant e_{j+2} c_j$$

$$g_j g_{j+1} \cdots g_i \frac{c_{i+1}}{e_{i+2}} \leqslant \frac{c_j}{e_{j+1}} \qquad (i \geqslant j).$$

Hence (i) $g_i = 1$ for all large i and (ii) the sequence of positive rational numbers $\{c_i/e_{i+1}\}$ with bounded numerators is decreasing in the wide sense for all large i. Hence $c_{i+1}/e_{i+2} = c_i/e_{i+1}$ for all large i.

Thus (2.6) becomes

$$e_{i+1}(e_{i+2}\,n_{i+2} - e_{i+3}) = e_{i+2}\,a_{i+2}\,n_{i+1}(e_{i+1}\,n_{i+1} - e_{i+2}), \tag{2.62}$$

for all large enough i.

We have now to show that from some stage on the bounded e_i in (2.62) are all equal. To prove this it is enough to show that from some stage on the e_i have the same canonical decomposition into prime factors.

For a given prime p let $p^{\alpha_i}\|e_i$ (i.e. $p^{\alpha_i}|e_i$ but $p^{\alpha_i+1}\nmid e_i$) so that $\alpha_i \geqslant 0$. In (2.62) the term $e_{i+1}\,e_{i+3}$ is divisible by exactly p to the power $\alpha_{i+1} + \alpha_{i+3}$. The other three terms are divisible by at least p to the respective powers

$$\alpha_{i+1} + \alpha_{i+2}, \qquad \alpha_{i+1} + \alpha_{i+2}, \qquad 2\alpha_{i+2}.$$

We prove that the α_i reach a common value for large i. If the sequence $\{\alpha_i\}$ is monotonic decreasing, this is clear since the α_i are non-negative integers. If the sequence is not monotonic decreasing then $\alpha_{i+1} \leqslant \alpha_{i+2}$ for some (large) suffix i. Hence

$$\alpha_{i+1} + \alpha_{i+3} \geqslant \alpha_{i+1} + \alpha_{i+2}, \qquad \alpha_{i+3} \geqslant \alpha_{i+2};$$

the sequence $\{\alpha_i\}$ continues to increase. But the α_i are bounded above since $1 \leqslant e_i \leqslant E$, $p \leqslant E$ if $p|e_i$. Again therefore the α_i reach a common value: the e_i for all large i have the same canonical decomposition and so are equal. The proof therefore of Theorem 1 is complete once we have shown that (2.4) implies the rationality of x. But (2.4) gives

$$\frac{1}{n_i - 1} = \frac{1}{n_i} + \frac{a_{i+1}}{n_{i+1} - 1} = \frac{1}{n_i} + \frac{a_{i+1}}{n_{i+1}} + \frac{a_{i+1}\,a_{i+2}}{n_{i+1} - 1} = \ldots,$$

$$x = \sum_{i=1}^{J} u_i + \frac{ea_1\,a_2 \ldots a_j}{n_j - 1},$$

a rational number.

3. Remarks

1. If $a_i = 1$ (all i), the theorem is that of Erdös and Straus (**1**).

2. If in addition to (2.1), (2.2), (2.3) there exist infinitely many pairs n_i, n_j which are not coprime ($i \neq j$), then x must be irrational.

3. If in addition to (2.1), (2.2), (2.3) there are infinitely many pairs a_i, n_i which are not coprime, then x must be irrational.

4. The condition (2.2) can be improved as in the case of Erdös and Straus for $a_i = 1$ (all i). Theorem 1 is still true if (2.1) is replaced by

$$\limsup \frac{a_1 \dots a_{i+1} N_i}{n_{i+1}} \left(a_{i+2} \frac{n_{i+1}^2}{n_{i+2}} - 1 \right) \leqslant 0. \tag{3.1}$$

The details are omitted.

5. Signs $\varepsilon_i = \pm 1$ can be introduced. Two points however need attention: (i) a modification in the definition of c_i, d_i, (ii) an addition to the proof after equation (2.55):

$$d_i = g_i c_{i+1}.$$

In place of (2.51) use

$$b N_i e_{i+1} a_1 \dots a_{i+1} = c_i n_{i+1} - d_i \varepsilon_{i+1} \varepsilon_{i+2}, \tag{3.2}$$
$$0 \leqslant d_i < n_{i+1}, \qquad 0 \leqslant c_i \text{ (in place of } 1 \leqslant c_i).$$

If $c_i = 0$, then necessarily $\varepsilon_{i+1} \varepsilon_{i+2} = -1$ and $d_i > 0$. If however $d_i = 0$, then $c_i \geqslant 1$.

The proof goes through until we reach (2.55). Here we must now show that $d_i = 0$ (and so $c_{i+1} = 0$) cannot occur for infinitely many i. But $d_i = 0$ implies that

$$0 < d_{i+1} = b N_{i+1} e_{i+2} a_1 \dots a_{i+2}$$

which is arbitrarily large for large i whereas d_{i+1} is bounded.

The rest of the proof is essentially the same. Thus we may state

THEOREM 2. *Suppose that the positive integers n_i, a_i, e_i satisfy the conditions*

$$\limsup a_{i+1} n_i^2/n_{i+1} \leqslant 1, \qquad 1 \leqslant e_i \leqslant E,$$
$$a_1 a_2 \dots a_{i+1} N_i/N_{i+1} \textit{ is bounded.}$$

Let $\varepsilon_i = \pm 1$; $u_i = (a_1 \dots a_i/n_i) e_i \varepsilon_i$. Then the series Σu_i (assumed to be convergent) is rational if and only if from some point on (i) the e_i are all equal and (ii) the a_i, n_i are connected by the relations

$$n_{i+1} - \varepsilon_{i+1} \varepsilon_{i+2} = a_{i+1} n_i (n_i - \varepsilon_i \varepsilon_{i+1}).$$

4. A theorem is now given for the series (4.4) below.

THEOREM 3. *Suppose that the four sequences of integers $\{a_i\}$, $\{n_i\}$, $\{e_i\}$, $\{\varepsilon_i\}$ satisfy the following conditions:*

$$a_i \geqslant 1, \qquad n_i \geqslant 1, \qquad \limsup a_{i+1} n_i/n_{i+1} \leqslant 1, \qquad n_i \to \infty, \tag{4.1}$$

$$\frac{a_1 a_2 \dots a_{i+1}}{n_{i+1}} \textit{ is bounded.} \tag{4.2}$$

$$1 \leqslant e_i \leqslant E, \qquad \varepsilon_i = \pm 1. \tag{4.3}$$

Suppose that

$$x = \Sigma u_i = \sum \frac{a_1 a_2 \dots a_i}{n_1 n_2 \dots n_i} e_i \varepsilon_i. \tag{4.4}$$

Then x is rational if and only if from some point on

$$n_{i+1} - \varepsilon_{i+1} \varepsilon_{i+2} = a_{i+1}(n_i - \varepsilon_i \varepsilon_{i+1}), \qquad e_{i+1} = e_i. \tag{4.5}$$

Remarks 1. If the condition $n_i \to \infty$ is omitted, the other conditions imply that either $n_i = n \geqslant 1, a_i = 1$ (all $i \geqslant i_0$) or else that $n_i \to \infty$. In the first case the question reduces to the rationality or irrationality of the series $\Sigma e_i \varepsilon_i / n^i$ $(n \geqslant 2)$. This series is certainly rational if the sequence $\{e_i \varepsilon_i\}$ is ultimately periodic so that (4.5) need not hold. The second case, $n_i \to \infty$, is that of the Theorem.

2. Theorem 2 can be deduced from Theorem 3 by substituting $a_{i+1} n_i$ for a_i in Theorem 3. But this requires the condition (for Theorem 2) $a_i \dots a_{i+1} n_i \dots n_i / n_{i+1}$ bounded, a stronger condition than $a_1 \dots a_{i+1} N_i / n_{i+1}$ bounded, since $N_i \leqslant n_1 \dots n_i$.

3. The proof of Theorem 3 differs only in detail from the proof of Theorem 2. It is therefore omitted.

4. Two special cases of Theorem 3 are worth giving in full. Take first $a_1 = a_2 = 1, a_3 = n_1, \dots a_{i+2} = n_i$. We obtain

THEOREM 4. *Suppose that*

$$\varepsilon_i = \pm 1, \qquad 1 \leqslant e_i \leqslant E,$$

$$\limsup n_{i-1} n_i / n_{i+1} \leqslant 1, \qquad n_i \to \infty,$$

$$n_1 n_2 \dots n_{i-1} / n_i \text{ is bounded.}$$

Then the series

$$\frac{\varepsilon_1 e_1}{n_1} + \frac{\varepsilon_2 e_2}{n_1 n_2} + \frac{\varepsilon_3 e_3}{n_2 n_3} + \dots$$

is rational if and only if from some point on

$$e_{i+1} = e_i, n_{i+1} - \varepsilon_{i+1} \varepsilon_{i+2} = n_{i-1}(n_i - \varepsilon_i \varepsilon_{i+1}).$$

The second special case deduces a result already obtained in (**2**) for infinite products. Take

$$a_{i+1} = n_i + 1, \qquad \varepsilon_i = 1, \qquad e_i = 1.$$

We obtain

THEOREM 5. *Suppose that the positive integers* $n_i(\to \infty)$ *satisfy the conditions*

$$\limsup n_i^2/n_{i+1} \leqslant 1,$$

$$n_1 n_2 \dots n_i/n_{i+1} \text{ is bounded.}$$

Then the infinite product $\Pi(1 + 1/n_i)$ *is rational if and only if from some point on* $n_{i+1} = n_i^2$.

A direct proof of Theorem 5 (and more general results) is given in (**2**).

References

1. ERDÖS, P. and STRAUS, E. G. On the irrationality of certain Ahmes series. *J. Indian Math. Soc.* **27** (1963), 129–133.
2. OPPENHEIM, A. The irrationality of certain infinite products. *J. London Math. Soc.* **43** (1968), 115–118.

Marginal Elements in Transversal Theory

HAZEL PERFECT

In 1953, Mann and Ryser (**10**) considered, and partially solved, the problem of finding under what conditions a given finite family of sets possesses a transversal which contains prescribed elements among its members. They introduced the term 'marginal elements' for these initially chosen elements. Later, the problem was completely solved by Hoffman and Kuhn (**7**). More general problems of a similar kind readily suggest themselves; thus, for example, we might ask for conditions for an independent transversal† of a family, or for a common transversal of two families, containing in each case marginal elements. Our purpose, in this paper, is to survey some of the various methods which have emerged in the last few years for dealing with this kind of situation. We describe in turn, in sections 2, 3, 4, methods based on 'elementary constructions', on the notion of abstract independence, and on Menger's theorem respectively. Section 5 is devoted to the study of independent transversals with marginal elements. A considerable part of our account is expository. Possibly the method described in 2.2, which generalizes that in (**19**), is new, and Theorem 5.1 in 5.1 may not have been stated in precisely these terms before. The last section 6 is in the nature of an appendix in which we supply some notes on a particular kind of 'induced' structure.

We mention, in passing, just two applications of the theory of marginal elements. The first, within transversal theory, is to the problem of finding conditions for the existence of a system of representatives of a family, or a system of common representatives of two families, where the frequency of occurrence of each element is bounded below and above. For some details of this kind of application, we refer to (**16**). Another application is to Latin rectangles. Here the problem is that of finding conditions under which a Latin rectangle can be built up to a Latin square. Reference may be made to Mann and Ryser's work (**10**).

It is a pleasure to me to record my indebtedness to Dr. L. Mirsky for much valuable advice on the content and presentation of this paper.

† See 1.1.

1. Preliminaries

1.1. We assume familiarity with the basic definitions and theorems of transversal theory. For general background see, for example, (**14**, **17**). Since our notation and terminology are somewhat at variance with that in (**14**), we remark that, in the present account, $X \subseteq E$ is a *transversal* of a family $\mathfrak{A} = (A_i : i \in I)$ of subsets of E if there exists a bijection $\phi : X \to I$ such that $x \in A_{\phi(x)}$ $(x \in X)$. A *partial transversal* (PT) of $\mathfrak{A}$ is a transversal of a subfamily of $\mathfrak{A}$. We shall use $|X|$ to denote the number of elements in X, and allow the function $|\cdot|$ to take values from $\{0, 1, 2, ..., \infty\}$.

Abstract independence features prominently in our account. For convenience, therefore, we recall the axioms of an independence structure and the statement of Rado's basic theorem on independent transversals (in its 'defect' form).

Let E be an arbitrary set. A non-empty collection $\mathscr{E}$ of subsets of E is a *pre-independence structure* on E if it has the properties I(1), I(2) below.

I(1) If $A \in \mathscr{E}$ and $B \subseteq A$, then $B \in \mathscr{E}$.

I(2) (*The replacement property*) If A, B $\in \mathscr{E}$ with $|A| = m$, $|B| = m+1$, then there exists $x \in B - A$ such that $A \cup \{x\} \in \mathscr{E}$.

If, in addition, $\mathscr{E}$ has finite character (so that a subset of E belongs to $\mathscr{E}$ if each of its own finite subsets belongs to $\mathscr{E}$), then it is an *independence structure*. In either case, the sets which belong to $\mathscr{E}$ are called the *independent* subsets† of E.

We associate with a pre-independence structure $\mathscr{E}$ on E a *rank function* ρ, taking values from $\{0, 1, 2, ..., \infty\}$, and defined on the collection of all subsets X of E by the equation

$$\rho(X) = \sup\{|Y| : Y \in \mathscr{E}, Y \subset\subset X\}.‡$$

It is easily shown that, for X, Y $\subseteq$ E, the *modular inequality*

$$\rho(X) + \rho(Y) \geqslant \rho(X \cup Y) + \rho(X \cap Y)$$

is valid.

The systematic study of abstract independence was initiated by Whitney in a fundamental paper (**27**). For some of the later history of the subject, see Rado's account in (**24**). A striking set-theoretic instance of a pre-independence structure is provided by the collection of partial transversals (PTs) of a family of sets. (If no element belongs to infinitely many of the sets, the collection of PTs is an independence structure.) For finite families, this fact was first

† In view of the finite character, maximal independent subsets exist in an independence structure.

‡ $Y \subset\subset X$ indicates that Y is a *finite* subset of X.

recognized by Edmonds and Fulkerson (**3**); see also (**15**). It accounts for much of the importance of abstract independence in relation to transversal theory.

THEOREM 1.1. [R. Rado (**22, 23**)] *Let* $\mathfrak{A} = (A_i : i \in I)$ *be a family of subsets of* E, *and let d be a non-negative integer. Let* $\mathscr{E}$ *be a pre-independence or independence structure on* E *according as* I *is finite or infinite. If* I *is infinite, assume that each* A_i $(i \in I)$ *is finite. Then there exists a subfamily* $(A_i : i \in J)$ *of* $\mathfrak{A}$ *with* $|I - J| \leqslant d$ *which has an independent transversal*† *if and only if*

$$\rho(A(I')) \geqslant |I'| - d \qquad (I' \subset\subset I).$$

Here, as is now customary, $A(I')$ stands for $\cup\{A_i : i \in I'\}$. The case $d = 0$ gives conditions for an independent transversal of $\mathfrak{A}$. The specialization that $\mathscr{E}$ is the power set of E yields the defect versions of the theorems of P. Hall (**6**) and M. Hall (**5**).

For a recent simple proof of Theorem 1.1, see (**21**). The method is an obvious generalization of Rado's own elegant proof of Hall's theorem (**25**).

1.2. There are various ways in which a given independence structure may 'induce' a new structure. One method, which will be of particular importance later, follows from Theorem 1.2 below. We supply a proof of this theorem in section 6.

THEOREM 1.2. *Let* $\mathscr{E}$ *be an independence structure on an arbitrary set* E, *and let* $M \subseteq E$ *be given. Define*

$$\mathscr{E}(M) = \{X \subseteq E : X \cup N \in \mathscr{E} \text{ for some maximal independent subset N of M}\}. \tag{1.1}$$

Then $\mathscr{E}(M)$ *is itself an independence structure on* E. *Further, if* ρ, ρ_M *denote the rank functions of* $\mathscr{E}$, $\mathscr{E}(M)$ *respectively, then, for* $X \subset\subset E$,

$$\rho_M(X) = \min_{\substack{F \subset\subset M \\ X \cap M \subseteq F}} \{\rho(X \cup F) + \rho(X \cap F) - \rho(F)\}. \tag{1.2}$$

In fact, we shall only use two special cases of Theorem 1.2; first, when M is finite and, second, when $M \in \mathscr{E}$. In this connection, we note the following corollaries, which are deduced from Theorem 1.2 in section 6.

COROLLARY 1. *Suppose* $M \subset\subset E$. *Then the rank formula* (1.2) *takes the simpler form*

$$\rho_M(X) = \rho(X \cup M) + \rho(X \cap M) - \rho(M)$$

and remains true for arbitrary (not necessarily finite) X. *Further, the term 'independence' may be replaced by 'pre-independence' throughout Theorem* 1.2.

† i.e. a transversal in $\mathscr{E}$.

COROLLARY 2. *When* $M \in \mathscr{E}$, *the rank formula of* $\mathscr{E}(M)$ *is given by*

$$\rho_M(X) = \min_{F \subset\subset M} \{\rho(X \cup F) + |X \cap F| - |F|\} \qquad (X \subset\subset E).$$

2. Methods based on 'elementary constructions'

2.1. In a semi-expository paper (**13**), Mirsky has demonstrated that the solutions of many problems in (finite) transversal theory may be obtained directly from Hall's theorem by means of 'elementary constructions'. The first problem on marginal elements which we consider can be solved very easily by these means.

THEOREM 2.1. [A. J. Hoffman and H. W. Kuhn (**7**)] *Let* $\mathfrak{A} = (A_i : i \in I)$, *with* $|I| = n$, *be a finite family of subsets of a given set* E, *and let* $M \subseteq E$ *be given. Then* $\mathfrak{A}$ *has a transversal containing* M *if and only if the conditions* (1), (2) *below are satisfied.*

(1) $|A(I')| \geqslant |I'| \qquad (I' \subseteq I)$,

(2) $|A(I') \cap M| \geqslant |I'| - n + |M| \qquad (I' \subseteq I)$,

Here, it will suffice to describe the elementary construction which allows us to deduce Theorem 2.1 from Hall's theorem. We may as well suppose that E is a finite set (with $|E| \geqslant n$), for the removal of this restriction is easily accomplished. Consider, then, a new family $\mathfrak{A}^*$ of subsets of E consisting of the sets A_i $(i \in I)$ together with $|E| - n$ copies of the set $E - M$. The crux of the argument is that $\mathfrak{A}$ has a transversal containing M if and only if $\mathfrak{A}^*$ has a transversal. This is readily verified, and a straightforward application of Hall's theorem to the family $\mathfrak{A}^*$ yields the conditions (1), (2) of the theorem.

Theorem 2.1 dates back to 1956 when Hoffman and Kuhn (**7**) established it by the techniques of linear programming. (We have stated Hoffman and Kuhn's second condition in a different, though equivalent, form.) Three years earlier sufficient, but not necessary, conditions had been given by Mann and Ryser.

2.2. The next result is the analogue of Theorem 2.1 for the case of two families.

THEOREM 2.2. *Let* $\mathfrak{A} = (A_i : i \in I)$, $\mathfrak{B} = (B_j : j \in J)$, *with* $|I| = |J| = n$, *be finite families of subsets of a given set* E, *and let* $M \subseteq E$ *be given. Then* $\mathfrak{A}, \mathfrak{B}$ *have a common transversal containing* M *if and only if*

$$|A(I') \cap M| + |B(J') \cap M| + |A(I') \cap B(J') \cap (E - M)|$$
$$\geqslant |I'| + |J'| + |M| - n \qquad (I' \subseteq I,\ J' \subseteq J). \tag{2.1}$$

In the proof below, we suppose that E is finite. Different proofs of Theorem 2.2 in sections 3.2, 4.1 require no such restriction on E.

Assume, without loss of generality, that I, J, E are pairwise disjoint, and define a new family

$$\mathfrak{X} = (X_k : k \in I \cup E)$$

of subsets of $E \cup J$ by the equations

$$\begin{aligned} X_k &= A_k \qquad (k \in I), \\ X_k &= \{k\} \cup \{j \in J : k \in B_j\} \qquad (k \in E - M), \\ X_k &= \{j \in J : k \in B_j\} \qquad (k \in M). \end{aligned}$$

By considering the obvious graphical interpretation of the problem (or by direct verification), we see that $\mathfrak{A}$ and $\mathfrak{B}$ have a common transversal (CT) which contains M if and only if $\mathfrak{X}$ has a transversal. The details of the application of Hall's theorem to the family $\mathfrak{X}$ are somewhat tedious but, ultimately, yield the conditions (2.1).

Theorem 2.2 is a special case of a theorem of Ford and Fulkerson (**4**, Ch. 2, Theorem 10.8) on common systems of representatives with repetitions. The method of proof just outlined, which reduces the problem to an application of Hall's theorem by means of an elementary construction, generalizes that given in (**19**) for the case $M = \emptyset$.

3. Methods based on the use of independence structures

3.1. We have recalled in 1.1 that the collection of PTs of a family of subsets of E forms a pre-independence structure on E. This fact gives the clue to what is perhaps the most transparent proof of Theorem 2.1. By Hall's criterion, condition (1) of the theorem holds if and only if $\mathfrak{A}$ has a transversal; by the defect form of Hall's criterion, condition (2) holds if and only if $(A_i \cap M : i \in I)$ has a PT of length $|M|$ or, equivalently, if and only if M is a PT of $\mathfrak{A}$. (Notice that, without loss of generality, we may assume $|M| \leqslant n$.) Manifestly, then, (1) and (2) are necessary if $\mathfrak{A}$ has a transversal containing M. Conversely, if (1) and (2) are satisfied, then, by the replacement property of transversal independence, the PT M of $\mathfrak{A}$ may be extended to a transversal of $\mathfrak{A}$ containing M; and the proof is complete.

3.2. Independence theory may also be employed to prove Theorem 2.2. Specifically, we use transversal independence and also the induced structure described in Corollary 1 to Theorem 1.2. The argument which we briefly indicate below is due to Welsh (**26**).

Let $\mathscr{E}$ be the collection of PTs of $\mathfrak{B}$ (which we know is an independence structure on E). Without loss of generality, we may suppose that M is a PT of

$\mathfrak{B}$, so that $M \in \mathscr{E}$. Next, let $\mathscr{E}(M)$ be defined as in Theorem 1.2. We may show without difficulty that $\mathfrak{A}$ and $\mathfrak{B}$ have a CT containing M if and only if $\mathfrak{A}$ has a transversal in $\mathscr{E}(M)$. An application of Rado's Theorem 1.1 on independent transversals, with the formula for ρ_M given in Theorem 1.2, Corollary 1, and the rank formula for transversal independence completes the proof of Theorem 2.2.

We remark that the common partial transversals (CPTs) of two families do not, in general, form an independence structure, and therefore the condition (2.1) is stronger than the two conditions that $\mathfrak{A}$ and $\mathfrak{B}$ shall have a CT and that M shall be a CPT of $\mathfrak{A}$ and $\mathfrak{B}$; for a CPT, in general, cannot be extended to a CT by replacement.

3.3. One way of proving the replacement property of transversal independence is to invoke the generalization of Banach's Mapping Theorem which is formulated in (**20**). More generally, from this theorem, we readily deduce that, if $\mathfrak{A} = (A_i : i \in I)$ is an arbitrary (i.e. not necessarily finite) family of subsets of E which possesses a transversal, and if $M \subseteq E$ is a PT of $\mathfrak{A}$, then $\mathfrak{A}$ possesses a transversal which contains M. This observation together with M. Hall's theorem yields the following infinite analogue of Theorem 2.1.

THEOREM 3.1. *Let* $\mathfrak{A} = (A_i : i \in I)$ *be a family of finite subsets of* E. *Let* $M \subseteq E$ *be given and suppose that no element of* M *belongs to* A_i *for infinitely many* $i \in I$. *Then* $\mathfrak{A}$ *has a transversal containing* M *as a subset if and only if the conditions* (1), (2) *below are satisfied.*

$$(1)\quad |A(I')| \geqslant |I'| \qquad (I' \subset\subset I),$$

$$(2)\quad |\{i \in I : F \cap A_i \neq \emptyset\}| \geqslant |F| \qquad (F \subset\subset M).$$

Theorem 3.1 is due to Rado (unpublished notes); the argument above appeared in (**15**).

Brualdi (**1**), as well as proving much more general results, has obtained an infinite analogue of Theorem 2.2. However, his proof requires the application of a more difficult mapping theorem than the one described in (**20**). In section 5 below, we shall obtain results on independent transversals with marginal elements, some of which will be applicable to both finite and infinite families. In particular, from these we are able to deduce a one-sided infinite version of Theorem 2.2.

4. Methods based on Menger's graph theorem

4.1. Yet another proof of Theorem 2.2 depends on Menger's graph theorem (**12**; see also **9**, Ch. 14). The brief account of this method which we give is based on (**18**). We write $G = (N, \mathscr{E})$ for the graph whose set of nodes is N and whose set of edges is $\mathscr{E}$; and we assume that all graphs are directed.

Consider the graphs G, G* defined in the following way. Assume I, E, J to be pairwise disjoint, and let $G = (N, \mathscr{E})$, where

$$N = I \cup E \cup J, \qquad \mathscr{E} = \mathscr{E}_1 \cup \mathscr{E}_2$$

and

$$\mathscr{E}_1 = \{(i, e) \in I \times E : e \in A_i\}, \qquad \mathscr{E}_2 = \{(e, j) \in E \times J : e \in B_j\}.$$

Let $M^{(1)}$, $M^{(2)}$ be sets with $|M^{(1)}| = |M^{(2)}| = |M|$, disjoint from each other and from $N - M$, and consider bijections of M into $M^{(1)}$, $M^{(2)}$. For each $e \in M$, denote by $e^{(1)}$, $e^{(2)}$ its images in $M^{(1)}$, $M^{(2)}$. Take $G^* = (N^*, \mathscr{E}^*)$, where

$$N^* = I \cup M^{(2)} \cup (E - M) \cup M^{(1)} \cup J, \quad \mathscr{E}^* = \mathscr{E}_{11}{}^* \cup \mathscr{E}_{12}{}^* \cup \mathscr{E}_{21}{}^* \cup \mathscr{E}_{22}{}^*$$

and

$$\mathscr{E}_{11}{}^* = \{(i, e^{(1)}) \in I \times M^{(1)} : e \in A_i\}, \quad \mathscr{E}_{12}{}^* = \{(i, e) \in I \times (E - M) : e \in A_i\},$$

$$\mathscr{E}_{21}{}^* = \{(e^{(2)}, j) \in M^{(2)} \times J : e \in B_j\}, \quad \mathscr{E}_{22}{}^* = \{(e, j) \in (E - M) \times J : e \in B_j\}.$$

Now $\mathfrak{A}$, $\mathfrak{B}$ have a CT containing M if and only if there are n disjoint paths from I to J in G whose set of intermediate (i.e. not initial or terminal) nodes contains M. It can be shown that this is so if and only if there are $n + |M|$ disjoint paths from $I \cup M^{(2)}$ to $M^{(1)} \cup J$ in G*. Menger's theorem applied to G* yields the desired result.

4.2. We refer to (**16**) for what is virtually a reinterpretation of the argument of 4.1. The construction of G* from G suggests how to define new families $\mathfrak{A}^*$, $\mathfrak{B}^*$ from $\mathfrak{A}$, $\mathfrak{B}$ with the property that $\mathfrak{A}$, $\mathfrak{B}$ have a CT containing M if and only if $\mathfrak{A}^*$, $\mathfrak{B}^*$ have a CT. The problem is therefore reduced to the special case $M = \emptyset$. The point of view here is similar to that in section 2, though the 'elementary construction' applied to $\mathfrak{A}$, $\mathfrak{B}$ does not reduce the problem to an application of Hall's theorem but instead to Ford and Fulkerson's analogue of Hall's theorem for two families (**4**, Ch. 2, Cor. 10.9).

5. Independent transversals with marginal elements

5.1. We have used independence theory as a tool in section 3. Now, on the other hand, we look at independent transversals for their own sake and examine an independence-theoretic analogue of Theorem 2.1. In fact, for the record, we prove a somewhat more general result.

THEOREM 5.1. *Let* E *be a given set, and let* $\mathscr{E}$ *be a pre-independence structure on* E *with rank function* ρ. *Let* $\mathfrak{A} = (A_i : i \in I)$, *with* $|I| = n$, *be a family of subsets of* E. *Let* $m \leqslant n$ *and* $M \subset\subset E$, *with* $\rho(M) \leqslant m$, *be given. Then* $\mathfrak{A}$ *has an independent partial transversal of length m containing a maximal independent subset of* M *if and only if the conditions* (1), (2) *below are satisfied.*

(1) $\rho(\mathrm{A(I')} \cup \mathrm{M}) + \rho(\mathrm{A(I')} \cap \mathrm{M}) \geqslant \rho(\mathrm{M}) + |\mathrm{I'}| - n + m \quad (\mathrm{I'} \subseteq \mathrm{I})$,

(2) $\rho(\mathrm{A(I')} \cap \mathrm{M}) \geqslant \rho(\mathrm{M}) + |\mathrm{I'}| - n \quad (\mathrm{I'} \subseteq \mathrm{I})$.

The case $m = n$ is, of course, the exact analogue of Theorem 2.1 in the context of independence theory.

To establish Theorem 5.1, we begin by defining a new independence structure $\mathscr{E}'$ on E (the 'truncation' of $\mathscr{E}$ at m) by the equation

$$\mathscr{E}' = \{\mathrm{X} \subseteq \mathrm{E} : \mathrm{X} \in \mathscr{E} \quad \text{and} \quad |\mathrm{X}| \leqslant m\}.$$

If its rank function is ρ', then, for $\mathrm{X} \subseteq \mathrm{E}$,

$$\rho'(X) = \min\{m, \rho(\mathrm{X})\}. \tag{5.1}$$

Next, let

$$\mathscr{E}'(\mathrm{M}) = \{\mathrm{X} \subseteq \mathrm{E} : \mathrm{X} \cup \mathrm{N} \in \mathscr{E}' \text{ for some maximal independent subset N of M in } \mathscr{E}' \text{ (or equivalently in } \mathscr{E})\}.$$

By Corollary 1 to Theorem 1.2, $\mathscr{E}'(\mathrm{M})$ is an independence structure on E and its rank function, ρ_{M}' say, is given by

$$\rho_{\mathrm{M}}'(\mathrm{X}) = \rho'(\mathrm{X} \cup \mathrm{M}) + \rho'(\mathrm{X} \cap \mathrm{M}) - \rho'(\mathrm{M}) \qquad (\mathrm{X} \subseteq \mathrm{E}). \tag{5.2}$$

Now, clearly, $\mathfrak{A}$ has an independent partial transversal (IPT) in $\mathscr{E}$ of length m containing a basis† of M in $\mathscr{E}$ if and only if $\mathfrak{A}$ has an IPT in $\mathscr{E}'$ of length m containing a basis of M in $\mathscr{E}'$. Assume $\mathfrak{A}$ has an IPT X in $\mathscr{E}'$ of length m containing a basis N of M in $\mathscr{E}'$. Then $\mathrm{X} \cup \mathrm{N} = \mathrm{X} \in \mathscr{E}'$ and so $\mathrm{X} \in \mathscr{E}'(\mathrm{M})$; i.e. $\mathfrak{A}$ has an IPT of length m in $\mathscr{E}'(\mathrm{M})$. Conversely, if $\mathfrak{A}$ has an IPT X of length m in $\mathscr{E}'(\mathrm{M})$ then, for some basis N of M (in $\mathscr{E}'$), $\mathrm{X} \cup \mathrm{N} \in \mathscr{E}'$. But $|\mathrm{X}| = m$, $|\mathrm{X} \cup \mathrm{N}| \leqslant m$ and so $\mathrm{X} \supseteq \mathrm{N}$. Therefore $\mathfrak{A}$ has an IPT in $\mathscr{E}'$ of length m containing a basis of M in $\mathscr{E}'$.

Finally, then, by Rado's Theorem 1.1, $\mathfrak{A}$ has an IPT in $\mathscr{E}$ of length m containing a basis of M in $\mathscr{E}$ if and only if

$$\rho_{\mathrm{M}}'(\mathrm{A(I')}) \geqslant |\mathrm{I'}| - n + m \qquad (\mathrm{I'} \subseteq \mathrm{I}); \tag{5.3}$$

and the use of (5.1), (5.2) readily converts (5.3) into the conditions (1), (2) of the theorem.

The proof of Theorem 2.2 outlined in section 3.2 is the special case of the argument just described when $m = n$ and when $\mathscr{E}$ is the collection of PTs of $\mathfrak{B}$. No initial truncation is needed in this case since $\mathscr{E}$ is of rank n.

5.2. It is perhaps worth remarking in passing that the argument of section

† i.e. a maximal independent subset.

5.1, when suitably specialized, provides yet another simple method of proof of Theorem 2.1. Specifically, let

$$\mathscr{E}(\mathrm{M}) = \{\mathrm{X} \subseteq \mathrm{E} : |\mathrm{X} \cup \mathrm{M}| \leqslant n\}.$$

Then $\mathscr{E}(\mathrm{M})$ is an independence structure with rank function ρ given by

$$\rho(X) = \min\{|\mathrm{X} \cup \mathrm{M}|, n\} + \min\{|\mathrm{X} \cap \mathrm{M}|, n\} - |\mathrm{M}| \qquad (\mathrm{X} \subseteq \mathrm{E}). \quad (5.4)$$

Now $\mathfrak{A}$ has a transversal containing M if and only if it has a transversal in $\mathscr{E}(\mathrm{M})$. By Rado's Theorem 1.1 and (5.4), this is so if and only if

$$\min\{|\mathrm{A}(\mathrm{I}') \cup \mathrm{M}|, n\} + \min\{|\mathrm{A}(\mathrm{I}') \cap \mathrm{M}|, n\} - |\mathrm{M}| \geqslant |\mathrm{I}'| \qquad (\mathrm{I}' \subseteq \mathrm{I});$$

i.e. if and only if

$$|\mathrm{A}(\mathrm{I}')| \geqslant |\mathrm{I}'|, \qquad |\mathrm{A}(\mathrm{I}') \cap \mathrm{M}| \geqslant |\mathrm{I}'| - n + |\mathrm{M}| \qquad (\mathrm{I}' \subseteq \mathrm{I}).$$

5.3. We digress briefly from our main theme in order to comment upon the conditions (1), (2) in Theorem 5.1. Condition (1) is necessary and sufficient for $\mathfrak{A}$ to have a PT of length m in $\mathscr{E}(\mathrm{M})$ and condition (2) is necessary and sufficient for a basis of M (in $\mathscr{E}$) to be a PT of $\mathfrak{A}$. Now (1) implies the following condition

$$(1') \quad \rho(\mathrm{A}(\mathrm{I}')) \geqslant |\mathrm{I}'| - n + m \qquad (\mathrm{I}' \subseteq \mathrm{I}).$$

To see this, we may either interpret (1′) as the condition for $\mathfrak{A}$ to possess a PT of length m in $\mathscr{E}$, when the implication (1) ⇒ (1′) is obvious; or we may employ the modular inequality for ρ to deduce (1′) from (1).

Conditions (1′), (2) are in general *insufficient* to ensure the conclusion of Theorem 5.1. However, in the situation where the independent partial transversals of $\mathfrak{A}$ themselves form an independence structure on E the conditions (1′), (2) are indeed sufficient, as is readily checked.

We are prompted to raise, therefore, questions of the following kind. (For simplicity we suppose that all sets considered are finite.)

(i) *For which independence structures $\mathscr{E}$ do the independent partial transversals of* every *family form an independence structure?*

(ii) *For which independence structures $\mathscr{E}$ do the independent partial transversals of a* given *family form an independence structure?*

(iii) *How are these matters related to the validity of the modular* equality *for ρ (when* (1) *and* (1′) *are equivalent)?*

In answer to (i), it is straightforward to prove that the IPTs of every family of subsets of E form an independence structure on E if and only if $\mathscr{E}$ is a truncated restriction of the universal structure on E. It would seem that (ii) is a more difficult question, and we are not able to give a useful answer. It is, of course, a special case of the following question. Given two independence structures on E, with rank functions ρ_1, ρ_2, when do their common independent sets form an independence structure? An answer of a kind is that this is so if and only if the function μ defined for $X \subseteq E$ by

$$\mu(X) = \min_{X_1 \subseteq X} (\rho_1(X_1) + \rho_2(X - X_1)),$$

satisfies the modular inequality.

In connection with (iii), we observe† that the modular inequality for the rank function ρ of $\mathscr{E}$ becomes an equality for all $X, Y \subseteq E$ precisely when $\mathscr{E}$ is a restriction of the universal structure on E. We have only formulated (iii) in rather vague terms, but it would seem to be of interest to investigate under what conditions (on $\mathscr{E}$) the modular inequality for ρ becomes an equality for certain prescribed collections of subsets of E.

5.4. Our last main result is an infinite analogue of Theorem 5.1. We shall, however, consider transversals of $\mathfrak{A}$ rather than partial transversals. Also, we are only able to handle the situation where $M \in \mathscr{E}$.

THEOREM 5.2. *Let* E *be a given set, and let* $\mathscr{E}$ *be an independence structure on* E *with rank function* ρ. *Let* $M \in \mathscr{E}$ *be given and let* $\mathfrak{A} = (A_i : i \in I)$ *be a family of finite subsets of* E. *Then* $\mathfrak{A}$ *has an independent transversal containing* M *if and only if the conditions* (1), (2) *below are satisfied.*

$$(1) \quad \rho(A(I') \cup F) + |A(I') \cap F| \geqslant |I'| + |F| \qquad (I' \subset\subset I, \ F \subset\subset M).$$

$$(2) \quad |\{i \in I : F \cap A_i \neq \emptyset\}| \geqslant |F| \qquad (F \subset\subset M).$$

First, suppose that $\mathfrak{A}$ has an independent transversal, T say, containing M. Then $T \cup M = T \in \mathscr{E}$; so $T \in \mathscr{E}(M)$. Therefore, by Rado's Theorem 1.1,

$$\rho_M(A(I')) \geqslant |I'| \qquad (I' \subset\subset I).$$

This is equivalent to condition (1) by virtue of Corollary 2 to Theorem 1.2. Also, condition (2), which simply asserts that M is a PT of $\mathfrak{A}$, is obviously satisfied.

Next, suppose that (1), (2) hold. Then, by Theorem 1.1 and Corollary 2 to Theorem 1.2, $\mathfrak{A}$ has a transversal, T say, which belongs to $\mathscr{E}(M)$; and M is a PT of $\mathfrak{A}$. Since $T \in \mathscr{E}(M)$, therefore $T \cup M \in \mathscr{E}$. Finally, a generalization of Banach's Mapping Theorem (see again 3.3) ensures that $\mathfrak{A}$ has a transversal T′ satisfying $M \subseteq T' \subseteq T \cup M$, which therefore belongs to $\mathscr{E}$.

The proof of the finite theorem in 5.1 employed an initial truncation of $\mathscr{E}$. We are able to avoid this in the case when $M \in \mathscr{E}$ by the use of a mapping

† For this remark, I am indebted to Dr. L. Mirsky.

theorem instead; and this is the reason why we succeed in generalizing to the infinite situation. Indeed, we can avoid the initial truncation in Theorem 5.1 without imposing the condition $M \in \mathscr{E}$, but this fact depends on a more difficult mapping theorem of Brualdi (**2**). It is not known whether, in this latter mapping theorem, certain finiteness assumptions can be relaxed.

In conclusion, we observe that Theorem 5.2 yields a one-sided infinite version of Theorem 2.2. Specifically, let $\mathfrak{B} = (B_j : j \in J)$ be a second family of subsets of E with no element of E belonging to more than a finite number of the sets B_j. Let $\mathscr{E}$ be the independence structure consisting of the PTs of $\mathfrak{B}$. Then Theorem 5.2 provides the conditions for $\mathfrak{A}$ and a subfamily of $\mathfrak{B}$ to possess a CT containing M as a subset. We refer to the work of Brualdi (**1**) for much more general results on CTs.

5.5. Certain more general problems in transversal theory than those which we have considered could be classified as problems about marginal elements. For instance, the theorem of Hoffman and Kuhn (Theorem 2.1) has a symmetrized generalization due to Mendelsohn and Dulmage (**11**) (see also (**15**) for its infinite analogue). A different generalization of Theorem 2.1 (also due to Hoffman and Kuhn (**8**)) gives necessary and sufficient conditions for a finite family to possess a transversal, the cardinals of whose intersections with the sets of a given partition are bounded below and above. These at once suggest further problems of a similar kind in the context of independence theory. But we need not look to such general situations before finding problems on marginal elements which are still defying solution. For example, we have already mentioned the infinite analogue of Theorem 5.1, which we were only able to solve in the special case where $M \in \mathscr{E}$.

We end by posing quite an 'elementary' problem on marginal elements which we believe is unsolved. Suppose, for simplicity, that all the sets considered are finite. Let $\mathfrak{A}$ be a family of subsets of a given set E, and let $M \subseteq E$. Let $\mathscr{E}$ be an independence structure on E, and let k ($\leqslant |M|$)be a given positive integer. We ask under what conditions $\mathfrak{A}$ has an independent transversal containing at least k elements of M. In the special case when $\mathscr{E}$ is the collection of PTs of a family $\mathfrak{B}$, we seek conditions for a CT of $\mathfrak{A}$ and $\mathfrak{B}$ (or a CPT of prescribed length perhaps) containing at least k elements of M. Again, so far as we know, the answer is not known.

6. Appendix: a proof of Theorem 1.2

6.1. For completeness, we give a proof of Theorem 1.2. It is closely related to known results, but it is difficult to supply an exact reference for the particular formulation that we have chosen.

To simplify the subsequent discussion we first establish three simple lemmas.

Lemma 6.1. *Let* N *be a arbitrary set, and* $\mathscr{F}(\mathrm{N})$ *the collection of all finite subsets of* N. *Let* $\mathscr{F}_i$ $(1 \leqslant i \leqslant k)$ *be collections of finite subsets of* N *with the properties*

(1) $\mathrm{A} \in \mathscr{F}_i, \mathrm{B} \subseteq \mathrm{A} \Rightarrow \mathrm{B} \in \mathscr{F}_i \; (1 \leqslant i \leqslant k)$,

(2) $\mathrm{A} \in \mathscr{F}(\mathrm{N}) \Rightarrow \mathrm{A} \in \mathscr{F}_i$ *for some* i $(1 \leqslant i \leqslant k)$.

Then $\mathscr{F}_i = \mathscr{F}(\mathrm{N})$ *for some* i $(1 \leqslant i \leqslant k)$.

Assume the contrary. Then there exist $\mathrm{A}_i \in \mathscr{F}(\mathrm{N})$ $(1 \leqslant i \leqslant k)$ with

$$\mathrm{A}_1 \notin \mathscr{F}_1, \ldots, \mathrm{A}_k \notin \mathscr{F}_k.$$

Now $\mathrm{A}_1 \cup \ldots \cup \mathrm{A}_k \in \mathscr{F}(\mathrm{N})$ and so $\mathrm{A}_1 \cup \ldots \cup \mathrm{A}_k \in \mathscr{F}_i$ for some i satisfying $1 \leqslant i \leqslant k$ (by (2)). Therefore, for this i, $\mathrm{A}_i \in \mathscr{F}_i$ (by (1)). This contradiction completes the proof.

If $\mathscr{F}$ is a collection of subsets of a set E and $\mathrm{X} \subseteq \mathrm{E}$, then $\mathscr{F}_{|\mathrm{X}}$ is used below to denote the *restriction* of $\mathscr{F}$ to X, namely

$$\mathscr{F}_{|\mathrm{X}} = \{\mathrm{Y} \subseteq \mathrm{X} : \mathrm{Y} \in \mathscr{F}\}.$$

Further, let $\mathrm{A}, \mathrm{B} \subseteq \mathrm{E}$ with $\mathrm{A} \cap \mathrm{B} = \varnothing$. If $\mathscr{F}$, $\mathscr{G}$ are collections of subsets of A, B, then $\mathscr{F} \oplus \mathscr{G}$, the *direct sum* of $\mathscr{F}$ and $\mathscr{G}$, is defined by the equation

$$\mathscr{F} \oplus \mathscr{G} = \{\mathrm{X} : \mathrm{X} = \mathrm{A}_1 \cup \mathrm{B}_1, \mathrm{A}_1 \in \mathscr{F}, \mathrm{B}_1 \in \mathscr{G}\}.$$

Other notation used in the next two lemmas is that laid down in the statement of Theorem 1.2. In the proof of Lemma 6.2, we employ the notion of 'dependence' associated with the independence structure $\mathscr{E}$ (in symbols, '$x \mid \mathrm{X}$' stands for the statement 'x depends on X', $\mathrm{X} \subseteq \mathrm{E}$); see **(24)**.

Lemma 6.2. *Let* $\mathrm{X} \subseteq \mathrm{E} - \mathrm{M}$. *If* $\mathrm{X} \cup \mathrm{N} \in \mathscr{E}$ *for some basis* N *of* M, *then* $\mathrm{X} \cup \mathrm{P} \in \mathscr{E}$ *for every independent subset* P *of* M.

Let $\mathrm{P} \subseteq \mathrm{M}$, $\mathrm{P} \in \mathscr{E}$. There exists a basis Q of $\mathrm{X} \cup \mathrm{P}$ with $\mathrm{Q} \supseteq \mathrm{P}$. If $\mathrm{Q} = \mathrm{X} \cup \mathrm{P}$, there is nothing further to prove. Suppose, then, that

$$x \in (\mathrm{X} \cup \mathrm{P}) - \mathrm{Q} = \mathrm{X} - \mathrm{Q}.$$

Then
$$x \mid \mathrm{Q}$$
and so
$$x \mid (\mathrm{X} \cup \mathrm{M}) - \{x\}.$$
Therefore
$$x \mid \mathrm{D}$$
for any basis D of $(\mathrm{X} \cup \mathrm{M}) - \{x\}$. There exists such a D with $\mathrm{D} \supseteq \mathrm{N}$ and, since N is a *maximal* independent subset of M, then

$$\mathrm{D} \subseteq \mathrm{X} \cup \mathrm{N} - \{x\}.$$

Therefore $$x \mid (X \cup N) - \{x\};$$

which contradicts the fact that $X \cup N \in \mathscr{E}$. The proof is complete.

LEMMA 6.3. $\mathscr{E}(M) = \mathscr{E}(M)_{|E-M} \oplus \mathscr{E}_{|M}$.†

Clearly, $\mathscr{E}(M) \subseteq \mathscr{E}(M)_{|E-M} \oplus \mathscr{E}_{|M}$. To prove the opposite inclusion, let $X \in \mathscr{E}(M)_{|E-M} \oplus \mathscr{E}_{|M}$, so that we may write

$$X = Y \cup Z$$

with $Y \in \mathscr{E}(M)_{|E-M}$, $Z \in \mathscr{E}_{|M}$. Then $Y \subseteq E - M$ and, by Lemma 6.2,

$$Y \cup N \in \mathscr{E}$$

for *any* basis N of M. Since $Z \subseteq M$, $Z \in \mathscr{E}$, we may choose N so that $N \supseteq Z$. Therefore

$$X \cup N = Y \cup N \in \mathscr{E}$$

and so $X \in \mathscr{E}(M)$. Thus Lemma 6.3 is established.

6.2. We turn now to the proof of the first assertion of Theorem 1.2. A direct sum of independence structures is at once seen to be itself an independence structure. Therefore, by Lemma 6.2, it is sufficient to show that $\mathscr{E}(M)_{|E-M}$ is an independence structure. All that requires proof is that $\mathscr{E}(M)_{|E-M}$ is of finite character and that the replacement property holds. We take these in turn.

Let, then, $X \subseteq E - M$ and suppose that, for each $Y \subset\subset X$, we have $Y \in \mathscr{E}(M)_{|E-M}$. Then, by Lemma 6.2, $Y \cup N \in \mathscr{E}$ for any basis N of M. Consider $X \cup N$. Every finite subset is a finite subset of $Y \cup N$ for some $Y \subset\subset X$ and so belongs to $\mathscr{E}$. Therefore $X \cup N \in \mathscr{E}$, and $X \in \mathscr{E}(M)_{|E-M}$.

Next, let $X, Y \in \mathscr{E}(M)_{|E-M}$, $|X| = m$, $|Y| = m + 1$. Notice, first, that if M is of finite rank the result is an immediate consequence of Lemma 6.2 and the replacement property of $\mathscr{E}$. In the general situation, let N be any basis of M. Write $Y - X = \{y_1 \ldots, y_k\}_{\neq}$. Let $\mathscr{F}_i$ be the collection of finite subsets A of N such that

$$X \cup \{y_i\} \cup A \in \mathscr{E}$$

$(1 \leqslant i \leqslant k)$. Clearly,

(1) $A \in \mathscr{F}_i, B \subseteq A \Rightarrow B \in \mathscr{F}_i \qquad (1 \leqslant i \leqslant k).$

Now let A be *any* finite subset of N; then $X \cup A \in \mathscr{E}$, $Y \cup A \in \mathscr{E}$. Therefore $X, Y \in \mathscr{E}(A)_{|E-A}$, which is an independence structure, and so $X \cup \{y_i\} \in \mathscr{E}(A)_{|E-A}$, i.e. $X \cup \{y_i\} \cup A \in \mathscr{E}$, for some i with $1 \leqslant i \leqslant k$. Therefore,

† $\mathscr{E}(M)_{|E-M}$ is our notation for what is often called the 'contraction' of $\mathscr{E}$ to $E - M$.

(2) $A \in \mathscr{F}(N) \Rightarrow A \in \mathscr{F}_i$ for some i $(1 \leqslant i \leqslant k)$ and so, by Lemma 6.1, $\mathscr{F}_i = \mathscr{F}(N)$ for some i with $1 \leqslant i \leqslant k$. For this i,

$$X \cup \{y_i\} \cup A \in \mathscr{E}$$

for every $A \subset\subset N$. Therefore

$$X \cup \{y_i\} \cup N \in \mathscr{E},$$

and so $X \cup \{y_i\} \in \mathscr{E}(M)_{|E-M}$ as required.

6.3. We show next that, for $X \subset\subset E - M$,

$$\rho_M(X) = \min_{F \subset\subset M} \{\rho(X \cup F) - \rho(F)\}. \tag{6.1}$$

First, then, suppose $\rho_M(X) = m$. Then there exists $Y \subseteq X$ with $|Y| = m$ such that $Y \cup N \in \mathscr{E}$ for every basis N of M. Therefore, for every $F \subset\subset M$, $Y \cup F$ contains a subset of cardinal $m + \rho(F)$ belonging to $\mathscr{E}$, which means that $\rho(X \cup F) - \rho(F) \geqslant m$. Therefore

$$\rho_M(X) \leqslant \min_{F \subset\subset M} \{\rho(X \cup F) - \rho(F)\}. \tag{6.2}$$

The proof of the reverse inequality is a little longer. Suppose

$$\min_{F \subset\subset M} \{\rho(X \cup F) - \rho(F)\} = m,$$

(then in particular $|X| \geqslant m$) and let N be a given basis of M. For each $Y \subseteq X$ with $|Y| = m$ denote by $\mathscr{F}_Y$ the collection of finite subsets F of N such that $Y \cup F \in \mathscr{E}$. Clearly $\{\mathscr{F}_Y : Y \subseteq X, |Y| = m\}$ is finite since X is finite; and it is readily seen that the conditions of Lemma 6.1 are satisfied for the collections $\mathscr{F}_Y$, $Y \subseteq X$, $|Y| = m$. Therefore $\mathscr{F}(N) = \mathscr{F}_Y$ for some $Y \subseteq X$, $|Y| = m$. For this Y, therefore,

$$Y \cup F \in \mathscr{E} \qquad (F \subset\subset N)$$

and hence $Y \cup N \in \mathscr{E}$; i.e. $\rho_M(X) \geqslant m$. Hence

$$\rho_M(X) \geqslant \min_{F \subset\subset M} \{\rho(X \cup F) - \rho(F)\}; \tag{6.3}$$

and now (6.1) follows from (6.2) and (6.3).

Finally, to establish the rank formula (1.2) of Theorem 1.2, let $X \subset\subset E$, $X = X_1 \cup X_2$, $X_1 \subseteq E - M$, $X_2 \subseteq M$. By Lemma 6.3,

$$\rho_M(X) = \rho_M(X_1) + \rho(X_2);$$

and it remains to show that

$$\min_{F \subset\subset M} \{\rho(X_1 \cup F) - \rho(F) + \rho(X_2)\}$$

$$= \min_{\substack{F \subset\subset M \\ X \cap M \subseteq F}} \{\rho(X \cup F) + \rho(X \cap F) - \rho(F)\}. \tag{6.4}$$

First, if $F \subset\subset M$ and $F \supseteq X \cap M$, then

$$\rho(X \cup F) + \rho(X \cap F) - \rho(F) = \rho(X \cup F) + \rho(X_2) - \rho(F)$$

and so the inequality $\leqslant$ holds in (6.4). To obtain the reverse inequality, we need only observe that, if $F \subset\subset M$,

$$\begin{aligned}\rho(X_1 \cup F) - \rho(F) + \rho(X_2) &\geqslant \rho(X_1 \cup X_2 \cup F) + \rho((X_1 \cup F) \cap X_2) - \rho(F) \\ &= \rho(X \cup F) + \rho(X_2 \cap F) - \rho(F) \\ &= \rho(X \cup F) + \rho(X \cap F) - \rho(F).\end{aligned}$$

The proof of Theorem 1.2 is now complete.

6.4. Next, we turn to the Corollaries 1, 2. To obtain the simplified rank formula when $M \subset\subset E$ we need only show that

$$\rho(X \cup M) + \rho(X \cap M) - \rho(M) \leqslant \rho(X \cup F) + \rho(X \cap F) - \rho(F)$$

for every $F \subseteq M$, $F \supseteq X \cap M$. But, for such F,

$$\begin{aligned}&\rho(X \cup F) + \rho(X \cap F) - \rho(F) - \rho(X \cup M) - \rho(X \cap M) + \rho(M) \\ &\quad = \rho(X \cup F) + \rho(M) - \rho(X \cup M) - \rho(F) \\ &\quad \geqslant \rho(X \cup F \cup M) + \rho((X \cup F) \cap M) - \rho(X \cup M) - \rho(F) \\ &\quad = 0.\end{aligned}$$

Also, since $\rho_M(X) = \sup\{\rho_M(Y) : Y \subset\subset X\}$ for arbitrary X, and since rank functions are isotone, the deduction of the result for arbitrary X from the special case of finite X is almost immediate. Finally, the last assertion in Corollary 1 is obviously true.

In Corollary 2, we note that the condition $F \supseteq X \cap M$ in the formula (1.2) is redundant when $M \in \mathscr{E}$. Indeed, in this case, if $X = X_1 \cup X_2$, $X_1 \subseteq E - M$, $X_2 \subseteq M$,

$$\begin{aligned}\rho(X \cup F) + \rho(X \cap F) - \rho(F) &= \rho(X \cup F) + |X \cap F| - |F| \\ &= \rho(X \cup F) + |X_2| - |X_2 \cap F| \\ &= \rho(X_1 \cup (X_2 \cup F)) - \rho(X_2 \cup F) + \rho(X_2) \\ &= \rho(X_1 \cup F') - \rho(F') + \rho(X_2),\end{aligned}$$

where $F' = X_2 \cup F \subset\subset M$. Therefore

$$\min_{F \subset\subset M} \{\rho(X \cup F) + \rho(X \cap F) - \rho(F)\}$$

$$\geqslant \min_{F \subset\subset M} \{\rho(X_1 \cup F) - \rho(F) + \rho(X_2)\};$$

and the reverse inequality follows as before. This condition $F \supseteq X \cap M$ is, however, not superfluous in general. For example, let $E = \{1, 2, 3, 4\}$, $M = \{2, 3, 4\}$, $\mathfrak{A} = (\{1\}, \{2, 3\}, \{3, 4\})$, and let $\mathscr{E}$ be the collection of PTs of $\mathfrak{A}$. If $X = \{1, 2, 3\}$, $F = \{4\}$, then

$$\rho_M(X) > \rho(X \cup F) + \rho(X \cap F) - \rho(F).$$

Our last observation is that, if M is infinite and $M \in \mathscr{E}$, and if $\mathscr{E}$ is only assumed to be a pre-independence structure, then $\mathscr{E}(M)$† need *not* be a pre-independence structure. As a counter example, let $E = \{1, 2, 3, \ldots\}$, $M = \{1, 3, 5, \ldots\}$ and let $\mathscr{E}$ consist of all finite subsets of E, all subsets of $\{2, 1, 3, 5, 7, \ldots\}$, and all subsets of $\{4, 6, 1, 3, 5, 7, \ldots\}$. Then $\{2\}$, $\{4, 6\} \in \mathscr{E}(M)$ whereas $\{2, 4\} \notin \mathscr{E}(M)$, $\{2, 6\} \notin \mathscr{E}(M)$.

References

1. Brualdi, R. A. A general theorem concerning common transversals. To appear in the Proceedings of the Conference on 'Combinatorial Mathematics and its Applications', Oxford 1969.
2. Brualdi, R. A. On families of finite independence structures. *Proc. London Math. Soc.* To appear.
3. Edmonds, J. and Fulkerson, D. R. Transversals and matroid partition. *J. Res. National Bureau of Standards* **69B** (1965), 147–153.
4. Ford, L. R. and Fulkerson, D. R. *Flows in Networks* (Princeton University Press, 1962).
5. Hall, M. Jr. Distinct representatives of subsets. *Bull. American Math. Soc.* **54** (1948), 922–926.
6. Hall, P. On representatives of subsets. *J. London Math. Soc.* **10** (1935), 26–30.
7. Hoffman, A. J. and Kuhn, H. W. Systems of distinct representatives and linear programming. *American Math. Monthly,* **63** (1956), 455–460.
8. Hoffman, A. J. and Kuhn, H. W. On systems of distinct representatives. *Linear Inequalities and Related Systems. Annals of Math. Studies* **38**, (1956), 199–206.
9. König, D. *Theorie der endlichen und unendlichen Graphen* (Leipzig, 1936. Reprinted by Chelsea N.Y.).
10. Mann, H. B. and Ryser, H. J. Systems of distinct representatives. *American Math. Monthly* **60** (1953), 397–401.
11. Mendelsohn, N. S. and Dulmage, A. L. Some generalizations of the problem of distinct representatives. *Canadian J. Math.* **10** (1958), 230–241.

† Which is defined, since M is a maximal independent subset of itself.

12. MENGER, K. Zur allgemeinen Kurventheorie. *Fund. Math.* **10** (1927), 96–115.
13. MIRSKY, L. Hall's criterion as a 'self-refining' result. *Monatsh. für Math.* **73** (1969), 139–146.
14. MIRSKY, L. and PERFECT, H. Systems of representatives. *J. Math. Anal. Appl.* **15** (1966), 520–568.
15. MIRSKY, L. and PERFECT, H. Applications of the notion of independence to problems of combinatorial analysis. *J. Comb. Theory* **2** (1967), 327–357.
16. MIRSKY, L. and PERFECT, H. Comments on certain combinatorial theorems of Ford and Fulkerson. *Archiv der Math.* **19** (1968), 413–416.
17. MIRSKY, L. and others. Some aspects of transversal theory. Seminar, University of Sheffield, 1967.
18. PERFECT, H. Applications of Menger's graph theorem. *J. Math. Anal. Appl.,* **21** (1968), 96–111.
19. PERFECT, H. Remark on a criterion for common transversals., *Proc. Glasgow Math. Assoc.* **10** (1969), 66–67.
20. PERFECT, H. and PYM, J. S. An extension of Banach's mapping theorem with applications to problems concerning common representatives. *Proc. Cambridge Phil. Soc.* **62** (1966), 187–192.
21. PYM, J. S. and PERFECT, H. Submodular functions and independence structures. *J. Math. Anal. Appl.* **30** (1970), 1–31.
22. RADO, R. A theorem on independence relations. *Quart. J. Math. (Oxford)* **13** (1942), 83–89.
23. RADO, R. Axiomatic treatment of rank in infinite sets. *Canadian J. Math.* **1** (1949), 337–343.
24. RADO, R. Abstract linear dependence. *Colloq. Math.* **14** (1966), 257–264.
25. RADO, R. Note on the transfinite case of Hall's theorem on representatives. *J. London Math. Soc.* **42** (1967), 321–324.
26. WELSH, D. J. A. Some applications of a theorem of Rado. *Mathematika* **15** (1968), 199–203.
27. WHITNEY, H. On the abstract properties of linear dependence. *American J. Math.* **57** (1935), 509–533.

On the Combinatorics of the Euler Characteristic

Gian-Carlo Rota

1. Introduction

The present work is motivated by the work of Hadwiger and Klee on the Euler characteristic of polytopes, as well as by the more recent work by Sallee and Shephard on valuations on convex polytopes other than the Euler characteristic. The work of Klee, in particular, seemed to indicate the possibility of a combinatorial tie-up between the Euler characteristic and some underlying order-theoretic structure. It is the main purpose of this note to establish such a connection: Theorem 2 below expresses the Characteristic of a distributive lattice in terms of the Möbius function of the underlying ordered set of join-irreducibles. A number of applications are given of this main result: for example, a q-analog of the Euler-characteristic, and the computation of the Möbius function for the incidence lattice of a convex polytope, which surprisingly turns out to equal ± 1 alternatingly.

We have prefixed these results by a general method for 'linearizing' computations in a distributive lattice, which I have not seen elsewhere, and which seems considerably simpler than the standard set-theoretic representations in the literature. Even in the special case of Boolean algebras, the valuation ring functor introduced below seems more pliable than the well-known Boolean ring functor.

The definition of Characteristic given below is only apparently less general than the one given by Klee; the two definitions can actually be shown equivalent; such a proof of equivalence would however require a detour into routine order-theoretic techniques of interest only to specialists; we have therefore decided to omit it.

The present note, which is a continuation of the program set forth in I, hopefully will be followed by a more detailed study of homological methods in combinatorial theory.

2. Notation

We shall freely make use of the standard notation of ordered set theory, in particular, distinguishing joins and meets—written $\vee$ and $\wedge$—from set-theoretic unions and intersections—written $\cup$ and $\cap$. The reader may refer to the author's paper (referred to as I), to the elementary introduction by Harper–Rota, or to the introductory treatise by MacLane–Birkhoff, for further explanations. Properties of distributive lattices used below are stated without proof before being used.

3. The valuation ring

Let L be a distributive lattice. Recall that a *valuation* on L, with values in a commutative ring $\mathbf{A}$ with identity, is a function v from L to $\mathbf{A}$ which satisfies:

$$v(a \vee b) + v(a \wedge b) = v(a) + a(b) \tag{3.1}$$

for all elements a, b of L.

Valuations have been largely studied on Boolean algebras, where they are usually called measures; although their definition superficially resembles the definition of a measure on a Boolean algebra, the theory for a distributive lattice is richer. An example of a valuation on a distributive lattice that has no counterpart in measure theory is the Euler characteristic on the lattice generated by convex polytopes in $\mathbf{R}^n$.

Just as the study of measures has been reduced to that of linear functionals on suitable function spaces, we reduce—in a 'functorial' way—the study of valuations on an arbitrary distributive lattice to the study of linear functionals on a suitable module. The same purpose can also be accomplished by the classical representation theorem of Birkhoff–Stone; the present method, however, besides being very simple and constructive, does not require the introduction of extraneous objects ('prime ideals').

To this end, we proceed to construct a ring $V(L, \mathbf{A})$, associated with the distributive lattice L, to be called the *valuation ring* of L.

Consider the (commutative) semigroup ring over the semigroup obtained from L by taking meet ($\wedge$) as product; call it $R(L, \mathbf{A})$. Recall that this is the set of all formal sums

$$\sum_i a_i x_i, \qquad a_i \in A, \qquad x_i \in L, \tag{3.2}$$

where i ranges over any finite set. Multiplication xy of two elements x, y is defined as $xy = x \wedge y$ and extended by linearity. If L has a maximal element I, it acts as the identity of L; otherwise adjoin an identity, so that $R(L, \mathbf{A})$ will have an identity in all cases.

In $R(L, \mathbf{A})$, consider the set of all linear combinations of elements of the form

$$x \vee y + x \wedge y - x - y; \tag{3.3}$$

call this set S.

LEMMA. *The set S is an ideal in the ring $R(L, \mathbf{A})$.*

Proof. Clearly S is a submodule; to prove it is an ideal, it suffices to show that for $z \in L$, then

$$z \wedge (x \vee y + x \wedge y - x - y) \tag{3.4}$$

is an element of S. Indeed, expanding (3.4), we get

$$z \wedge (x \vee y) + z \wedge (x \wedge y) - z \wedge x - z \wedge y. \tag{3.5}$$

The first summand can be expanded by the distributive law, giving

$$(z \wedge x) \vee (z \wedge y);$$

the second summand can be rewritten in the form

$$(z \wedge x) \wedge (z \wedge y),$$

so that altogether (3.5) becomes

$$(z \wedge x) \vee (z \wedge y) + (z \wedge x) \wedge (z \wedge y) - z \wedge x - z \wedge y, \tag{3.6}$$

which is an element of the form (3.3), with $z \wedge x$ for x and $z \wedge y$ for y.

The quotient ring $V(L, \mathbf{A}) = R(L, \mathbf{A})/S$ is the *valuation ring of* L, relative to the ring of values $\mathbf{A}$.

In the present work the ring $\mathbf{A}$ will ordinarily consist of the integers.

The correspondence between a distributive lattice and its valuation ring, $L \to V(L, \mathbf{A})$, is a functor from the category of distributive lattices (where morphisms are functions which preserve $\wedge$ and $\vee$) and the category of algebras over the commutative ring $\mathbf{A}$. This functor is monomorphic on both objects and maps.

THEOREM 1. *The functor $L \to V(L, \mathbf{A})$ induces a biunique natural correspondence between valuations on L and linear functionals on $V(L, \mathbf{A})$ considered as an $\mathbf{A}$-module.*

Proof. First, let v be a valuation on L. Define a linear functional v' on $R(L, \mathbf{A})$ by extending v by linearity. Because of (3.1), v' vanishes on the ideal S, hence it defines a unique linear functional $\hat{v}$ on $V(L, \mathbf{A})$. Clearly the correspondence $v \to \hat{v}$ is monomorphic.

Conversely, let u be a linear functional on the $\mathbf{A}$-module $V(L, \mathbf{A})$. For $x \in L$, let $\hat{x}$ be the image of x under the composite map

$$L \to R(L, \mathbf{A}) \to R(L, \mathbf{A})/S = V(L, \mathbf{A}).$$

Set

$$v(x) = u(\hat{x}).$$

Clearly v is a valuation; furthermore, $\hat{v} = u$, which shows the correspondence is biunique, and completes the proof.

From now on, we identify $x \in L$ with its image $\hat{x}$ in $V(L, \mathbf{A})$, and v with $\hat{v}$. Identity (3.1) can now be rewritten as

$$v(x \vee y) = v(1) - v((1 - x)(1 - y)); \tag{3.7}$$

more generally, we have the identity

$$x \vee y = 1 - (1 - x)(1 - y). \tag{3.8}$$

It is now an easy matter to iterate (3.7):

COROLLARY 1. *For any subset $x_1, x_2, \ldots, x_n$ of the distributive lattice L, the identity*

$$v(x_1 \vee x_2 \vee \ldots \vee x_n) = v(1) - v((1 - x_1)(1 - x_2) \ldots (1 - x_n)) \tag{3.9}$$

holds for any valuation v.

The right side, once expanded, gives an expression entirely within the lattice L, independent of the valuation ring.

The statement of the Corollary is a variant of the classical inclusion–exclusion principle. Note however that, having introduced the notion of a valuation ring, statement (3.9) is no longer 'purely symbolic' (as it is billed in many treatments of inclusion–exclusion, for example Klee). In fact, (3.9) can be more generally stated as

$$x_1 \vee x_2 \vee \ldots \vee x_n = 1 - (1 - x_1)(1 - x_2) \ldots (1 - x_n). \tag{3.10}$$

EXAMPLE: Let L be the real line, with the usual order. Formula (3.10) becomes the classical formula (Pólya–Szegö, Vol. II, p. 121:)

$$\begin{aligned} \max(a, b, c, \ldots, k, l) = a + b + c + \ldots + k + l \\ - \min(a, b) - \min(a, c) \ldots - \min(k, l) \\ + \min(a, b, c) + \ldots \\ \ldots \\ \pm \min(a, b, c, \ldots, k, l). \end{aligned}$$

As an easy application of Corollary 1, we have the known result:

COROLLARY 2. *A valuation in a finite distributive lattice is uniquely determined by the values it takes on the set of join-irreducibles of L, and these values can be arbitrarily assigned.*

Recall that a join-irreducible of L is an element $x_1 \neq 0$ such that, if

$x_1 = u \vee v$, then $x_1 = u$ or $x_1 = v$. It is easily shown (and well-known) that every element $x \neq 0$ of a finite distributive lattice is the unique supremum of an irredundant set of join-irreducibles. A set of join-irreducibles is irredundant when no proper subset has the same supremum.

The proof of Corollary 2 is by induction over the partial order. Assuming that the values $v(j)$ have been assigned for all join-irreducibles j, we show that $v(x)$ is uniquely determined for all $x \in L$.

Express $x = x_1 \vee x_2 \vee \ldots \vee x_n$ as a (unique) supremum of an irredundant set of join-irreducibles x_i. Every element in the expansion of the right side of (3.10) lies below x; therefore, the right side can be assumed to be already defined by the induction hypothesis; we can therefore define $v(x)$ as the right side of (3.10).

The conclusion extends trivially to every locally finite distributive lattice having a minimal element.

4. The Characteristic

From now on, let L be a finite distributive lattice.

The *Characteristic* χ of L is defined as the valuation, unique by Corollary 2, such that $\chi(x) = 1$ for all join-irreducibles x other than the minimal one, if any, and $\chi(x) = 0$ if x is the minimal join-irreducible of L.

Recall that a subset J of an ordered set P is said to be an *order-ideal* when if $q \in J$ and $p \leqslant q$, then $p \in J$. The set-theoretic union or intersection of order-ideals is an order-ideal. Hence, the set of all order-ideals of an ordered set is a distributive lattice, denoted by $J(P)$. Conversely, every finite distributive lattice L is isomorphic to the lattice $J(P)$, where P is the ordered set of all join-irreducibles of L. We identify L with $J(P)$ whenever convenient.

A *generator* of an order-ideal J is a maximal element of J, considered as an ordered set in the induced order. An element of the lattice $J(P)$ is a join-irreducible if and only if it has a unique generator; such subsets of P have been sometimes called prime or principal ideals.

EXAMPLE 1. Let $P = P(S)$ be the family of all subsets of a set S, ordered by inclusion. An element of $L = J(P(S))$ is more familiarly known as a *simplicial complex*. On the lattice $J(P(S))$ the Characteristic, as defined above, coincides with the classical Euler characteristic of a simplicial complex. Indeed, the Euler characteristic, $c(x)$, of a simplicial complex x, considered as an integer-valued function c on L, is a valuation (see e.g. Spanier, p. 205). If j is a join-irreducible of $L = J(P(S))$, then j is a simplex, and $c(j) = 1$. Since the Characteristic is uniquely determined by its value on simplices, (Corollary 2 to Theorem 1), it follows that χ coincides with it. We shall give a simpler proof that $c = \chi$ for $J(P(S))$ below.

The preceding example displays a motivation for the present definition of the Characteristic. An element of a distributive lattice $L = J(P)$ will be considered as a generalization of the notion of a simplicial complex; an ordinary simplicial complex corresponds to the special case when L is a *free* distributive lattice. (A finite distributive lattice L is free if and only if it is of the form $L = J(P(S))$ as in the preceding Example).

We are now ready to connect the notion of Characteristic with the notion of Möbius function of an ordered set. Recall that the *Möbius function* of a finite ordered set P is the unique integer-valued function μ on $P \times P$ such that

$$(1) \quad \mu(x, x) = 1, \qquad x \in P,$$

$$(2) \quad \sum_{x \leq z \leq y} \mu(x, z) = 0 \qquad x < y,$$

$$(3) \quad \mu(x, y) = 0 \qquad \text{if } x \not\leq y.$$

THEOREM 2. *Let χ be the Characteristic of a finite distributive lattice $L = J(P)$, and let μ be the Möbius function of the ordered set P of join-irreducibles of L. Assume that P has a unique minimal element* 0, *and let μ be the Möbius function of P. Then, for every non-empty order-ideal $A \in J(P)$, the identity*

$$\chi(A) = - \sum_{\substack{p \in A \\ p > 0}} \mu(0, p) \tag{4.1}$$

holds.

Proof. For every element p of P, define a function v_p on $J(P)$ as

$$v_p(A) = \begin{cases} 1 & \text{if } p \in A \\ 0 & \text{if } p \notin A. \end{cases}$$

Evidently, v_p is a valuation. By Theorem 1, any linear combination of valuations is a valuation; in particular, the following function v is a valuation:

$$v(A) = - \sum_{p \neq 0} \mu(0, p)\, v_p(A), \quad A \in J(P), \quad A \neq \emptyset. \tag{4.2}$$

$$v(\emptyset) = 0.$$

But the right side of (4.2) coincides with the right side of (4.1). If A is a join-irreducible, with maximal element q, then the right side of (4.1) gives

$$v(A) = - \sum_{0 < p \leq q} \mu(0, p) = \mu(0, 0) = 1.$$

The conclusion now follows from Corollary 2 to Theorem 1.

Upon comparing the statement of Theorem 2 with the assertion of Example 1, the following question arises: is there a homology theory on L, whose Euler characteristic coincides with the Characteristic of L? To answer this question, associate to an ordered set P a simplicial complex $K(P)$, whose simplices are all linearly ordered subsets of P. The simplicial homology of $K(P)$ may be called the *order homology* of P.

THEOREM 3. *The Characteristic of a finite distributive lattice $L = J(P)$ is the Euler characteristic in the order homology of P, whenever the ordered set P has a unique minimal element.*

First proof. The ordinary Euler characteristic χ on simplicial complexes is a valuation, when a family of simplicial complexes is made into a distributive lattice by taking union and intersection as the lattice operations. Furthermore, it takes the value 1 on simplices. Associate with every ideal $A \subseteq J(P)$ a subcomplex $K(A)$ of $K(P)$. This correspondence preserves union and intersections; therefore, we can define a valuation c on $J(P)$ by $c(A) = \chi(K(A))$.

If A is a join-irreducible in $J(P)$ with maximal element a, then $K(A)$ is isomorphic to the cone constructed on $K(A-a)$, and hence (Hilton and Wylie, p. 84) $K(A)$ is acyclic; it follows that $c(A) = \chi(K(A)) = 1$.

Thus, we have shown that the two valuations χ and c on $J(P)$ coincide on join-irreducibles; by the Uniqueness Theorem, we conclude that they coincide everywhere.

Second proof. Let B be a non-empty order-ideal in $J(P)$. Let $\hat{B}$ be the ordered set obtained by adding to B an element I such that $I > b$ for all $b \in B$. By a result of Philip Hall (cf. Rota, p. 346), the Möbius function of B is given by

$$\mu(0, I) = -1 + r_0 - r_1 + r_2 - \dots, \tag{4.3}$$

where r_k is the number of k-simplices (that is, simplices of size $k+1$) contained in $B-\{0\}$.

It follows from the definition of the Möbius function that

$$\mu(0, I) = -\sum_{p \in B} \mu(0, p), \tag{4.4}$$

and upon comparing with (4.1) we find

$$\mu(0, I) = \chi(B) - \mu(0, 0) = \chi(B) - 1. \tag{4.5}$$

Comparing (4.5) and (4.3) we obtain

$$\chi(B) = r_0 - r_1 + r_2 - \dots. \tag{4.6}$$

The right side is the classical expression of the Euler characteristic of the simplicial complex $K(B)$ as the alternating sum of the number of faces of each dimension. The proof is therefore complete.

The argument of the second proof can be reversed, to give a generalization to arbitrary finite distributive lattices of the classical Euler formula:

COROLLARY 1. *In a finite distributive lattice L, let r_k be the number of linearly ordered subsets of k join-irreducibles lying below the element x. Then the Characteristic of x is given by the formula*

$$\chi(x) = r_0 - r_1 + r_2 - \dots \tag{4.7}$$

Proof. Adjoin an element $\bar{0}$ to L, so that $\bar{0} < x$ for all $x \in L$; call $\bar{L}$ the resulting distributive lattice. Then $\bar{L} = J(P)$, where P has a unique minimal element 0, the argument of the preceding second proof can be applied, and the conclusion follows from formula (4.6).

For a simplicial complex P, the simplicial complex $K(P)$ is order-isomorphic to the barycentric subdivision of P; therefore, the order homology on simplicial complexes coincides with the ordinary homology, and Corollary 1 is a special case of the classical theorem.

In the course of the proof of the preceding Theorem we have also established

COROLLARY 2. *Let P be a finite ordered set with* 0. *For any $p \in P$, let $\hat{p}$ be the order-ideal $\{x\colon x < p\}$. Then*

$$\mu(0, p) = \chi(\hat{p}) - 1, \qquad p \neq 0.$$

EXAMPLE 2. What is the Characteristic of the distributive lattice D of positive integers, ordered by divisibility? The Möbius function $\mu(k, n) = \bar{\mu}(n/k)$ of L is the classical Möbius function of number theory: $\bar{\mu}(n) = (-1)^k$ if n is the product of k district primes, and 0 otherwise. An element of D other than the integer one is a join-irreducible if and only if it is the power of a prime. Hence, (4.2) gives

$$\chi(n) = -\sum_{p^k|n} \mu(p^k), \qquad n \in D,$$

where the sum on the right ranges over all primes p and all positive integers k such that p^k divides n. But $\bar{\mu}(p^k) = 0$ unless $k = 1$, and thus $\bar{\mu}(p) = -1$. Hence, the characteristic $\chi(n)$ equals the number of distinct prime divisors of n, usually written $d(n)$.

Theorem 3 can be applied in two ways: to compute an Euler characteristic, when the Möbius function is known, and *vice-versa* to compute the Möbius function of an ordered set by the techniques of homology theory. As an instance of the second application, we prove the following generalization of a result of Philip Hall (Rota, p. 349): if the maximal element I of P covers exactly one element, then $\mu(0, I) = 0$. Indeed, under the circumstances the simplicial complex $K(P)$ is isomorphic to the cone stretched from the simplicial complex $K(P - I)$ to the 'vertex' I, hence its homology vanishes identically.

By other homological arguments, one can obtain Crapo's complementation theorem, the Cross-Cut Theorem (Rota, p. 352), and several other results to be presented elsewhere.

We conclude this section with a few remarks about the *relative* Characteristic. This may be defined as a function $\chi(y, x)$ on an element $y \geqslant x$ of a distributive lattice L, with the following properties:

(1) $\chi(x, x) = 0, \qquad x \in L.$

(2) $\chi(z, y) + \chi(y, x) = \chi(z, x), \qquad z \geqslant y \geqslant x.$

(3) If the segments $[x, y]$ and $[u, v]$ are projective, then $\chi(y, x) = \chi(v, u)$.

(4) If y covers x, then $\chi(y, x) = 1$.

It can be shown, using the above results, that under these conditions $\chi(y, x) = \chi(y) - \chi(x)$, and that $\chi(z, x)$ is the Characteristic of the distributive lattice $\{z \in L : z \geqslant x\}$.

5. Applications

(a) *The theta Characteristic.* A combinatorial generalization of the notion of simplicial complex is obtained by replacing the word 'subset' by 'subspace of a vector space' throughout. To ensure finiteness, we take here a vector space V of finite dimension over a finite field $GF(q)$, and define a *q-complex* as a family Q of subspaces of V, such that if $W \in Q$ and $M \subseteq W$, then $M \in Q$.

A q-complex is simply an order ideal in the lattice $L(V)$ of subspaces of V, ordered by inclusion, and this should make the analogy with simplicial complexes apparent. The Characteristic of a q-complex can be computed by Theorem 2. Recalling that the Möbius function of the lattice $L(V)$ equals the so-called 'theta factor' (Rota, p. 352):

$$\mu(A, B) = (-1)^k q^{k(k-1)/2}, \qquad A, B \in L(V), \tag{5.1}$$

where k is the difference of the two dimensions, we have from Theorem 2:

PROPOSITION 1. *The Characteristic of a q-complex Q with r_k faces of dimension k is the 'theta' characteristic given by the formula*

$$\chi(Q) = \sum_{k>0} (-1)^{k+1} q^{k(k-1)/2} r_k. \tag{5.2}$$

The q-analog of a simplex is a join-irreducible in $L(V)$, that is, a q-complex which is the set of all subspaces of some vector space. The theta characteristic of a 'q-simplex' equals one (by definition!), and (5.2) gives the identity of Euler and Cauchy

$$1 = \sum_{k>0} (-1)^{k+1} q^{k(k-1)/2} \begin{bmatrix} n \\ k \end{bmatrix}, \tag{5.3}$$

where the brackets on the right stand for the Gaussian coefficients counting the number of k-dimensional subspaces of an n-space; other q-identities can be similarly established by use of the theta characteristic.

A *q-sphere* S_n is the q-complex obtained from a q-simplex C of dimension n by removing the maximal element. The Betti numbers of $K(C)$ vanish, and those of $K(S_n)$, vanish except for the nth, which equals $q^{n(n-1)/2}$.

As $q \to 1$ (for an imaginary field with 'one' element) a q-complex becomes an ordinary simplicial complex, and a q-sphere becomes an ordinary homology sphere.

It is possible to prove a q-analog of Euler's theorem on subdivision of polyhedra, stating that the theta characteristic remains invariant under certain 'q-subdivisions' (projections and sections).

(b) *The partition characteristic.* A *partition complex* on a set S is a family R of partitions of S, with the property that if $\pi \in R$ and π is a refinement of σ (that is, every block of π is contained in a block of σ), then $\sigma \in R$. In other words, a partition complex is an order ideal in the dual $\pi(S)^*$ of the lattice $\pi(S)$ of partitions of S ($\pi(S)^*$ is obtained from $\pi(S)$ by inverting the order relation). Once the Möbius function of $\pi(S)$ is known the Characteristic is easily computed by Theorem 2 (cf. Rota, p. 359), giving

$$\chi(R) = \sum_{k \geqslant 1} (-1)^k (k-1)!\, r_k, \tag{5.4}$$

where r_k is the number of partitions with k blocks in the partition complex R.

Again it is possible to prove 'subdivision-invariance' and 'non-intersection' results, analogous to the classical ones.

(c) *The incidence lattice of a polytope.* With a polytope H in Euclidean n-space one can associate a lattice $L(H)$, whose elements are the faces of H, ordered by inclusion, sometime known as the *incidence lattice* of H. It is an open problem, posed by Rademacher and Steinitz, to characterize combinatorially the incidence lattice of convex polytopes. As a step in this direction, we prove:

THEOREM 4. *The Möbius function of the incidence lattice of a convex polytope takes alternately the values* $+1$ *and* -1; *more precisely,*

$$\mu(0, F) = (-1)^{f-1}, \tag{5.5}$$

where f is the dimension of the face F, and 0 *is the null face.*

Proof. By uniqueness, the Characteristic on the distributive lattice $J(L(H))$, where H is a convex polytope, coincides with the ordinary Euler characteristic; note that every element of $J(L(H))$ is a subpolytope of H. Let n be the dimension of H. The Euler characteristic of the boundary of H is the Euler characteristic of an $(n-1)$-sphere, which equals $1 + (-1)^{n-1}$. This must equal the Characteristic of the ideal $L(H) - I$ in $J(L(H))$. Corollary 2 to Theorem 3 now gives $\mu(0, I) = (-1)^{n-1}$.

6. Open problems

Theorem 4 can be greatly generalized: *every* valuation defined on the distributive lattice generated by all closed convex polytopes in $\mathbf{R}^n$ translates, by much the same method, into a combinatorial condition on the incidence lattice of convex polytopes. Thus, we are led to conjecture that a 'basis' for the set of all such valuations on polytopes will translate into a set of necessary and sufficient conditions for a lattice to be the incidence lattice of a convex polytope. In three dimensions this reasoning gives the theorem of Rademacher–Steinitz. In higher dimensions, the recent work of Sallee and Shephard seems to lend support to this conjecture.

One such valuation is the valuation χ^+ which is obtained by applying the Riesz decomposition $\chi = \chi^+ - \chi^-$ to the Characteristic. What is the geometric meaning of χ^+ for polytopes?

Corollary 1 to Theorem 3 can be used to extend the definition of the Möbius function to non-finite situations (for example, for a q-complex over *any* field, other than $GF(q)$), for in such cases the homology may still be finite-dimensional. What is the analog of Möbius inversion in this context?

The theta characteristic, and formulas computing it for a variety of q-complexes, bear a striking resemblance to certain formulas in the theory of partitions, and suggest that it may be related to the 'Euler characteristic' of algebraic surfaces defined by A. Weil.

Non-intersection theorems of Helly type (in their topological form, not in their convex form, as in e.g. Alexandroff–Hopf p. 295ff) probably exist for the theta characteristic and the partition characteristic, but such possibility remains to be investigated.

Corollary 2 to Theorem 1 is valid more generally for modular lattices (Birkhoff, p. 236). We have preferred the present approach, through the valuation ring, because it puts the still all-too-frequent naive 'symbolic' computations with valuations on a rigorous basis. It may be noted that Theorem 1 associates functorially with every distributive lattice a semialgebra of type 1 in the sense of Bonsall, and provides a scheme for translation of all 'distributive lattice' concepts into 'semialgebra of type 1' concepts, a welcome simplification. For example, a 'prime ideal' in the distributive lattice sense translates into a genuine prime ideal in the algebraic sense.

Theorem 3 also generalizes to arbitrary valuations, and yields module-isomorphisms of the incidence algebra of an ordered set into the set of valuations (see the preceding paragraph), and again extends the notion of incidence algebra to non-finite situations. Curiously, in this correspondence the Characteristic turns out to be the inverse of the 'number of elements of' valuation (at least for finite lattice), corresponding to the inverse relationship between zeta function and Möbius function of an ordered set, a fact which is surely not a coincidence, but which I haven't been able to explain.

An interesting class of valuations to be studied are those on geometric lattices; for example, the chromatic polynomial of a graph G defines a valuation on L, the bond lattice of G, which is closely related to the Characteristic; a discussion of these concepts would take us too far afield.

We conclude with two remarks. The Betti numbers can be treated in the spirit of the present note, giving some further connections between homology and combinatorial invariants. Finally, the Characteristic of infinite distributive lattices can also be defined, by a process of subdivision adapted from classical topology.

References

1. Alexandroff, P. and Hopf, H. *Topologie* (Berlin, Springer, 1935).
2. Birkhoff, Garrett. *Lattice Theory* (Third edition, Amer. Math. Soc. Colloquium Publications, Providence, 1966).
3. Bonsall, F. F. Semialgebras of continuous functions. *Proceedings Intern. Symp. Linear Spaces* (Jerusalem, 1960), 101–114.
4. Crapo, H. H. The Möbius function of a lattice. *J. Combinatorial Theory* **1** (1966), 126–131.
5. Folkman, J. The homology groups of a lattice. *J. Math. Mech.* **15** (1966), 126–131.
6. Grünbaum, B. *Convex Polytopes* (Interscience, New York, 1967).
7. Hadwiger, H. Über eine symbolisch-topologische Formel. *Elem. Math.* **2** (1947), 35–41.
8. Hadwiger, H. Über additive Funktionale k-dimensionaler Eipolyeder. *Publ. Math. Debrecen* **3** (1953), 87–94.
9. Hadwiger, H. Eulers Charakteristik und kombinatorische Geometrie. *J. reine angew. Math.* **194** (1955), 101–110.
10. Hadwiger, H. Zur Eulerschen Charakteristik euklidischer Polyeder. *Monatsh. für Math.* **64** (1960), 349–354.
11. Hilton, P. J. and Wylie, S. *Homology Theory* (Cambridge University Press, 1960).
12. Klee, V. The Euler characteristic in combinatorial geometry. *Amer. Math. Monthly* **70** (1963), 119–127.
13. MacLane, S. and Birkhoff, G. *Algebra* (New York, Macmillan, 1967).
14. Perles, M. A. and Sallee, G. T. Cell complexes, valuations, and the Euler relation. To appear.
15. Pettis, B. J. On the extension of measures. *Annals of Math.* (2), **54** (1951), 186–197.

16. Pólya, G. and Szegö, G. *Aufgaben und Lehrsätze aus der Analysis*, 2 vols. (Third edition; Springer, Berlin, 1964).

17. Rademacher, H. and Steinitz, E. *Vorlesungen über die Theory der Polyeder*. (Springer, Berlin, 1934).

18. Robertson, J. B. Uniqueness of measures, *Amer. Math. Monthly* **74** (1967), 50–53.

19. Rota, G.–C. On the foundations of combinatorial theory. I. Theory of Möbius functions. *Z. Wahrscheinlichkeitstheorie* **2** (1964), 340–368.

20. Sallee, G. T. Polytopes, valuations, and the Euler relation. *Canad. J. Math.* **20** (1968), 1412–1424.

21. Shephard, G. C. Euler-type relations for convex polytopes. To appear.

22. Spanier, E. H. *Algebraic Topology* (McGraw–Hill, New York, 1966).

23. Weil, A. Number of solutions of equations over finite fields. *Bull. Amer. Math. Soc.* **55** (1949), 497–508.

Some Remarks on the Matrix Operator ad A

Olga Taussky*

This note concerns mainly the finite-dimensional version of Fuglede's theorem (**3**). This was discussed by Drazin (**2**) who refers it back to Halmos (**4**) and also links it with an identity of von Neumann (**6**). The theorem in question is:

THEOREM 1A. *Let A be a matrix over the complex numbers. Then A is normal if and only if $AB = BA$ implies $A^*B = BA^*$ for every matrix B.*

Each of the two parts can be proved in one line.

Remark 1. A further understanding of the theorem can be achieved via the matrix ad A. This can be done in two different ways. On the one hand, one can say that $AB = BA$ means that the commutator operator defined by A applied to B is zero. This operator can be expressed by the $n^2 \times n^2$ -dimensional matrix $(I \times A)$–$(A' \times I)$, called ad A. The statement ad $A \cdot B = 0$ is equivalent to saying that ad A has the characteristic vector B (in a suitable ordering) with respect to the characteristic root 0.

Hence the theorem states that normal matrices are characterized by the fact that ad$A$ and ad A^* have the same characteristic vectors corresponding to the characteristic root 0. On the other hand, one can reformulate the theorem in the following way:

THEOREM 1B. *Let A be a matrix over the complex numbers. Then A is normal if and only if $AB = BA$ implies $AB^* = B^*A$ for all B.*

This then can be interpreted as follows: if A is normal and if B is a characteristic vector of ad A corresponding to the characteristic value 0 then so is B^*. This will now be proved: If A is normal, then for a suitable unitary U, the

* This work was carried out (in part) under NSF Grant 11236.

matrix $U^{-1}AU =$ diagonal $(\alpha_1, \ldots, \alpha_n)$ where α_i are the characteristic roots of A. For any unitary matrix V we have

$$V^{-1}(AB - BA)V = V^{-1}AV \cdot V^{-1}BV - V^{-1}BV \cdot V^{-1}AV$$

and

$$V^{-1}(AB^* - B^*A)V = V^{-1}AV(V^{-1}BV)^* - (V^{-1}BV)^*V^{-1}AV.$$

Hence, we may assume that A is already in diagonal form. The matrix ad A is then also diagonal and the diagonal elements are all n^2 elements $\alpha_i - \alpha_k$. Every characteristic vector $B = (b_{ik})$ corresponding to 0 has an element $b_{ik} = 0$ if $\alpha_i - \alpha_k \neq 0$ and an arbitrary entry for b_{ik} if $\alpha_i - \alpha_k = 0$. This then proves the assertion for a diagonal A.

Remark 2. Drazin obtains an alternative proof for the fact that A is normal if the above condition holds by referring to the following known theorem: If B commutes with every X which commutes with A, then B is a polynomial in A. In this way this part of Theorem 1A becomes a special case of the fact just mentioned.

It seems of interest to ask: consider the generalized commutator

$$A_1X - XA_2$$

where A_1, A_2 are square matrices of not necessarily equal dimension and X a rectangular matrix of appropriate dimensions. One can then ask to characterize pairs of matrices B_1, B_2 of the same dimensions as A_1, A_2 with the property that whenever

$$A_1X - XA_2 = 0$$

also

$$B_1X - XB_2 = 0.$$

This would then be linked with Putnam's generalization (**5**) of the Fuglede theorem (see also Berberian (**1**)): If A_1, A_2 are normal, then $A_1B = BA_2$ implies $A_1{}^*B = BA_2{}^*$.

Remark 3. If A is normal then ad A is normal. This follows from the fact that (ad $A)^* =$ ad A^* and the fact that for a commuting pair A, B also ad A, ad B commute (and conversely).

Proof. Since ad A is given by the matrix

$$(I \times A) - (A' \times I)$$

we have to study the product

$$[(I \times A) - (A' \times I)]\,[(I \times B) - (B' \times I)].$$

Using the identity $(A \times B)(C \times D) = (AC \times BD)$ it follows easily that the product coincides with the product taken in the reverse order. Conversely, the coincidence of the two products implies

$$(I \times AB) + (A'B' \times I) = (I \times BA) + (B'A' \times I).$$

This leads to

$$\left(I \times (AB - BA)\right) = \left((B'A' - A'B') \times I\right);$$

hence

$$\left(I \times (AB - BA)\right) = \left((AB - BA)' \times I\right);$$

hence $\mathrm{ad}(AB - BA) = 0$; hence $AB - BA = 0$.

Remark 4. The number of common characteristic vectors of ad A and ad A^* corresponding to the characteristic root 0 could perhaps be used as a measure for the normality of A.

References

1. BERBERIAN, S. K. Note on a theorem of Fuglede and Putnam. *Proc. Amer. Math. Soc.* **10** (1959), 175–182.
2. DRAZIN, M. P. On diagonable and normal matrices. *Quart. J. Math.* Oxford (2), **2** (1951), 189–198.
3. FUGLEDE, B. A commutativity theorem for normal operators. *Proc. Nat. Acad. Sci.* **36** (1950), 35–40.
4. HALMOS, P. R. *Finite Dimensional Vector Spaces,* (Princeton, 1942).
5. PUTNAM, C. R. On normal operators in Hilbert space. *Amer. J. Math.* **73** (1951), 357–362.
6. VON NEUMANN, J. Approximate properties of matrices of high finite order. *Portugaliae Math.* **3** (1942), 1–62.

Graphs on Spheres

W. T. Tutte

Summary

Consider an elastic model of a graph whose vertices are constrained to lie on a sphere, and whose edges are stretched along chords. Does it have an equilibrium position in which it is not confined to a single plane; and, if so, can such a position be found which corresponds, under projection from the centre, to a realization of the graph on the sphere (without crossings)? In this paper a preliminary survey of the problem is presented.

1. Realizations

A finite graph G is said to be a *topological graph* in a metric space S if it satisfies the following conditions.

(i) The vertices of G are distinct points of S.

(ii) The links of G are simple closed arcs in S whose end-points are their incident vertices.

(iii) The loops of G are simple closed curves in S, each passing through its incident vertex.

(iv) No edge contains a vertex with which it is not incident.

(v) Any common point of two distinct edges is a vertex.

If G and H are isomorphic graphs and G is a topological graph in a metric space S, then we say that G is a *realization* of H in S.

We are concerned here only with the cases in which S is the Euclidean plane or the 2-sphere. Using the device of stereographic projection we can show that a finite graph having a realization in one of these surfaces has also a realization in the other. Such a graph is said to be *planar*. A combinatorial condition for the planarity of a graph is given by Kuratowski's Theorem (**2, 3**).

We may distinguish special kinds of realization. Thus a realization in the plane is *straight* if the edges are straight segments, and a realization on the sphere is *geodetic* if the edges are great circular arcs. The condition that a graph

H shall have a straight realization in the plane is that it shall be planar and *strict*, i.e., have no loops or multiple edges (**1**). From a straight realization of H in a plane we can obtain a geodetic realization of H on a tangent sphere by projection from the centre of the sphere. However, there are obvious examples of graphs that are not strict and yet have geodetic realizations on the sphere.

If G is a topological graph in the space S, we define its *complex* $|G|$ as the point-set which is the union of the edges of G and the set of vertices of G. The *faces* of G, with respect to S, are the components of the complement of $|G|$ in S. If G is non-separable, and S is the 2-sphere or Euclidean plane, it can be shown that the boundary of each face is a simple closed curve made up of edges and vertices of G. Moreover each edge of G lies in the boundary of exactly two faces. In the planar case exactly one face is unbounded.

We say that a graph H is *nodally* 3-*connected* if it has the following property. Whenever H is represented as the union of two edge-disjoint proper subgraphs J and K, then either J and K have three or more common vertices or they have exactly two, and in the latter case either J or K is an arc-graph whose ends are these two vertices.

Let H be nodally 3-connected and let C be a circuit of H which corresponds to the boundary of a face for some realization of H in the plane. We construct a realization C' of C in the plane in which the edges and vertices are the edges and vertices respectively of a convex polygon Q. The *representative point* $P(v)$ of a vertex v of C is then the corresponding vertex of C', with respect to a given isomorphism of C onto C'. A representative point $P(w)$ can be assigned to each other vertex w of H so as to satisfy the following rule: for each such vertex w, the point $P(w)$ is the centroid of the representative points of the vertices of H adjacent to w. This rule can be reduced to a set of linear equations connecting the Cartesian coordinates of the representative points of the vertices of G. It is shown in (**4**) that the equations have a unique solution for the coordinates of the representative points of the vertices of H not belonging to C. It is also shown in (**4**) that H has a straight representation G such that the vertex of G corresponding to a given vertex v of H is the representative point of v. We refer to G as a *barycentric* realization of H.

We may visualize the construction of the above barycentric realization of H as the stretching of an elastic model of H across the frame C'. The barycentric condition minimizes the sum of the squares of the lengths of the edges.

2. Vector equations

Suppose an elastic model of a graph G to be stretched over a globe. Will it fly off the globe or can it take up an equilibrium position on it? Before we can discuss this question mathematically we must agree on the form of the law of elasticity.

Let us enumerate the vertices of G as $v_1, v_2, \ldots, v_n$. We write the number of edges joining two distinct vertices v_i and v_j as c_{ij}. Thus

$$c_{ij} = c_{ji}. \tag{1}$$

We write also

$$c_{ii} = 0 \qquad (1 \leqslant i \leqslant n). \tag{2}$$

To each vertex v_i let there be assigned a representative point P_i on a sphere S of unit radius. An assignment of representative points corresponds to a possible position of our model of G on the globe. If we regard the edges of the model as lying along chords of S it is natural to use a law of elasticity in which the energy associated with an edge of the model is measured by the square of its length. An equilibrium position of the model corresponds to a stationary value of the total energy (with respect to displacements of the vertices of the model on the globe). We are led to the mathematical problem of finding those assignments of the representative points P_i that correspond to stationary values of the function

$$Q = \sum_{i=1}^{n} \sum_{j=1}^{n} c_{ij}|V_i - V_j|^2, \tag{3}$$

where V_k denotes the vector, of unit length, from the centre of S to the point P_i.

Now $|V_i - V_j|^2$ is the scalar product $(V_i - V_j) . (V_i - V_j)$, that is

$$|V_i|^2 + |V_j|^2 - 2V_i . V_j = 2 - 2V_i . V_j.$$

Hence, differentiating (3) with respect to V_i, we find that, when Q is stationary,

$$dV_i . \left(\sum_{j=1}^{n} c_{ij} V_j \right) = 0. \tag{4}$$

But dV_i can be directed along any tangent to S at P_i. We deduce that the vector

$$\sum_{j=1}^{n} c_{ij} V_j$$

is parallel or antiparallel to V_i, or is zero. Hence

$$\sum_{j=1}^{n} c_{ij} V_j + \lambda_i V_i = 0 \tag{5}$$

for each i, where λ_i is a scalar depending only on i.

Conversely, if (5) holds, then (4) is true for each i, and so Q is stationary.

In what follows we give a procedure for solving equations (5), admitting that it is of practical utility only in very simple cases. We do not enquire as to whether or not a particular solution of (5) represents a stable equilibrium.

3. Solutions of the vector equations

Let us introduce a system of rectangular Cartesian coordinates with the centre of S as origin. Then the equation of S is

$$x^2 + y^2 + z^2 = 1.$$

We write the coordinates of the point P_i as (x_i, y_i, z_i).

Put

$$m_{ij} = c_{ij} + \lambda_i \delta_{ij}, \tag{6}$$

and denote by M that square matrix of order n whose (i, j)th element is m_{ij}. Then equations (5) can be rewritten as

$$\sum_{j=1}^{n} m_{ij} x_j = \sum_{j=1}^{n} m_{ij} y_j = \sum_{j=1}^{n} m_{ij} z_j = 0. \tag{7}$$

Write X, Y and Z for the n-vectors $(x_1, x_2, \dots, x_n)$, $(y_1, y_2, \dots, y_n)$, and $(z_1, z_2, \dots, z_n)$ respectively.

Now we can obtain a trivial solution of equations (5) by making all the points P_i coincide, or by putting some of them at one end of a diameter of S and the others at the other end. There may be other solutions in which the points P_i are confined to a single great circle. We describe all such solutions as *degenerate* and we interest ourselves only in non-degenerate solutions. We note that a non-degenerate solution is a solution in which the vectors V_i are not coplanar.

Evidently a solution is non-degenerate if and only if the n-vectors X, Y and Z associated with it are linearly independent. This is possible if and only if the rank of M is at most $n - 3$. In solving (5) it is thus initially necessary to constrain the λ_i so that

$$\text{rank}\,(M) \leqslant n - 3, \tag{8}$$

that is so that all the square submatrices of M of order $n - 2$ have zero determinants.

Suppose the λ_i chosen so that

$$\text{rank}\,(M) = n - 3.$$

In this exploratory study we can perhaps leave aside the case in which strict inequality occurs in (8). That case would however be the important one if we were trying to represent G in a k-sphere with $k > 2$. We now obtain three independent solutions U_1, U_2 and U_3 of the homogeneous linear equations

$$\sum_{j=1}^{n} m_{ij}\xi_j = 0$$

and argue that any solution of (5) corresponding to our special choice of the λ_i must be such that X, Y and Z are linear combinations of U_1, U_2 and U_3.

$$X = \alpha_1 U_1 + \alpha_2 U_2 + \alpha_3 U_3,$$
$$Y = \beta_1 U_1 + \beta_2 U_2 + \beta_3 U_3,$$
$$Z = \gamma_1 U_1 + \gamma_2 U_2 + \gamma_3 U_3.$$

We can regard X, Y and Z as the rows of a $3 \times n$ matrix N. Then the ith column of N gives the coordinate vector V_i of the point P_i. We then have a valid solution of equations (5) provided that in each column of N the sum of the squares of the three entries is unity. This condition of course restricts the numbers α_i, β_j, γ_k, and it may require further constraints on the λ_i.

A slight simplification results if we choose the x-axis to pass through P_1, and the (x, y)-plane to pass through P_2. A different but analogous simplification is used in Section 4.

4. The complete 4-graph

As a very simple example we apply the foregoing theory to the case of the complete 4-graph, which has four vertices v_1, v_2, v_3 and v_4, each pair being joined by exactly one edge. In this case

$$M = \begin{pmatrix} \lambda_1 & 1 & 1 & 1 \\ 1 & \lambda_2 & 1 & 1 \\ 1 & 1 & \lambda_3 & 1 \\ 1 & 1 & 1 & \lambda_4 \end{pmatrix}.$$

In order that (8) may hold we must put

$$\lambda_1 = \lambda_2 = \lambda_3 = \lambda_4 = 1.$$

The rank of M is then 1.

We take the U_i to be as follows.

$$U_1 = (1, \quad 0, \quad 0, \quad -1),$$
$$U_2 = (0, \quad 1, \quad 0, \quad -1),$$
$$U_3 = (0, \quad 0, \quad 1, \quad -1).$$

We then have

$$N = \begin{pmatrix} \alpha_1, & \alpha_2, & \alpha_3, & -\alpha_1 & -\alpha_2 & -\alpha_3 \\ \beta_1, & \beta_2, & \beta_3, & -\beta_1 & -\beta_2 & -\beta_3 \\ \gamma_1, & \gamma_2, & \gamma_3, & -\gamma_1 & -\gamma_2 & -\gamma_3 \end{pmatrix}.$$

Let the coordinate system be chosen so that V_1 and V_2 lie in the (x, y)-plane, and the x-axis bisects the angle between them. Then

$$\alpha_1 = \alpha_2,$$
$$\beta_1 = -\beta_2,$$
$$\gamma_1 = \gamma_2 = 0.$$

For each column of N we equate the sum of the squares of the entries to unity. We thus obtain the equations

$$\alpha_1{}^2 + \beta_1{}^2 = 1,$$
$$\alpha_3{}^2 + \beta_3{}^2 + \gamma_3{}^2 = 1,$$
$$(-2\alpha_1 - \alpha_3)^2 + \beta_3{}^2 + \gamma_3{}^2 = 1.$$

These imply

$$\alpha_3 = \pm (2\alpha_1 + \alpha_3).$$

We take the minus sign here; otherwise we would have $\alpha_1 = \alpha_2 = 0$, and N would have only two independent columns thus making the solution degenerate. We deduce that

$$\alpha_3 = -\alpha_1.$$

The solution is now easily completed. It requires merely that the angle between V_1 and V_2 shall be equal to that between V_3 and V_4, and that the bisecting rays of these two angles shall be opposite.

5. The triangular prism

As our second example we take the triangular prism, a graph made up of two triangles $v_1 v_2 v_3$ and $v_4 v_5 v_6$, together with the three extra edges $v_1 v_4$, $v_2 v_5$ and $v_3 v_6$. In this case we find that there is essentially only one non-degenerate solution. It corresponds to a realization of G on the sphere, each edge $v_i v_j$ being represented by the shorter of the two great circular arcs joining P_i, and P_j. Curiously, the two spherical triangles $P_1 P_2 P_3$ and $P_4 P_5 P_6$ are found to have different areas in the solution.

For the triangular prism we have

$$M = \begin{Bmatrix} \lambda_1 & 1 & 1 & 1 & 0 & 0 \\ 1 & \lambda_2 & 1 & 0 & 1 & 0 \\ 1 & 1 & \lambda_3 & 0 & 0 & 1 \\ 1 & 0 & 0 & \lambda_4 & 1 & 1 \\ 0 & 1 & 0 & 1 & \lambda_5 & 1 \\ 0 & 0 & 1 & 1 & 1 & \lambda_6 \end{Bmatrix}.$$

It is clear that the first three rows of M are linearly independent, whatever values the λ_i may have. If the rank of M is to be 3, the other rows must be linear combinations of the first three. Hence

$$\begin{aligned}(\text{row } 4) &= \lambda_4(\text{row } 1) + (\text{row } 2) + (\text{row } 3),\\ (\text{row } 5) &= (\text{row } 1) + \lambda_5(\text{row } 2) + (\text{row } 3),\\ (\text{row } 6) &= (\text{row } 1) + (\text{row } 2) + \lambda_6(\text{row } 3).\end{aligned}$$

Applying these row-equations to each column of M we obtain the following equations for the λ_i.

$$\begin{array}{lll}\lambda_1\lambda_4 = -1, & -\lambda_5 = \lambda_1 + 1, & -\lambda_6 = \lambda_1 + 1,\\ -\lambda_4 = \lambda_2 + 1, & \lambda_2\lambda_5 = -1, & -\lambda_6 = \lambda_2 + 1,\\ -\lambda_4 = \lambda_3 + 1, & -\lambda_5 = \lambda_3 + 1, & \lambda_3\lambda_6 = -1.\end{array}$$

They have the following consequence:

$$\lambda_1 = \lambda_2 = \lambda_3 = -\tau$$

and

$$\lambda_4 = \lambda_5 = \lambda_6 = -\tau^*,$$

where τ and τ^* are the roots of $x^2 - x - 1 = 0$. Using permutations of the suffixes consistent with the symmetry of G we can arrange that

$$\tau = (1 + \sqrt{5})/2, \qquad \tau^* = (1 - \sqrt{5})/2.$$

We may now write

$$\begin{aligned}U_1 &= (1,\ 0,\ 0,\ \tau,\ -1,\ -1),\\ U_2 &= (0,\ 1,\ 0,\ -1,\ \tau,\ -1),\\ U_3 &= (0,\ 0,\ 1,\ -1,\ -1,\ \tau\ ).\end{aligned}$$

As usual

$$N = \begin{Bmatrix}\alpha_1 U_1 + \alpha_2 U_2 + \alpha_3 U_3\\ \beta_1 U_1 + \beta_2 U_2 + \beta_3 U_3\\ \gamma_1 U_1 + \gamma_2 U_2 + \gamma_3 U_3\end{Bmatrix}.$$

Put

$$\begin{aligned}Q_1 &= \alpha_2\alpha_3 + \beta_2\beta_3 + \gamma_2\gamma_3,\\ Q_2 &= \alpha_1\alpha_3 + \beta_1\beta_3 + \gamma_1\gamma_3,\\ Q_3 &= \alpha_1\alpha_2 + \beta_1\beta_2 + \gamma_1\gamma_2.\end{aligned}$$

We proceed to equate to zero the sum of the squares of the entries in each column of N. From the first three columns we obtain

$$\alpha_i^2 + \beta_i^2 + \gamma_i^2 = 1,$$

for $i = 1, 2, 3$.

From the fourth column of N we obtain

$$(\alpha_1\tau - \alpha_2 - \alpha_3)^2 + (\beta_1\tau - \beta_2 - \beta_3)^2 + (\gamma_1\tau - \gamma_2 - \gamma_3)^2 = 1,$$

whence

$$-2Q_1 + 2\tau Q_2 + 2\tau Q_3 = \tau + 2.$$

Similarly the fifth and sixth columns of N yield the equations

$$2\tau Q_1 - 2Q_2 + 2\tau Q_3 = \tau + 2,$$
$$2\tau Q_1 + 2\tau Q_2 - 2Q_3 = \tau + 2.$$

On solving these three linear equations for the Q_i we find that

$$Q_1 = Q_2 = Q_3 = \tau/2 = \cos 36°.$$

Let us write θ_{ij} for the angle between V_i and V_j. Then

$$\theta_{12} = \theta_{23} = \theta_{13} = 36°.$$

To find θ_{14} we observe that, by the linear relations between the columns of N,

$$V_4 = \tau V_1 - V_2 - V_3.$$

Hence

$$\begin{aligned}\cos\theta_{14} &= (V_1 . V_4) = \tau(V_1 . V_1) - (V_1 . V_2) - (V_1 . V_3)\\ &= (2\tau - \tau - \tau)/2\\ &= 0.\end{aligned}$$

We deduce that $\theta_{14} = 90°$. Similarly $\theta_{25} = \theta_{36} = 90°$.

An analogous argument shows that $\theta_{15} = \theta_{16} = \theta_{24} = \theta_{26} = \theta_{34} = \theta_{35} = 120°$.

We have also

$$\cos\theta_{45} = (\tau V_1 - V_2 - V_3).(-V_1 + \tau V_2 - V_3).$$

By multiplying out the product on the right and using the preceding results we find that $\cos\theta_{45} = \tau^*/2$. Hence $\theta_{45} = 72°$. Similarly $\theta_{56} = \theta_{46} = 72°$.

The solution of equations (5) in the case of the triangular prism is now completely determined.

6. Progress report

The author has found the non-degenerate equilibrium positions for a number of 3-connected planar graphs of not more than 6 vertices.

One of these graphs is the square pyramid, the join of a vertex v_1 to a quadrilateral $v_2\, v_3\, v_4\, v_5$. When P_1 is taken to be the point $(1, 0, 0)$ it is found that the other four points P_i lie on the circle of intersection of the sphere with the plane $x = -1/2$. The quadrilateral can be represented by any rectangle inscribed in this circle. The solution evidently corresponds to a geodesic realization of the graph on the sphere.

The triangular bipyramid consists of a triangle $v_1 v_2 v_3$, two other vertices v_4 and v_5, and all possible joins from these two vertices to the vertices of the triangle. In the non-degenerate solution P_4 and P_5 are diametrically opposite while P_1, P_2 and P_3 are distributed at angles of 120° around a great circle. There is no further restriction except that $P_4 P_5$ must not lie in the plane $P_1 P_2 P_3$. Again we have a geodesic realization of the graph.

The 5-wheel or pentagonal pyramid is the join of a vertex v_1 to a circuit $v_2 v_3 v_4 v_5 v_6$. There are two non-degenerate solutions for this graph. We take P_1 to be the point $(1, 0, 0)$. Then in one solution the other points P_i lie on the circle of intersection of the sphere with the plane $x = -(5+\sqrt{5})/10$, and the angular distance on this circle from P_i to P_{i+1}, measured in a positive sense of description of the circle, is 72° $(2 \leqslant i \leqslant 6)$. The other solution is similarly described except that $x = -(5-\sqrt{5})/10$ on the plane and the angular distance is 144°. The first solution evidently corresponds to a geodesic realization, but the second does not.

For some graphs the equations for the λ_i proved to have no solution. One such graph is obtained from the triangular prism, as described in §5, by adjoining an edge $v_1 v_5$. Another is obtained from the pentagonal pyramid, as described above, by adjoining an edge $v_2 v_4$. In the case of the graph obtained from the octahedron by deleting one edge, real solutions for the λ_i were obtained, but they led only to degenerate equilibria.

The author tried to clarify the algebraic situation by studying the matrix

$$M = \begin{Bmatrix} \lambda_1 & a_{12} & a_{13} & a_{14} & a_{15} & a_{16} \\ a_{12} & \lambda_2 & a_{23} & a_{24} & a_{25} & a_{26} \\ a_{13} & a_{23} & \lambda_3 & a_{34} & a_{35} & a_{36} \\ a_{14} & a_{24} & a_{34} & \lambda_4 & a_{45} & a_{46} \\ a_{15} & a_{25} & a_{35} & a_{45} & \lambda_5 & a_{56} \\ a_{16} & a_{26} & a_{36} & a_{46} & a_{56} & \lambda_6 \end{Bmatrix}.$$

This is the general symmetric matrix of order 6 with unknowns as diagonal elements. The problem was to find what values of the λ_i forced the rank of the matrix to be less than or equal to 3.

For convenience we write $a_{ij} = a_{ji}$.

It was found that the required values of the λ_i could be expressed in terms of the following sums.

$$Q_i = \sum_{(i,j,k,l,m,n)} \varepsilon(i,j,k,l,m,n)\, a_{jk}\, a_{kl}\, a_{lm}\, a_{mn}\, a_{nj},$$

$$H_i = \sum_{(i,j,k,l,m,n)} \varepsilon(i,j,k,l,m,n)\, a_{ij}\, a_{jk}\, a_{kl}\, a_{lm}\, a_{mn}\, a_{ni}.$$

Here (i, j, k, l, m, n) is a permutation of the integers $(1, 2, 3, 4, 5, 6)$, and $\varepsilon(i, j, k, l, m, n)$ is $+1$ or -1 according as the permutation is even or odd. In Q_i there is just one term for each undirected cyclic sequence (j, k, l, m, n). By 'undirected' we mean that (j, k, l, m, n) is not to be distinguished from (n, m, l, k, j). Thus if M corresponds to a graph G the sum Q_i has just one non-zero term corresponding to each 5-circuit not passing through v_i. In H_i there is just one term for each unordered cyclic sequence (i, j, k, l, m, n), and this term is to be written with i in the first position so as to fix $\varepsilon(i, j, k, l, m, n)$. Thus, if M corresponds to a graph G, the non-zero terms of H_i correspond to the Hamiltonian circuits of G.

It can be shown that the polynomial

$$H_i^2 + 4Q_i \sum_j a_{ij}^2 Q_j$$

is independent of i. We denote it by D.

It was found that there are in general two solutions for the λ_i, corresponding to the two square roots of D. Each is given by

$$\lambda_i = \frac{-H_i + \sqrt{D}}{2Q_i},$$

for a particular choice of $\sqrt{D}$.

It appears from this result that if, for some graph of six vertices, it is impossible to solve the equations for the λ_i, then one of the expressions Q_i must take the value zero. In the two such cases mentioned above it is easy to verify that this effect does indeed occur.

The following problems are suggested for investigation.

(i) To find combinatorial conditions for a graph G to have a non-degenerate equilibrium position.

(ii) To determine if the existence of such an equilibrium position implies the existence of a non-degenerate equilibrium position corresponding to a geodetic realization.

References

1. FÁRY, I. On straight line representation of planar graphs. *Acta Sci. Math. Szeged* **11** (1948), 229–233.

2. KURATOWSKI, C. Sur le problème des courbes gauches en topologie. *Fund. Math.* **15** (1930), 271–283.

3. ORE, O. *The Four-Color Problem,* (New York, 1967).

4. TUTTE, W. T. How to draw a graph. *Proc. London Math. Soc.* (3), **13** (1963), 743–768.

On Equal Unions of Sets

H. TVERBERG

B. Lindström (**1**) recently proved the following

THEOREM 1. *If* $A_1, \ldots, A_{rn-n+1}$ *is a sequence of non-empty subsets of* $\{1, \ldots, n\}$, *then there are non-empty, disjoint subsets of* $\{1, \ldots, rn-n+1\}$, $B_1, \ldots, B_r$, *so that*

$$\bigcup_{i \in B_1} A_i = \ldots = \bigcup_{i \in B_r} A_i. \tag{1}$$

In this note we deduce Theorem 1 from

THEOREM 2. *If* $P_1, \ldots, P_{rn+r-n}$ *is a sequence of points in* R^n, *then there are r disjoint subsets of* $\{1, \ldots, rn+r-n\}$, $Q_1, \ldots, Q_r$, *so that*

$$\bigcap_{i=1}^{r} \text{convex hull}\,(\{P_j : j \in Q_i\}) \neq \emptyset. \tag{2}$$

Theorem 2 was proved (in a slightly different form) in (**4**), and is a generalization of Radon's well-known theorem (which is obtained by letting $r = 2$). The first such generalization was proved by R. Rado (**3**).

Let now the sequence $A_1, \ldots$ be given. We construct a sequence $P_1, \ldots$ of points, $P_i = (p_{i,1}, \ldots, p_{i,n})$ as follows:

$$k \notin A_i \Rightarrow p_{i,k} = 0, \qquad k \in A_i \Rightarrow p_{i,k} = |A_i|^{-1}.$$

The points are then in the hyperplane $x_1 + \ldots + x_n = 1$ in R^n. By Theorem 2, applied to R^{n-1}, there are $Q_1, \ldots, Q_r$ so that (2) is satisfied. Choose a point $W = (w_1, \ldots, w_n)$ in the intersection occurring in (2), and put

$$C = \{i : w_i > 0\}.$$

Consider any m in $\{1, \ldots, r\}$. As $W \in$ convex hull $(\{P_j ; j \in Q_m\})$, we have

$$W = \mu_1 P_{s_1} + \ldots + \mu_t P_{s_t}, \tag{3}$$

where $\mu_1 \geqslant \ldots \geqslant \mu_t > 0$, $\mu_1 + \ldots + \mu_t = 1$, while $\{s_1, \ldots, s_t\} \subset Q_m$.

Then (3) implies

$$C = A_{s_1} \cup \ldots \cup A_{s_t}.$$

Thus each one of $Q_1, \ldots, Q_r$ has a subset so that the union of the A_i's with i in that subset equals C. As the Q_i's are disjoint, Theorem 1 is proved.

Clearly Theorem 1 implies a similar theorem on equal intersections. In order to see that Theorem 1 is best possible, in a certain sense, one may consider the following sequence of sets.

$$A_1 = A_2 = \ldots = A_{r-1} = \{1\}, \ldots, A_{(n-1)(r-1)+1} = \ldots = A_{n(r-1)} = \{n\}.$$

In view of our proof of Theorem 1, this sequence also shows that Theorem 2 is best possible, a fact which was explained in a complicated way in (**4**).

B. Lindström has also obtained some transfinite versions of Theorem 1. If, for instance, a sequence $\{A_i, i \in I\}$ of *finite* subsets of an infinite set S is given, with $|I| > |S|$, then there are, for any finite r, r non-empty, disjoint subsets of I, say $B_1, \ldots, B_r$, so that (1) holds.

The proof, which I sketch here with Lindström's kind permission, is as follows. If, for some r, $B_1, \ldots, B_r$ could not be found, then one would have, for every finite n,

$$|B_{i_1} \cup \ldots \cup B_{i_{rn-n+1}}| \geqslant n + 1 \tag{4}$$

for every subset $\{i_1, \ldots, i_{rn-n+1}\}_{\neq}$ of I. This is because of Theorem 1. But the condition (4) is the same as R. Rado's condition for the existence of a system of representatives of the sequence A_i in which no element occurs more than $r - 1$ times (see (**2**) theorem 3.2.) Hence

$$|I| \leqslant (r-1) \left| \bigcup_{i \in I} A_i \right| \leqslant (r-1)\,|S| = |S|,$$

a contradiction.

References

1. LINDSTRÖM, B. A theorem on families of sets. *J. Combinatorial Theory*.
2. MIRSKY, L. and PERFECT, H. Systems of representatives. *J. Math. Anal. Applic.* **15** (1966), 520–568.
3. RADO, R. Theorems on the intersection of convex sets of points. *J. London Math. Soc.* **27** (1952), 320–328.
4. TVERBERG, H. A generalization of Radon's theorem. *J. London Math. Soc.* **41** (1966), 123–128.

How the Proof of Baudet's Conjecture was Found

B. L. van der Waerden*

The psychology of invention in mathematics is an interesting but difficult subject. Classical books on this subject are:

J. Hadamard: Psychology of Invention in the Mathematical Field, Princeton 1949.

G. Pólya: How to Solve It, Princeton 1945.

G. Pólya: Mathematics and Plausible Reasoning, 2 Vols., Princeton 1954.

In my little pamphlet 'Einfall und Ueberlegung' (2nd ed., Basel 1968) I have attempted a synthesis of the points of view of Hadamard and Pólya. The present paper is an elaboration of Part II of this pamphlet.

Once in 1926, while lunching with Emil Artin and Otto Schreier, I told them about a conjecture of the Dutch mathematician Baudet:

If the sequence of integers 1, 2, 3, ... *is divided into two classes, at least one of the classes contains an arithmetic progression of l terms*:

$$a, a + b, \ldots, a + (l - 1) b,$$

no matter how large the given length l is.

After lunch we went into Artin's office in the Mathematics Department of the University of Hamburg, and tried to find a proof. We drew some diagrams on the blackboard. We had what the Germans call 'Einfälle': sudden ideas that flash into one's mind. Several times such new ideas gave the discussion a new turn, and one of the ideas finally led to the solution.

One of the main difficulties in the psychology of invention is that most mathematicians publish their results with condensed proofs, but do not tell us how they found them. In many cases they do not even remember their original ideas. Moreover, it is difficult to explain our vague ideas and tentative attempts in such a way that others can understand them. To myself I am accustomed to

* The present article is based on and is largely a translation of a paper entitled 'Wie der Beweis der Vermutung von Baudet gefunden wurde', *Abh. Math. Sem. Univ. Hamburg*, vol. **28**. It is printed here with the permission of the original publishers.

talk in short hints which I alone can understand. Explaining these hints to others requires making them more precise and thus changing their nature.

In the case of our discussion of Baudet's conjecture the situation was much more favourable for a psychological analysis. All ideas we formed in our minds were at once put into words and explained by little drawings on the blackboard. We represented the integers 1, 2, 3, ... in the two classes by means of vertical strokes on two parallel lines. Whatever one makes explicit and draws is much easier to remember and to reproduce than mere thoughts. Hence, this discussion between Artin, Schreier and myself offers a unique opportunity for analysing the process of mathematical thinking.

It was clear to us from the very beginning that the case $l = 2$ is trivial. One need not even consider the infinite sequence of integers; it is sufficient to consider the three integers 1, 2, 3. If they are divided into two classes, one of the classes contains a pair of numbers (in arithmetic progression).

The next case we considered was $l = 3$. In this case, too, it is not necessary to consider all integers: it suffices to take the integers from 1 to 9. The numbers from 1 to 8 can be divided, in several ways, into 2 classes without obtaining an arithmetic progression of 3 terms in one class, e.g. like this:

$$\begin{array}{llllllllll} 1 & 2 & & & 5 & 6 & & & \text{in the first class} \\ & & 3 & 4 & & & 7 & 8 & \text{in the second class.} \end{array}$$

However, in any one of these cases, the number 9 cannot escape. If we put it into the first class, we have the progression 1 5 9, and if we put it into the second class, we get the progression 7 8 9. Just so in all other possible cases. I had observed this already the day before.

Next, Schreier asked: If Baudet's conjecture is at all true for a certain value of l, is it always possible to find an integer $N(l)$ such that the conjecture holds already for the segment

$$1 \ 2 \ 3 \ \ldots \ N(l),$$

in the sense that every division of this segment into two classes yields an arithmetical progression of length l in one class?

Schreier himself found the answer: it was Yes. If Baudet's conjecture holds for a fixed value of l, it is possible to find an N such that the conjecture holds already for the segment $1 \ 2 \ \ldots \ N$. This was proved by a well known procedure from set theory, the 'diagonal procedure'. The argument is as follows.

If no such N existed, then for every N there would be a division D_N of the numbers from 1 to N into 2 classes such that no class contains an arithmetic progression of length l. Thus one could obtain an infinite sequence

$$D_1 \, D_2 \ldots$$

of such divisions. The number 1 lies, in every one of these divisions, in one of the two classes. Hence it happens an infinity of times that 1 is in the same (first or second) class, and an infinite subsequence $D'_1, D'_2, \ldots$ exists such that in all these divisions 1 is in the same class, say in class number i_1 ($i_1 = 1$ or 2).

In the divisions $D'_2, D'_3, \ldots$ the number 2 belongs to one of the two classes. Hence, by the same argument, an infinite subsequence $D''_2, D''_3, \ldots$ exists such that 2 is always in the same, i_2th class.

And so on. For every n one obtains a subsequence of divisions

$$D_n^{(n)}, \qquad D_{n+1}^{(n)}, \qquad \ldots$$

such that in all these divisions the integers 1, 2, ..., n are always in the same classes:

$$\begin{array}{l} 1 \text{ in class } i_1 \\ 2 \text{ in class } i_2 \\ \quad \ldots \\ n \text{ in class } i_n. \end{array}$$

Next, one can form a 'diagonal division' DD of all integers 1, 2, 3, ..., in which 1 lies in class i_1, 2 in class i_2, and so on. In this division, the number n lies in the same class as in the division $D_n^{(n)}$, hence the name 'diagonal procedure'.

In this division DD no arithmetic progression of length l could exist in which all terms belong to the same class. For if it existed, it would exist already in $D_n^{(n)}$, i.e. in one of the original divisions. But we have assumed Baudet's conjecture to be true for the sequence of all integers 1 2 3 ... and for this particular value of l. Thus we obtain a contradiction.

From this point onward, we tried to prove the 'strong conjecture', as we called it, for a finite segment from 1 to $N(l)$, i.e. we tried to find a number $N(l)$ having the desired property. For $l = 2$ and $l = 3$ such numbers had been found already:

$$N(2) = 3, \qquad N(3) = 9.$$

So we tried to go from $l - 1$ to l. For this induction proof, the replacement of the original conjecture by a stronger one is a definite advantage, as Artin rightly remarked. If one can assume for $l - 1$ the existence of a finite bound $N(l - 1)$, one has a better chance to find a proof for the next number l.

Next, Artin observed: If the strong conjecture is true for 2 classes and for all values of l, it must also be true for an arbitrary number of classes, say for k classes. To prove this assertion, he first supposed k to be 4. The 4 classes can be grouped into 2 and 2. This gives us a rough division of the integers into 2 big classes, every big class consisting of 2 smaller classes. In one of the big classes an arithmetic progression of $N(l)$ terms exists. The terms of this progression can be numbered from 1 to $N(l)$. These numbers are now divided into two smaller classes, and hence in one of the smaller classes an arithmetic progression of length l exists. Thus, if the strong conjecture is true for 2 classes, it is also true for 4 classes. By the same argument, one finds that it also holds for 8 classes, etc., hence, for any number of classes $k = 2^n$. But if it holds for $k = 2^n$, it also holds for every $k \leqslant 2^n$, because we may always add a few empty classes. Hence, if Baudet's conjecture holds for 2 classes it also holds, even in the strong form, for an arbitrary number of classes.

We now tried to prove the 'strong conjecture' for arbitrary k and l by induction from $l - 1$ to l. This means: we tried to find a bound $N = N(l, k)$ such that, if the integers from 1 to N are divided into k classes, one of the classes contains an arithmetic progression of length l.

Artin expected—and he proved right—that the generalization from 2 to k classes would be an advantage in the induction proof. For, he argued, we might now try to prove the strong conjecture for an arbitrary *fixed* value of k and for length l under the induction hypothesis that it holds for *all* k and for length $l - 1$. This means: we have a very strong induction hypothesis to start with, which is a definite advantage.

Following the line indicated by Artin, we now tried to prove Baudet's conjecture for 2 classes and for progressions of length l, assuming the strong conjecture to hold for all k for progressions of length $(l - 1)$.

Next, Artin had another very good idea. If the integers 1, 2, ... are divided into 2 classes, blocks of (say) 3 successive integers are automatically partitioned into $2^3 = 8$ classes. For each of the 3 numbers within the block can lie in the first or second class, and this gives us 8 possibilities for the whole block. Now the blocks of 3 successive integers can be numbered: block number n consists of the integers n, $n + 1$, $n + 2$. If the blocks are partitioned into 8 classes, their initial numbers n are also partitioned into 8 classes, and to this partition we can apply the induction hypothesis. Thus we obtain the following result: among sufficiently many successive blocks we can find an arithmetic progression of $(l - 1)$ blocks all in the same class. The pattern of the distribution of integers over the two classes in the first block will be repeated, exactly as it is, in the other $(l - 2)$ blocks.

The same holds for blocks of arbitrary length m, each consisting of m successive numbers

$$n, n + 1, \ldots, n + m - 1.$$

The number of classes for those blocks is 2^m. Once more one can obtain arithmetic progressions of $(l - 1)$ blocks in the same class, with exact repetition of the pattern in the first block. Moreover, if the blocks are long enough, we can also find arithmetic progressions of $(l - 1)$ integers within each block.

In the simplest case $l = 2$ the conjecture is certainly true for all k, for if the integers from 1 to $k + 1$ are divided into k classes, there must be two integers in one of the classes. This is Dirichlet's 'box principle': if $k + 1$ objects are in k boxes, one of the boxes contains two of them. A very useful principle in Number Theory.

Thus, starting with the obvious case $l = 2$, we tried to treat the case of 2 classes and $l = 3$ (although this case had been dealt with already by an enumeration of all possible cases). We represented the integers in the two classes by small vertical strokes on two parallel lines, as in Fig. 1.

Among three successive integers there are always two in the same class, by the induction hypothesis, i.e. in this case by the 'box principle'. Now consider a block of 5 successive integers. Among the first three there are two in the same class; this gives us an arithmetic progression of length 2. The third term of this progression still lies within the block of 5. If it is in the same class as the first two terms, we have in this class a progression of length 3, as desired. Therefore we may suppose that the third term lies in the other class, and we have, within every block of 5, a pattern like the one of Fig. 1.

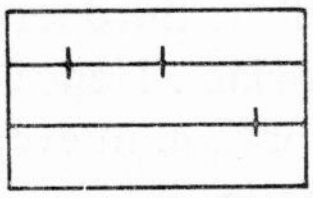

FIGURE 1

I was drawing such blocks on the blackboard, and I thought: There are $2^5 = 32$ classes of blocks of 5, hence among 33 successive blocks of 5 there must be 2 blocks in the same class. In the first of these blocks a pattern like the one of Fig. 1 exists, and in the second block of 5 this pattern is exactly repeated (Fig. 2).

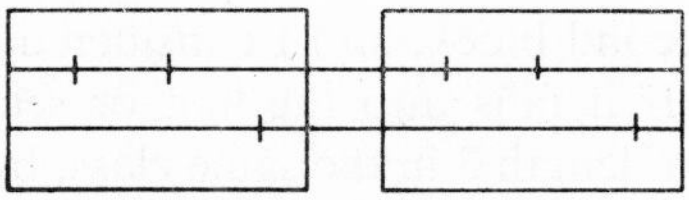

FIGURE 2

What we wanted to construct were progressions of length 3. Hence I drew one more block at the same distance from the second block as the second from the first, and I drew three strokes in the third block in the same position as the strokes in the first and second block (Fig. 3).

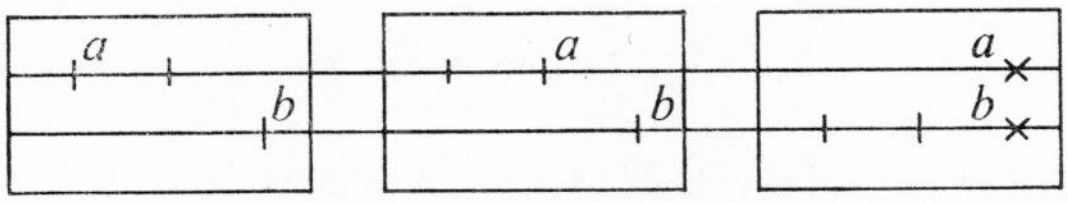

FIGURE 3

The third of these strokes represents an integer, which may be in the first or second class. If it is in the first, we have in this class an arithmetic progression *a a a* (Fig. 3). If it is in the second class, we have in this class a progression *b b b*. Hence we have in any case within the block of integers from 1 to

$$5 + 32 + 32 = 69,$$

an arithmetic progression of 3 terms in one class.

After having found this proof in the special case $k = 2$ and $l = 3$, I explained it to Artin and Schreier. I felt sure that the same proof would work in the general case. They did not believe it, and so I proceeded to present the proof for the next higher case $k = 3$, $l = 3$.

In stead of considering blocks of $3 + 2 = 5$, I now considered blocks of $4 + 3 = 7$ successive integers. Since the first four numbers of such a block are distributed among 3 classes, two of them must belong to the same class. The third term of the arithmetic progression starting with these two terms still belongs to the same block of 7. If the third term lies in the same class, we have a progression of length 3 in this class. Hence we may suppose the third term to lie in another class. Thus we obtain, in every block of seven, a pattern like the one in the first small block of Fig. 4.

The blocks of 7 are partitioned into 3^7 classes. Hence among $3^7 + 1$ successive blocks of 7 there are two belonging to the same class. In the first block we have three integers in arithmetic progression, two of which belong to the same class, and this pattern repeats itself in the second block. If the second block is shifted once more over the same distance, one obtains 3 blocks forming an arithmetic progression of blocks, as shown in Fig. 4.

In the third block, I drew 3 strokes in positions corresponding to the 3 strokes in the first or second block, and I considered the possibilities for the third of these strokes. If it falls into the first or second class, we have an arithmetic progression of length 3 in the same class, by the same argument as before; but now the third stroke can escape into the third class. Thus we obtain the pattern drawn in Fig. 4.

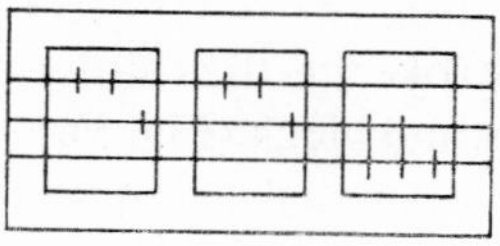

FIGURE 4

In every large block of $3^7 + 3^7 + 7 = h$ successive integers we have such a pattern. Now the large blocks of h are divided into 3^h classes. Hence among

$3^h + 1$ successive large blocks there are two belonging to the same class. Drawing the small blocks within the large ones, I obtained the picture of Fig. 5.

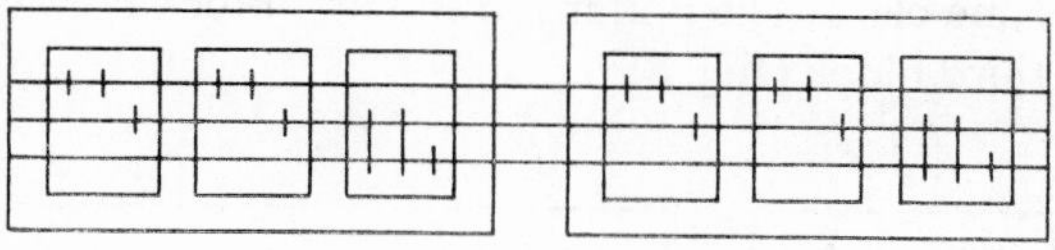

FIGURE 5

Now shifting the second large block over the same distance, and considering the third stroke in the third small block in the third large block, I showed that it cannot escape any more. If it lies in the first class, there is a progression $a\ a\ a$ in the first class. If it lies in the second class, there is a progression $b\ b\ b$ in that class, and if in the third class, a progression $c\ c\ c$ in this class. (Fig. 6).

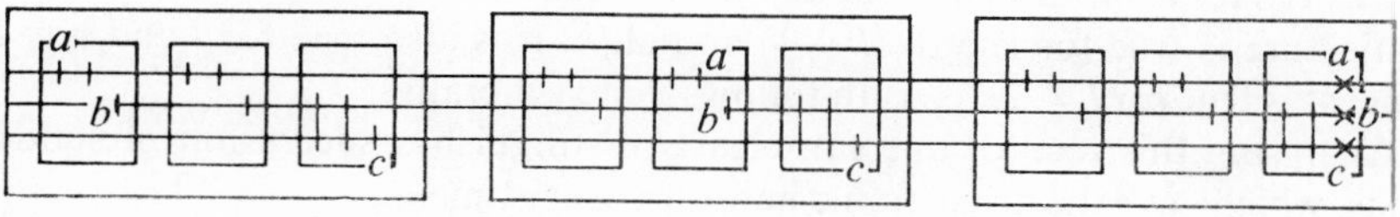

FIGURE 6

After this, all of us agreed that the same kind of proof could be given for arbitrary k. However, Artin and Schreier still wanted to see the case $l = 4$.

As before, I first considered the case of 2 classes. For this case I had already proved that among sufficiently many, say n, successive integers there is a progression of 3 terms in the same class. We may suppose n to be odd. The distance between the first and last term of this progression is $(n - 1)$ at most, hence the difference between two successive terms is $\frac{1}{2}(n - 1)$ at most. Now consider the fourth term of the same progression. All four terms lie within a block of

$$g = n + \tfrac{1}{2}(n - 1)$$

successive integers. If the fourth term belongs to the same class as the other three, we are satisfied. Suppose it lies in the other class; then we have the pattern of Fig. 7.

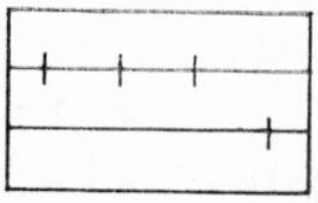

FIGURE 7

In every block of g successive integers such a pattern must occur. Now the blocks of g are divided into 2^g classes. Hence among sufficiently many, say $N(3, 2^g)$ blocks of length g, there are 3 blocks in arithmetical progression belonging to the same class. The pattern in the first block is exactly repeated in the second and third block (Fig. 8).

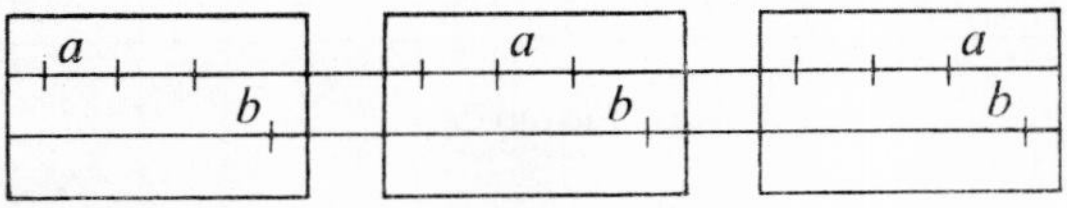

FIGURE 8

Adding a fourth block to this progression, I easily obtained a progression $a\ a\ a\ a$ in the first or $b\ b\ b\ b$ in the second class.

Now it was clear to every one of us that the induction proof from $(l - 1)$ to l works for arbitrary l and for any fixed value of k. Hence if Baudet's strong conjecture is true for length $(l - 1)$ and all k, it is also true for l and any k. Since it is true for $l = 2$, its truth follows quite generally.

Analysing this record, one can clearly distinguish a succession of sudden ideas, which gave the discussion a new turn every time.

1. The first was Schreier's idea of restricting oneself to a finite segment from 1 to N. This idea was fundamental for the whole proof.

2. The second idea was: to try an induction from $l - 1$ to l. This was quite a natural idea, because the case $l = 2$ was obvious and the case $l = 3$ could be solved by enumerating all possible cases.

3. Artin proved: if the strong conjecture is true for 2 classes, it is also true for 4 classes. In his proof another idea was implicit, viz.: if the conjecture is true for a segment of all integers from 1 to N it is also true for any arithmatical progression of length N

$$a, a + b, \ldots, a + (N - 1)\,b$$

because the terms of this progression can be numbered by the integers 1 to N. This is also a central idea in the proof.

4. Next, Artin said: in an induction it is always an advantage to have a strong induction hypothesis to start with. Therefore let us start with the assumption that the conjecture holds for progressions of length $(l - 1)$ and for *all* k, and try to prove the conjecture for progressions of length l and for *one* value of k, say $k = 2$. Thus the plan for the proof was devised.

5. The next idea, which also came from Artin, was of decisive importance. He said: we can apply the induction hypothesis not only to single integers, but also to blocks, for they too are divided into classes. Thus we are sure that whole blocks are repeated $(l - 1)$ times.

6. After this, it was only natural to consider progressions of $(l - 1)$ blocks and progressions of $(l - 1)$ integers within the blocks, and to try to extend these progressions of length $(l - 1)$ to progressions of length l. The simplest non-trivial case is $l = 3$, and thus I was led, quite naturally, to consider patterns like the one of Fig. 2.

7. This pattern still does not contain a progression of length 3 in one class. Therefore, it was necessary to extend the progression of length 2 occurring in the second class in Fig. 2 to a progression of length 3. Hence I extended the pattern of Fig. 2 by drawing the third block of Fig. 3, and I considered the third term of the progression *b b b*. As soon as attention was focussed upon this term, it was clear that it cannot escape from forming an arithmetic progression of length 3 in the first or second class.

This final idea was accompanied by a feeling of complete certainty. I felt quite sure that this method of proof would work for arbitrary k and l. I cannot explain this feeling; I can only say that mathematicians often have such a conviction. When a decisive idea comes to our mind, we feel that we have the whole proof we are looking for: we have only to work it out in detail.

However, I can explain, to a certain extent, why Artin and Schreier did not feel so sure. They saw only the result: the presence of the progression *a a a* in the first class or *b b b* in the second one, but I had discovered a method for finding such progressions, and I was convinced that this method would work in higher cases as well.

It is like picking apples from a tree. If one has got an apple and another is hanging a little higher, it may happen that one knows: with a little more effort one can get that one too. The man standing next to me only sees that I have just got the first apple, and he is in doubt whether I can get the other too, but I myself have not only got the apple, but I also have a feeling of the movement that enabled me to pick it.

The feeling that a method of proof can be carried over to other cases is sometimes deceptive. Often the higher cases offer additional difficulties. Still, feelings of this kind are extremely useful in mathematical research.

Finding the proof of Baudet's conjecture was a good example of teamwork. Each of the three of us contributed essential ideas. After the discussion with Artin and Schreier I worked out the details of proof and published it in *Nieuw Archief voor Wiskunde* **15**, p. 212 (1927). (Interesting applications and generalizations of the theorem proved in my paper were given by Richard Rado†).

A. J. Khinchin included the theorem among his 'Three Pearls of the Theory of Numbers' (1952) and published a proof due to M. A. Lukomskaja, which is in all essentials the same as mine, the only difference being that in her proof the blocks are required to be non-overlapping.

† R. Rado: Studien zur Kombinatorik, Ph.D-Thesis Berlin 1931, *Math. Zeitschr.* **36,** p. 424. Verallgemeinerung eines Satzes von van der Waerden, *Sitzungsber. preuss. Akad.,* Berlin 1933, p. 589. Note on Combinatorial Analysis, *Proc. London Math. Soc.* (2) **48,** p. 122.

Related Classes of Set Functions

D. J. A. WELSH

1. Introduction

P. Hall's theorem **(3)** that a finite family $\mathbf{A} = (A_i : i \in I)$ of sets has a transversal if and only if

$$\left| \bigcup_{i \in J} A_i \right| \geqslant |J| \qquad (J \subseteq I),$$

is not the best possible in the following sense: the class of set functions f such that $\mathbf{A}$ has a transversal X with $f(X) \geqslant |I|$ if and only if

$$f\left(\bigcup_{i \in J} A_i \right) \geqslant |J| \qquad (J \subseteq I),$$

contains functions other than the cardinality function. The first theorem of this paper shows that R. Rado's theorem **(6)** is, essentially, the best possible.

Throughout this paper S denotes a fixed finite set, I will denote a finite index set, and if $\mathbf{A} = (A_i : i \in I)$ is a family of sets, for any $J \subseteq I$,

$$A(J) = \bigcup_{i \in J} A_i.$$

$\mathscr{F}$ will denote the family of non-negative set functions on S, that is, functions on the set of all subsets of S taking non-negative real values. If $(x_i : i \in I)$ is a family of elements of S we write $\{(x_i : i \in I)\}$ to denote the set consisting of the distinct members of $(x : i \in I)$. If f, g are two members of $\mathscr{F}$ we write $f \leqslant g$ if, for all $X \subseteq S$, $f(X) \leqslant g(X)$. $|\cdot|$ denotes the cardinality function, and if f is any function $[f]$ is the function defined by

$$[f](X) = [f(X)],$$

(where as usual, $[x]$ denotes the maximum integer less than or equal to x).

The transversal theory terminology is that of the review paper by Mirsky and Perfect **(5)** and the matroid terminology is that of **(9)**.

We say that a member f of $\mathscr{F}$ is a *transversal function* if for any family $(A_i : i \in I)$ of subsets of S, the following statements are equivalent:

(T1) $(A_i : i \in I)$ has a transversal X with $f(X) \geqslant |I|$.

(T2) For any $J \subseteq I$,

$$f(A(J)) \geqslant |J|.$$

Then P. Hall's theorem says that the cardinality function $|.|$ is a transversal function. The basic theorem of R. Rado (**6**) says that the rank function of a matroid is a transversal function. Clearly there exist other transversal functions, for example if $0 \leqslant g(X) < 1$ for all subsets X of S, then g is a transversal function. We denote the family of transversal functions on S by $\mathscr{T}$.

We define a member f of $\mathscr{F}$ to be a *representative function* on S if for any family $(A_i : i \in I)$ of subsets of S the following statements are equivalent:

(R1) $(A_i : i \in I)$ has a system of representatives (SR) $(x_i : i \in I)$ such that, for any $J \subseteq I$,

$$f(\{(x_i : i \in J)\}) \geqslant |J|.$$

(R2) For any $J \subseteq I$,

$$f(A(J)) \geqslant |J|.$$

We denote the family of representative functions by $\mathscr{R}$. In (**10**) I use the methods of Rado (**8**) to show that if f has the properties (i), (ii), (iii) below, then $f \in \mathscr{R}$.

(i) f is integer-valued.

(ii) f is *increasing*, that is if $A \subseteq B$, $f(A) \leqslant f(B)$.

(iii) f is *submodular*, that is for any subsets A, B, of S,

$$f(A \cup B) + f(A \cap B) \leqslant f(A) + f(B).$$

Again it is easy to find functions not satisfying (i)–(iii) but which belong to $\mathscr{R}$.

Finally I define the family $\mathscr{E}$ of *matroid functions* as follows. If f is a non-negative set function on S, let $M(f)$ be the following family of subsets of S,

$$M(f) = \{X : X \subseteq S, \text{ and } f(Y) \geqslant |Y| \quad \forall\, Y \subseteq X\}.$$

Then f is a member of $\mathscr{E}$ if and only if $M(f)$ is the family of independent sets of a matroid.

The reason for this definition is that an extremely fruitful theorem of Edmonds (**2**) says that every non-negative, integer-valued, increasing, submodular function is a member of $\mathscr{E}$.

Here we characterise the families $\mathscr{T}$ and $\mathscr{R}$ and show that

$$\mathscr{T} \subseteq \mathscr{R} \subseteq \mathscr{E}$$

for any set S, and that the inclusion relation is strict. The results obtained show that Rado's theorem **(6)** and the main theorem of **(10)** are essentially best possible.

2. Transversal functions

The family of transversal functions is essentially characterised by the following theorem of **(6)**, which for finite sets can be stated as follows.

THEOREM 1. (Rado). *Let M be a family of subsets of S such that for any family $\mathbf{A} \equiv (A_i : i \in I)$ of subsets of S the following statements are equivalent*:

(i) $\mathbf{A}$ *has a transversal X which belongs to M.*

(ii) *The union of any k members of $\mathbf{A}$ ($k \leqslant |I|$) contains a member Y of M with $|Y| \geqslant k$.*

Then M is the family of independent sets of a matroid.

Using this together with the following lemmas, we see that the main theorem of Rado **(6)** is essentially best possible, by proving

THEOREM 2. *A function f is a transversal function if and only if $[f]$ is the rank function of a matroid.*

LEMMA 1. *If $f \in \mathscr{T}$, then $f < |.| + 1$.*

Proof. Let $f(X) = a \geqslant |X| + 1$. Consider the family $\mathbf{A} \equiv (A_i : i \in I)$ of subsets of S, where $|I| = |X| + 1$ and $A_i = X$ $(i \in I)$. Then, for any $J \subseteq I$,

$$f(A(J)) = f(X) = a \geqslant |J|,$$

and since $f \in \mathscr{T}$, $\mathbf{A}$ has a transversal, say Y, with $f(Y) \geqslant |I| = |X| + 1$. But $\mathbf{A}$ has no transversal. Hence this is impossible and $f(X) < |X| + 1$.

LEMMA 2. *If $f \in \mathscr{T}$, then $[f] \in \mathscr{T}$.*

Proof. Suppose $[f](A(J)) \geqslant |J|$ for all $J \subseteq I$. Then $f(A(J)) \geqslant |J|$ for all $J \subseteq I$ and therefore $(A_i : i \in I)$ has a transversal X with $f(X) \geqslant |I|$. Since $|I|$ is an integer, $[f](X) \geqslant |I|$. The converse follows similarly.

LEMMA 3. *Let $f \in \mathscr{T}$ and let f be integer-valued. If $g \in \mathscr{F}$ and $f \leqslant g < f + 1$, then $g \in \mathscr{T}$.*

Proof. Suppose $\mathbf{A} = (A_i : i \in I)$ is a family of subsets of S such that, for all $J \subseteq I$, $f(A(J)) \geqslant |J|$. Since f is integer-valued, it is easy to see that

$f(A(J)) = |J|$ for all $J \subseteq I$, and hence $\mathbf{A}$ has a transversal X with $f(X) \geqslant |I|$. Clearly $g(X) \geqslant |I|$. Conversely if $\mathbf{A}$ has a transversal X with $g(X) \geqslant |I|$, then $f(X) \geqslant |I|$ and hence $f(A(J)) \geqslant |J|$ for all $J \subseteq I$ and therefore $g(A(J)) \geqslant |J|$ for all $J \subseteq I$. Hence $g \in \mathscr{T}$.

LEMMA 4. *If $f \in \mathscr{T}$ and $f(X) \geqslant d$, where d is a non-negative integer, there exists $Y \subseteq X$ with $|Y| = d$ and $f(Y) \geqslant d$.*

Proof. Consider the family $(A_i\colon 1 \leqslant i \leqslant d)$ of subsets of S, with $A_i = X$ $(1 \leqslant i \leqslant d)$. Then for any $J \subseteq \{1, ..., d\}$, $f(A(J)) = f(X) \geqslant d \geqslant |J|$ and hence, since $f \in \mathscr{T}$, $\mathbf{A}$ has a transversal Y with $f(Y) \geqslant d$. Clearly $|Y| = d$ and $Y \subseteq X$.

LEMMA 5. *If $f \in \mathscr{T}$ and f is integer-valued, then f is increasing.*

Proof. Let $f(X) \leqslant d - 1, f(X - x) = d$ where d is an integer. By Lemma 4, there exists $Y \subseteq X - x$ with $f(X) \geqslant d$, and $|Y| = d$. Consider the family $\mathbf{A} = (A_i\colon 1 \leqslant i \leqslant d)$ where $A_i = Y$ $(1 \leqslant i \leqslant d)$. $\mathbf{A}$ has a transversal Y with $f(Y) \geqslant d$ and hence the family $(A_i'\colon 1 \leqslant i \leqslant d)$, where $A_i' = X$, has a transversal Y with $f(Y) \geqslant d$. Since $f \in \mathscr{T}$, $f(A'(J)) \geqslant |J|$ for all $J \subseteq I$. But $A'(J) = X$, hence $f(X) \geqslant d$ which is a contradiction.

Proof of Theorem 2. If $[g]$ is the rank function of a matroid, then $[g] \in \mathscr{T}$ by Rado's theorem (**6**). Hence, by Lemma 3, $g \in \mathscr{T}$. Conversely, suppose $g \in \mathscr{T}$. Then by Lemma 2, $[g] \in \mathscr{T}$. Let $f = [g]$ and let M be the family of subsets of S defined by $X \in M$ if and only if $f(X) = |X|$. Clearly f will be the rank function of a matroid if M is the family of independent sets of a matroid. Now a family $\mathbf{A} = (A_i\colon i \in I)$ has a transversal X belonging to M if and only if, for each $J \subseteq I$,

$$f(A(J)) \geqslant |J|.$$

By Lemma 4, $A(J)$ contains a set Y with $f(Y) \geqslant |J|$ and $|Y| = |J|$. Conversely suppose that, for each $J \subseteq I$, $A(J)$ contains a set Y with $|Y| = |J|$ and $Y \in M$. By Lemma 5, f is increasing and therefore $f(A(J)) \geqslant |J|$ so that since $f \in \mathscr{T}$, $\mathbf{A}$ has a transversal X with $f(X) \geqslant |I|$, that is a transversal $X \in M$. Thus M satisfies the conditions of Rado's Theorem 1 and is the family of independent sets of a matroid.

3. Representative functions

To characterise $\mathscr{R}$ we need the following lemmas.

LEMMA 6. *If f* belongs to *$\mathscr{R}$, then $[f] \in \mathscr{R}$.*

LEMMA 7. *Let f be an integer-valued member of $\mathscr{R}$. Then any member g of $\mathscr{F}$ satisfying $f \leqslant g < f + 1$ also belongs to $\mathscr{R}$.*

The proofs are easy, almost identical with the proofs of Lemmas 2 and 3. Combining them, we get

LEMMA 8. *A function $f \in \mathscr{R}$ if and only if $[f] \in \mathscr{R}$.*

Hence, since $f \in \mathscr{T}$ implies that $[f]$ is the rank function of a matroid which clearly belongs to $\mathscr{R}$, by Lemma 8 we have

THEOREM 3. *Every transversal function is a representative function.*

LEMMA 9. *If f is an integer-valued member of $\mathscr{R}$, then f is increasing.*

Proof. Suppose $X \subseteq S$ and $y \in S$ and $f(X \cup y) < f(X)$. Let $f(X) = d$ and consider the family $\mathbf{A} = (A_i : 1 \leqslant i \leqslant d)$, where $A_i = X$ $(1 \leqslant i \leqslant d)$. Then, for any $J \subseteq \{1, \ldots, d\}$,

$$f(A(J)) = f(X) = d \geqslant |J|.$$

Hence $\mathbf{A}$ has an SR $(x_i : 1 \leqslant i \leqslant d)$ such that, for $J \subseteq \{1, \ldots, d\}$,

$$f(\{x_i : i \in J\}) \geqslant |J|. \tag{1}$$

Hence if $\mathbf{A}' = (A_i' : 1 \leqslant i \leqslant d)$ where $A_i' = X \cup \{y\}$ $(1 \leqslant i \leqslant d)$, then $\mathbf{A}'$ also has an SR $(x_i : 1 \leqslant i \leqslant d)$ satisfying (1). Since $f \in \mathscr{R}$, this implies that

$$f(A'(J)) \geqslant |J|, \qquad (J \subseteq \{1, \ldots, d\}).$$

But taking $J = \{1, \ldots, d\}$, we get

$$f(A'(J)) = f(X \cup \{y\}) \geqslant d$$

which is a contradiction. Thus f is increasing.

Suppose now that f is an integer-valued function which belongs to $\mathscr{R}$. Define an associated sequence function $\bar{f}$ as follows. For any finite sequence $(x_1, x_2, \ldots, x_n)$ let $\bar{f}(x_1, \ldots, x_n) = 1$ if and only if, for all $J \subseteq \{1, \ldots, n\}$, $f(\{(x_i : i \in J)\}) \geqslant |J|$. Otherwise let $\bar{f}(x_1, \ldots, x_n) = 0$.

We will show that $\bar{f}$ has the following properties for any positive integer n and any $x_1, \ldots, x_{2n+1} \in S$,

$$\text{(J1)} \quad \bar{f}(x_1, \ldots, x_n) \leqslant \bar{f}(x_1, \ldots, \hat{x}_i, \ldots, x_n), \qquad (i = 1, \ldots, n);$$

$$\text{(J2)} \quad \text{if } \bar{f}(x_1, \ldots, x_n) = \bar{f}(x_{n+1}, \ldots, x_{2n+1}) = 1, \quad \text{then}$$

$$\bar{f}(x_1, \ldots, x_i, x_j, x_{i+1}, \ldots, x_n) = 1$$

$$\text{for some } i, \ \ 0 \leqslant i \leqslant n \text{ and some } j, \ \ 1 \leqslant j \leqslant 2n + 1.$$

(The symbol ^ signifies that the term beneath it is to be omitted). Thus in the language of Ingleton (**4**), we will have proved

LEMMA 10. *If f is an integer-valued member of $\mathscr{R}$, the associated sequence function $\bar{f}$ is a J-function.*

Proof. Clearly $\bar{f}$ satisfies (J1). Suppose that for the elements $x_1, x_2, \ldots, x_{2n+1}$ of S

$$\bar{f}(x_1, \ldots, x_n) = \bar{f}(x_{n+1}, \ldots, x_{2n+1}) = 1.$$

Let $\mathbf{A} = (A_i\colon 1 \leqslant i \leqslant n + 1)$ be the family of sets

$$A_i = \{x_i\} \qquad (1 \leqslant i \leqslant n)$$

$$A_{n+1} = \{(x_1, \ldots, x_{2n+1})\}.$$

It is easy to see that, for any $J \subseteq \{1, \ldots, n + 1\}$,

$$f(A(J)) \geqslant |J|,$$

since $f \in \mathscr{R}$ and is therefore increasing. Hence $\mathbf{A}$ has an SR $(x_1, \ldots, x_n, y)$ where $x_i \in A_i$ $(1 \leqslant i \leqslant n)$ and $y \in A_{n+1}$, and also if $J \subseteq \{1, \ldots, n\}$

$$f(\{(x_i\colon i \in J)\}) \geqslant |J|$$

$$f(\{(x_i\colon i \in J)\} \cup \{y\}) \geqslant |J| + 1.$$

Hence, by definition,

$$\bar{f}(x_1, \ldots, x_n, y) = 1$$

and therefore $\bar{f}$ satisfies (J2) and is a J-function.

The relationship between J-functions and Rado's family of I-functions (**7**) is explicitly pointed out in (**4**). I-functions are essentially sequence functions derived from matroids and every I-function is a J-function, but not conversely.

Now let r_f be the associated rank function of the J-function $\bar{f}$. For any set $A \subseteq S$, Ingleton defines $r_f(A)$ to be the maximum integer n such that there exists a sequence $(x_i\colon 1 \leqslant i \leqslant n)$ of elements of A such that $\bar{f}(x_i\colon$

$1 \leqslant i \leqslant n) = 1$. Suppose $r_f(A) = k < \infty$. Then there exists $(x_i: 1 \leqslant i \leqslant k)$ such that $x_i \in A$ $(1 \leqslant i \leqslant k)$ and

$$f(\{(x_i: i \in J)\}) \geqslant |J| \qquad (J \subseteq \{1, \ldots, k\}).$$

Since f is increasing, taking $J = \{1, \ldots, k\}$ we get

$$f(A) \geqslant k = r_f(A).$$

Conversely if $f(A) = k$, then letting $\mathbf{A} = (A_i: 1 \leqslant i \leqslant k)$ be the family of sets $A_i = A$ $(1 \leqslant i \leqslant k)$, we see that $f(A(J)) \geqslant |J|$ for all $J \subset \{1, \ldots, k\}$ and hence there exists an SR $(x_i: 1 \leqslant i \leqslant k)$ of $\mathbf{A}$ with

$$f(\{(x_i: i \in J)\}) \geqslant |J|.$$

Thus

$$\bar{f}(x_1, \ldots, x_k) = 1$$

and $r_f(A) \geqslant k$. Thus we have proved that, if $f \in \mathscr{R}$, f is the rank function of the associated J-function $\bar{f}$. But Ingleton (**4**) shows that the rank function of any J-function is increasing and submodular. Hence, combining this with the previous lemmas and the main result of (**10**), we have

LEMMA 11. *An integer-valued function f belongs to $\mathscr{R}$ if and only if it is increasing and submodular.*

But, by Lemma 8, $f \in \mathscr{R}$ if and only if $[f] \in \mathscr{R}$ and therefore we have a characterisation of $\mathscr{R}$.

THEOREM 4. *A function f is a representative function if and only if $[f]$ is increasing and submodular.*

4. Matroid functions

It seems to be very difficult to characterise the family $\mathscr{E}$. The following lemmas are easy to see.

LEMMA 12. *A function f belongs to $\mathscr{E}$ if and only if $[f] \in \mathscr{E}$ and*

$$M(f) = M([f]).$$

LEMMA 13. *Let $f \in \mathscr{E}$ and let f^* be defined by*

$$f^*(X) = \min(|X|, [f](X)) \qquad (X \subseteq S).$$

Then $f \in \mathscr{E}$ if and only if $f^* \in \mathscr{E}$ and $M(f) = M(f^*)$.

Since Edmonds (**2**) has shown that every increasing, integer-valued, submodular function is a member of $\mathscr{E}$, from Lemmas 10 and 11 and Theorem 4 we obtain

THEOREM 5. *Every representative function is a matroid function.*

However we can easily find integer-valued functions belonging to $\mathscr{E}$ which are not increasing and hence are not representative functions. Indeed, even when we consider only the family $\mathscr{E}^+$ of increasing integer-valued members of $\mathscr{E}$ we get non-submodular functions.

EXAMPLE: Take $S = \{1, 2, 3, 4, 5\}$, let

$$f(\emptyset) = 0, \quad f\{x\} = 1 \qquad (1 \leqslant x \leqslant 5),$$

$$f\{1,2\} = f\{1,3\} = f\{1,4\} = f\{1,5\} = 2,$$

$$f\{x,y\} = 1 \qquad (x \neq 1, y \neq 1),$$

$$f\{1,2,x\} = 2 \qquad (x = 3,4,5),$$

$$f(X) = |X| \text{ otherwise.}$$

Then $M(f)$ is a matroid, with bases

$$\{1,2\}, \{1,3\}, \{1,4\}, \{1,5\}.$$

However f is not submodular even though it has the additional property $f \leqslant |.|$.

When f is increasing, integer-valued, and submodular Edmonds (**2**) obtains the very useful result that the rank function r_f of $M(f)$ is given by

$$r_f(X) = \min_{A \subseteq X} \big(f(A) + |X - A|\big), \qquad (X \subseteq S).$$

It is easy to prove that, for any member f of $\mathscr{E}$,

$$r_f(X) \leqslant \min_{A \subseteq X} \big([f](A) + |X - A|\big), \qquad (X \subseteq S)$$

and the above example with $X = \{1, 2\}$ shows that the above inequality may be strict. However, using Lemma 13, we can state

LEMMA 14. *If $f \in \mathscr{E}$, the rank function r_f of $M(f)$ satisfies*

$$r_f(X) \leqslant \min_{A \subseteq X} \big(\min(|A|, \ [f](A)) + |X - A|\big).$$

There seems no hope of obtaining a 'nice' general result for the rank function.

The reason is not hard to see. Take M to be any matroid on S. Let f be a set function on S satisfying

$$f(X) = |X| \qquad (X \text{ independent in } M),$$

$$f(X) = |X| - 1 \qquad (X \text{ a circuit of } M).$$

On all other subsets of S let f be arbitrary. Then $f \in \mathscr{E}$.

References

1. Edmonds, J. Submodular set functions, (Abstract, Waterloo 1966).
2. Edmonds, J. Submodular functions, matroids, and certain polyhedra, *Lectures, Calgary Intern. Symp. on Comb. Structures. June* 1969.
3. Hall, P. On representatives of subsets, *J. London Math. Soc.* **10** (1935), 26–30.
4. Ingleton, A. W. A note on independence functions and rank, *J. London Math. Soc.*, **34** (1959), 49–56.
5. Mirsky, L. and Perfect, H. Systems of representatives, *J. Math. Anal. Appl.* **15** (1966), 520–568.
6. Rado, R. A theorem on independence relations, *Quart. J. Math.* (Oxford) **13** (1942), 83–89.
7. Rado, R. Note on independence functions, *Proc. Lond. Math. Soc.* (3), **7** (1957), 300–320.
8. Rado, R. Note on the transfinite case of Hall's theorems on representatives, *J. London Math. Soc.* **42** (1967), 321–324.
9. Welsh, D. J. A. On matroid theorems of Edmonds and Rado, *J. London Math. Soc.* (2), **2** (1970), 251–256.
10. Welsh, D. J. A. Generalized versions of Hall's theorem, *J. Comb. Theory* (1970) (to appear).

Publications of Richard Rado

1. Über stetige Fortsetzung reeller Funktionen. *Sitzber. Bayer. Akad. Wiss.* (Math.-Naturw. Abt.), 1931, 81–84.
2. Zur Boltzmannschen Theorie des zweiten Hauptsatzes. *Erkenntnis* **3**, 101–102.
3. Studien zur Kombinatorik. *Math. Zeitschrift* **36** (1933), 424–480.
4. Verallgemeinerung eines Satzes von van der Waerden mit Anwendungen auf ein Problem der Zahlentheorie. *Sitzber. Preuss. Akad. Wiss.* (Phys.-Math. Kl.), 1933, 589–596.
5. Fragen der Kombinatorik in der Theorie der diophantischen Gleichungen. *Jber. Deutsch. Math.-Ver.* **42** (1933), 121–124.
6. Bemerkungen zur Kombinatorik im Anschluss an Untersuchungen von Herrn D. König. *Sitzber. Berlin. Math. Ges.* **32** (1933), 60–75.
7. A new proof of a theorem of v. Staudt. *J. London Math. Soc.* **9** (1934), 85–88.
8. A note on the Bernoullian numbers. *J. London Math. Soc.* **9** (1934), 88–90.
9. A proof of Minkowski's theorem on homogeneous linear forms. *J. London Math. Soc.* **9** (1934), 164–165.
10. A remark on Minkowski's theorem about linear forms. *J. London Math. Soc. Soc.* **10** (1935), 115.
11. A new proof of a theorem of Hardy and Littlewood. *J. London Math. Soc.* **11** (1936), 87–92.
12. Theorems about the maximum modulus of polynomials. *Proc. London Math. Soc.* (2) **41** (1936), 221–242.
13. Linear transformations of sequences. *Phil. Trans. Roy. Soc.* (A) **235** (1936), 367–414.
14. Note on a mean value theorem of Littlewood. *J. London Math. Soc.* **12** (1937), 222–229.
15. Some recent results in combinatorial analysis. *Comptes rendus du Congrès International des Mathématiciens, Oslo 1936*, **2**, 20–21.
16. A theorem on general measure functions. *Proc. London Math. Soc.* (2) **44** (1938), 61–91.
17. Some elementary Tauberian theorems (I). *Quart. J. Math.* (Oxford) **9** (1938), 274–282.
18. Some elementary Tauberian theorems (II). *Quart. J. Math.* (Oxford) **10** (1939), 28–37.
19. The distributive law for products of infinite series. *Quart. J. Math.* (Oxford) **11** (1940), 229–242.

20. Some solved and unsolved problems in the theory of numbers. *Math. Gazette* **25** (1941), 72–78.

21. A theorem on independence relations. *Quart. J. Math.* (Oxford) **13** (1942), 83–89.

22. Theorems on linear combinatorial topology and general measure. *Annals of Math.* (2) **44** (1943), 228–270.

23. Note on combinatorial analysis. *Proc. London Math. Soc.* (2) **48** (1943), 122–160.

24. Two theorems on graphs. *Annals of Math.* (2) **46** (1945), 429–467.

25. The irreducible factors of certain polynomials. *Quart. J. Math.* (Oxford) **17** (1946), 111–115.

26. A theorem on the geometry of numbers. *J. London Math. Soc.* **21** (1946), 34–47

27. A theorem on general measure. *J. London Math. Soc.* **21** (1946), 291–300.

28. A theorem on Abelian groups. *J. London Math. Soc.* **22** (1947), 219–226.

29. A sequence of polyhedra having intersections of specified dimensions. *J. London Math. Soc.* **22** (1947), 287–289.

30. An arithmetical property of the exponential function. *J. London Math. Soc.* **23** (1948), 267–271.

31. Covering theorems for ordered sets. *Proc. London Math. Soc.* (2) **50** (1949), 509–535.

32. Factorization of even graphs. *Quart. J. Math.* (Oxford) **20** (1949), 95–104.

33. Axiomatic treatment of rank in infinite sets. *Canad. J. Math.* **1** (1949), 337–343.

34. Some covering theorems (I). *Proc. London Math. Soc.* (2) **51** (1949), 232–264.

35. G. H. Hardy's contribution to the study of inequalities. *J. London Math. Soc.* **25** (1950), 129–135.

36. A combinatorial theorem. *J. London Math. Soc.* **25** (1950), 249–255. (With P. Erdös.)

37. A proof of the basis theorem for finitely generated Abelian groups. *J. London Math. Soc.* **26** (1951), 74–75.

38. Some covering theorems (II). *Proc. London Math. Soc.* (2) **53** (1951), 243–267.

39. An inequality. *J. London Math. Soc.* **27** (1952), 1–6.

40. Covering theorems for systems of similar sets of points. *Proceedings of the International Congress of Mathematicians, Harvard University, 1950*, **1,** 498–499.

41. Sets having a divisor property. *Amer. Math. Monthly* **59** (1952), 255–257. (With P. Erdös.)

42. Theorems on the intersection of convex sets of points. *J. London Math. Soc.* **27** (1952), 320–328.

43. A theorem on sequences of convex sets. *Quart. J. Math.* (Oxford) (2) **3** (1952), 183–186.

44. Combinatorial theorems on classifications of subsets of a given set. *Proc. London Math. Soc.* (3) **2** (1952), 417–439. (With P. Erdös.)

45. A problem on ordered sets. *J. London Math. Soc.* **28** (1953), 426–438. (With P. Erdös.)

46. Direct decomposition of partitions. *J. London Math. Soc.* **29** (1954), 71–83.

47. The minimal sum of a series of ordinal numbers. *J. London Math. Soc.* **29** (1954), 218–232.

48. A partition calculus. *Proceedings of the International Congress of Mathematicians, Amsterdam, 1954*, **2**, 55–56.

49. Partial well-ordering of sets of vectors. *Mathematika* **1** (1954), 89–95.

50. Minimal points of convex sets in sequence spaces. *Math. Zeitschrift* **63** (1956), 486–495.

51. Note on generalized inverses of matrices. *Proc. Cambridge Phil. Soc.* **52** (1956), 600–601.

52. A partition calculus in set theory. *Bull. Amer. Math. Soc.* **62** (1956), 427–489. (With P. Erdös.)

53. Note on independence functions. *Proc. London Math. Soc.* (3) **7** (1957), 300–320.

54. A note on matrix polynomials. *Quart. J. Math.* (Oxford) (2) **8** (1957), 128–132. (With L. Mirsky.)

55. Common transversals of plane sets. *J. London Math. Soc.* **33** (1958), 85–95. (With R. Harrop.)

56. Partition relations connected with the chromatic number of graphs. *J. London Math. Soc.* **34** (1959), 63–72. (With P. Erdös.)

57. A theorem on partial well-ordering of sets of vectors. *J. London Math. Soc.* **34** (1959), 222–224. (With P. Erdös.)

58. Intersection theorems for systems of sets. *J. London Math. Soc.* **35** (1960), 85–90. (With P. Erdös.)

59. A theorem on infinite series. *J. London Math. Soc.* **35** (1960), 273–276.

60. A construction of graphs without triangles having pre-assigned order and chromatic number. *J. London Math. Soc.* **35** (1960), 445–448. (With P. Erdös.)

61. Intersection theorems for systems of finite sets. *Quart. J. Math.* (Oxford) (2) **12** (1961), 313–320. (With P. Erdös and Chao Ko.)

62. Monotone functions mapping the set of rational numbers on itself. *J. Australian Math. Soc.* **3** (1963), 282–287. (With B. H. Neumann.)

63. Universal graphs and universal functions. *Acta Arith.* **9** (1964), 331–340.

64. The pigeon-hole principle for ordinal numbers. *Proc. London Math. Soc.* (3) **15** (1965), 750–768. (With E. C. Milner.)

65. Partition relations for cardinal numbers. *Acta Math. Acad. Scient. Hungaricae* **16** (1965), 93–196. (With P. Erdös and A. Hajnal.)

66. Abstract linear dependence. *Colloq. Math.* **14** (1966), 257–264.

67. A theorem on chains of finite sets. *J. London Math. Soc.* **42** (1967), 101–106.

68. On the number of systems of distinct representatives of sets. *J. London Math. Soc.* **42** (1967), 107–109.

69. Note on the transfinite case of Hall's theorem on representatives. *J. London Math. Soc.* **42** (1967), 321–324.

70. Partition relations and transitivity domains of binary relations. *J. London Math. Soc.* **42** (1967), 624–633. (With P. Erdös.)

71. An extension of Sylvester's law of inertia. *Linear Algebra Appl.* **1** (1968), 29–31.

72. Some covering theorems (III). *J. London Math. Soc.* **43** (1968), 127–130.

73. A plane set of measure zero containing circumferences of every radius. *J. London Math. Soc.* **43** (1968), 717–719. (With A. S. Besicovitch.)

74. Intersection theorems for systems of sets (II). *J. London Math. Soc.* **44** (1969), 467–479. (With P. Erdös.)

75. The partition calculus. *Recent Progress in Combinatorics* (Academic Press, 1969), 151–159.

76. Some partition theorems. *Colloq. Math. Soc. János Bolyai* **4** (Combinatorial Theory and its Applications, Balatonfüred, Hungary) (1969), 929–936.

77. Partition relations for η_α-sets. *J. London Math. Soc.* To appear. (With P. Erdös and E. C. Milner.)

78. A theorem on chains of finite sets (II). *Acta Arith.* To appear.

79. Theorems on the colouring of the edges of a graph. *Proceedings of the Second Chapel Hill Conference on Combinatorial Mathematics and its Applications, March 1970.* To appear.

80. A selection lemma. *J. Combinatorial Theory.* To apear.

81. Two mean value theorems. *J. Math. Analysis Appl.* To appear.

82. *The Partition Calculus in Set Theory.* (With P. Erdös and A. Hajnal.) Monograph to be published by the Hungarian Academy of Sciences.

List of Contributors

REINHOLD BAER, Forschungsinstitut für Mathematik, Eidgenössische Technische Hochschule, Zürich, Switzerland.

R. A. BRUALDI, Department of Mathematics, University of Wisconsin, Madison, Wisconsin, U.S.A.

N. G. DE BRUIJN, Department of Mathematics, Technological University, Eindhoven, The Netherlands.

H. S. M. COXETER, Department of Mathematics, University of Toronto, Canada.

H. G. EGGLESTON, Department of Mathematics, Royal Holloway College, University of London, England.

P. D. T. A. ELLIOTT, Department of Mathematics, University of Nottingham, England.

P. ERDÖS, Mathematical Institute of the Hungarian Academy of Sciences, Budapest, Hungary.

T. ESTERMANN, University College, London, England.

D. R. FULKERSON, The RAND Corporation, Santa Monica, California, U.S.A.

A. HAJNAL, Mathematical Institute of the Hungarian Academy of Sciences, Budapest, Hungary.

H. HALBERSTAM, Department of Mathematics, University of Nottingham, England.

MARSHALL HALL, JR, California Institute of Technology, Pasadena, California, U.S.A.

H. HEILBRONN, Department of Mathematics, University of Toronto, Canada.

EDMUND HLAWKA, Mathematisches Institut der Universität, Wien, Austria.

ALAN J. HOFFMAN, IBM Research Center, Yorktown Heights, New York, U.S.A.

H. A. JUNG, Mathematisches Institut der Technischen Universität, Berlin, Germany.

A. MÉIR, Department of Mathematics, University of Alberta, Edmonton, Canada.

N. S. MENDELSOHN, Department of Mathematics and Astronomy, University of Manitoba, Winnipeg, Canada.

E. C. MILNER, Department of Mathematics, University of Calgary, Alberta, Canada.

L. MIRSKY, Department of Pure Mathematics, University of Sheffield, England.

C. ST.J. A. NASH-WILLIAMS, Department of Combinatorics and Optimization, University of Waterloo, Ontario, Canada.

B. H. NEUMANN, Institute of Advanced Studies, Australian National University, Canberra, Australia.

A. OPPENHEIM, Department of Mathematics, University of Ghana, Legon, Ghana.

HAZEL PERFECT, Department of Pure Mathematics, University of Sheffield, England.

J. S. PYM, Department of Pure Mathematics, University of Sheffield, England.

GIAN-CARLO ROTA, Department of Mathematics, Massachusetts Institute of Technology, Cambridge, Mass. U.S.A.

VERA T. SÓS, Department of Mathematics, Eötvös Loránd University, Budapest, Hungary.

OLGA TAUSSKY, California Institute of Technology, Pasadena, California, U.S.A.

P. TURÁN, Department of Mathematics, Eötvös Loránd University, Budapest, Hungary.

W. T. TUTTE, Department of Combinatorics and Optimization, University of Waterloo, Ontario, Canada.

H. TVERBERG, Department of Mathematics, University of Bergen, Norway.

B. L. VAN DER WAERDEN, Mathematisches Institut der Universität, Zürich, Switzerland.

D. J. A. WELSH, Merton College, Oxford, England.